BASIC PROCEDURES
IN TEACHING ARITHMETIC

Basic Procedures in Teaching Arithmetic

CHARLES F. HOWARD
Sacramento State College

ENOCH DUMAS
University of California
Berkeley

D. C. HEATH AND COMPANY BOSTON

Library of Congress Catalog Card Number 63-9703

PRINTED IN THE UNITED STATES OF AMERICA

PREFACE

A CHILD'S MOTIVATION for learning arithmetic and his confidence in using it are derived from his teacher. A teacher who has depth of understanding of what he is to teach, knows sound teaching procedures, and is enthusiastic in his approach to teaching may inspire many a youngster who otherwise would be an indifferent student to enjoy the wonders of mathematics.

Basic Procedures in Teaching Arithmetic has been written for elementary school teachers and for students preparing to teach. Each will find in this book (1) mathematical explanations for the arithmetic to be taught, (2) effective teaching procedures, (3) recommended materials of instruction, (4) descriptions of how children grow and what this means in terms of teaching them arithmetic, (5) practical ways of evaluating children's learning and providing for their individual differences, (6) an overview of contemporary mathematics some of which may be taught in the upper grades and some of which may affect what is taught in lower grades, (7) activities for using what has been studied, and (8) references to supplement the material in the book.

The need for schools to adjust to the current technological revolution as they did fifty years ago to the Industrial Revolution has given rise to a careful scrutiny of traditional arithmetic teaching. Experimental programs have been initiated throughout the country, which include more rigorous mathematical emphases than most elementary school teachers have been accustomed to providing. While it is too early to draw final conclusions, it seems certain that arithmetic will be given more attention and will include the teaching of deeper insights and more accurate communication skill. Since the authors believe that teachers must know more than they will teach, *Basic Procedures in Teaching Arithmetic* includes more mathematical explanations and more precise mathematical language than will be expected of children.

Both of the authors have taught in elementary schools and have supervised teachers and student teachers. The reader, therefore, may be assured that only classroom-tested teaching procedures and materials have been suggested.

The questions under "Guided Supplementary Reading" found at the end of each chapter are intended to encourage readers to delve into articles and books either giving additional information or presenting points of view at variance with each other and with those of the authors. A manual giving suggestions for using *Basic Procedures in Teaching Arithmetic* and indicating expected responses to "Suggested Learning Activities" and "Guided Supplementary Reading" is available from the publisher to college instructors.

The authors are indebted to innumerable persons for assistance, direct or indirect, in the preparation of this book. Special recognition, however, must be given to the following people each of whom has read parts or all of the manuscript and has made helpful suggestions: Robert J. Griffin, Director, Division of Instructional Services, Richmond Schools, Richmond, California; Jens Lloyd Lund, Supervisor of the Teaching of Mathematics, University of California, Berkeley; Joseph N. Payne, Associate Professor of Education, University of Michigan, Ann Arbor. We wish to thank Fearon Publishers for permission to use charts from *Arithmetic Charts Handbook*. Further, we wish to acknowledge the patience and various other kinds of assistance given by members of our families.

CHARLES F. HOWARD
ENOCH DUMAS

TABLE OF CONTENTS

BASIC PROCEDURES
IN TEACHING ARITHMETIC

PART *1*

The Arithmetic Program in Kindergarten, Grade One, and Grade Two

CHAPTER 1

An Overview of the Program in Kindergarten, Grade 1, and Grade 2

Miss Smith, an experienced, competent first grade teacher, has a problem which must be reconsidered each time she starts planning the arithmetic program for a new group of children. This problem is how to utilize most effectively the relatively small amount of time available to the children for the study of arithmetic, when each pupil comes to her with a background of experience which differs from that of all the other pupils. The interests and abilities of these six-year-olds vary considerably. Their needs in the areas of reading, language, health, and in social and emotional development are immediate and pressing. The time available for the direct study of arithmetic is short, but still an adequate foundation for this important area must be prepared for each child. What subject matter in arithmetic is most suitable for each group of children? How should all the primary grade experiences of a particular group of boys and girls be organized so that these children will develop interest and skill in arithmetic as well as in other areas of the curriculum? In what sequence should the important concepts of arithmetic be introduced to the children so that the psychological factors operating in each situation will contribute to the most effective learning?

One purpose of Part I of this book is to assist a teacher in kindergarten, grade 1, or grade 2 to identify the various factors which should be considered before planning a sequence of experiences in arithmetic for any particular group of children, and to suggest general procedures for organizing an effective program of arithmetic experiences for that group. A second purpose is to suggest educationally sound techniques and procedures which are suitable for a teacher to use prior to the third grade level to extend the pupils' number concepts and increase their skill in using number in social settings. A third purpose is to suggest sequences of arithmetic topics which may be used by the teacher as a basis from which to do more detailed planning.

Planning a Sequence of Arithmetic Experiences

When a primary teacher examines various courses of study or other publications which suggest arithmetic curricula for children in kindergarten, grade 1, or grade 2, she will note the wide areas of agreement as to the types of experiences which are suggested. She can hardly fail to note, however, that there seems to be a lack of agreement in suggesting the organization of these various experiences into a definite and complete sequential pattern. Usually publications suggest no detailed sequence which will assist the children to reorganize their former number experiences through new learnings in such a way that there will be a reasonable certainty that they will broaden and deepen their number concepts steadily and systematically throughout kindergarten and the first and second grades.

The omission in suggesting a definite and detailed sequence for introducing various number experiences to children in kindergarten and in grade 1 and grade 2 is not due to a lack of study of this important problem, nor is it the result of an unawareness of how valuable such a sequence would be, were it available, to a classroom teacher who is endeavoring to plan her work carefully in order to make it most effective. The problem arises initially from the many interrelated and opposing factors which must be considered in planning an effective sequence of learning experiences for any specific group of children entering school for the first time. A lack of a common sequence of number experiences for the various classes of children in kindergarten will make planning difficult for the teacher of the first grade, and this in turn leads to difficulties in planning the work in the second grade. Consequently the third grade teacher often may be mistaken in assuming that certain common arithmetic experiences have been completed by her pupils in earlier grades, and she might be incorrect in believing that the best sequence to follow from this point would be that which is suggested by the logical nature of the structure of arithmetic.

The fact that children differ in their physical, mental, and emotional characteristics is well known to teachers in the primary grades. Differences are apparent in intelligence, general health, eyesight, hearing, home background, community experiences, personality factors, and in children's reactions to teachers, adults, and to other boys and girls. These factors directly affect a child's ability to learn arithmetic because they determine the extent and the quality of a child's earlier experiences with number. The ways in which certain aspects of a child's development are related to his ability to learn arithmetic are discussed in Chapter 2.

Learning is complicated further for primary grade children by the fact that number and the number systems are abstract. Although the number concepts may be illustrated by using concrete materials, the relationships themselves are abstract and cannot be perceived directly. These concepts may be understood only after the child has succeeded in making generalizations based upon various experiences with number in situations which help him to identify the abstract number relationships.

Through the use of counting experiences the child is provided with an approach to understanding number and the number system, number relationships, and some of the principles of number operations, but there are many applications of number in social settings which he also needs to recognize. He must learn how number is used in connection with linear measure, with measuring time, liquid capacity, temperature, weight, and with money concepts. The new vocabulary needed to express these ideas and the need for learning to read and to write the symbols used to express number ideas provide the child with further tasks. As these new learnings require considerable effort on the part of the child, motivation becomes very important in order to help him maintain interest in arithmetic, and this maintenance becomes a problem for the teacher.

If children had all the time they needed to achieve the above named learnings, the task still would be a heavy one, but usually only a small part of the time a child has in kindergarten and in the first and second grades is available for learning arithmetic. Reading, language, and health activities must take priority over the other activities in time allotments. Various other activities which are important for their own content and are needed to provide the relaxation and the variety necessary to take into account the short interest span of children at these grade levels are required. Other activities are needed to provide social insights and the type of conduct expected in school where pupils are taught in group situations. Desirable attitudes toward school must be developed if the child is to conform to the requirements of group instructional procedures without unnecessary difficulties.

At the present time, there seems to be no other recourse for the teacher in the kindergarten or in the first and second grades than that she herself should plan a sequence of arithmetic experiences for each group of children she is teaching. This is the most effective way of taking into account all the various factors which influence the learning of a particular group of primary grade children. The difficulty of the task, as well as its importance, demands a high degree of knowledge and skill on the part of the primary grade teacher.

A plan which the teacher may use as a basis for organizing the arithmetic program in kindergarten and in the first and second grades is suggested in Chapter 3. This plan of necessity leaves to the teacher the task of deciding upon the best time to introduce new material, as this depends upon the ability of the particular group of children she is teaching. The teacher must use her judgment in selecting the specific daily experiences for the children in such a way that they may integrate the concepts derived from the new experience with those derived from their previous school experience and home background. The plan does provide a suggestion for an overall organization of the program which will enable a teacher to systematize the arithmetic program in kindergarten and the first and second grades, and thereby lead the pupils to develop their arithmetical concepts steadily and systematically in preparation for the new arithmetic experiences they will encounter at higher grade levels.

Evaluating the Capabilities of Kindergarten Children

One of the first tasks of the kindergarten teacher is that of learning as much as possible about the capabilities of the children who comprise her class. Such information is needed for planning the work in every area of the kindergarten child's curriculum. In the area of arithmetic, the teacher should determine, through questions and discussion, what each child knows about counting and the extent to which he is familiar with common quantitative terms and quantitative concepts. As the past experience of the child will form the basis upon which he can form new arithmetical concepts, an evaluation of what he already knows will provide a guide in planning new learnings. As a result of this evaluation, the teacher usually will find that it will be necessary to help the child to clarify many partially understood concepts as well as to build new number concepts. Procedures for evaluating the individual differences of children are discussed in Chapter 14.

During evaluation procedures and also while planning a sequence of arithmetic experiences for primary children, the teacher should keep in mind two aspects of the work. Both are important and both should be developed concurrently. One aspect of the task deals with developing in the child an understanding of common quantitative concepts and the vocabulary involved, while the second aspect is that of developing an understanding of our number system and how it is used to express these quantitative concepts.

These two phases of arithmetic should be evaluated and developed at the same time, as each supplements the other. At first, the heavier emphasis should be upon building concepts and vocabulary, but as the child progresses increasing emphasis should be placed upon building number concepts and upon the use of the number system, until that phase occupies the larger part of the time which is devoted to the direct study of arithmetic in the first and second grades. Apart from the direct study of the numbers of arithmetic, the child's understanding and use of quantitative vocabulary should continue to receive careful attention throughout all areas of school work, wherever it might apply, throughout all of the primary grades.

The development of these two phases of arithmetic is discussed in detail in Chapter 3.

Counting as a Basis for Understanding Number

While the child is developing quantitative concepts and vocabulary through various activities, both planned and incidental, the teacher can use counting as a basis upon which to lead him into an understanding of the number system itself. As number relationships are abstract and are difficult for the child to understand, it is desirable for him to meet these relationships in many different social settings and through the use of concrete materials, such as counting discs, tickets, beads, or an abacus. The use of materials enables him to see number relationships illustrated and gradually to grasp the abstract concepts which he will study in arithmetic. The vocabulary needed to describe these concepts must be developed also and made meaningful. Finally the child must learn to read and to write the number symbols which we employ to indicate numbers and number operations. He must be able to indicate with arithmetic symbols the concepts which were illustrated when he used manipulative materials.

The child is introduced to our familiar numeration system through his counting experiences. From rote counting, where he gives the number names only as a succession of sounds and without number meaning, he can make rapid progress to where he can answer the question, "How many?" by matching each of the names in his counting series with one of the objects in the group being counted, and know that the last number name he uses will indicate how many there are in the group as a whole. Procedures for developing counting are discussed in Chapter 4.

Analyzing Groups in the First and Second Grades

The counting process, although basic to other number operations and to the understanding of number, is not alone sufficient. Probably the pupil could deal with most of the simple arithmetic situations with which he is confronted in the early grades by counting, either forward or backward. The teacher knows, however, that to work more effectively with numbers at higher grade levels, the pupil will eventually need to understand other processes, and that as soon as the pupil is ready he should start to learn the meaning of addition and subtraction.

In the early grades, it is sufficient if the child thinks of addition as the process of combining small groups into larger groups, and if he thinks of subtraction as breaking up a group or as finding the difference between two groups. These processes can be illustrated easily with groups of discs or other counters, and the meaning may be grasped without much difficulty. Suggestions for teaching this aspect of arithmetic are given in Chapter 4 and are discussed in further detail in Chapter 7.

A step which is preliminary to teaching the child the meaning of either addition or subtraction is that of helping him understand that he can think of a group of objects as being made up of two or more smaller groups. He should then be led to understand that, in somewhat the same way, a number may be thought of sometimes as being made up of other numbers. A number may be expressed in terms of two or more numbers, as $6 + 8$, as well as by the standard form of the numeral, such as "14."

The child should perceive also that there are not necessarily only two smaller groups in a larger group, but although a number like five may be thought of as being made up of more than two smaller numbers, as $2 + 2 + 1$, we are particularly interested in how two numbers may be added to make a new number because when using the operations of addition or subtraction we work with only two numbers at a time, even though the problem requires the eventual consideration of many numbers.

The teacher should keep in mind the distinction between analyzing groups, where the pupil counts to find his answer, and the abstract operations of addition and subtraction in which the pupil is using the basic facts of addition and subtraction. The analysis of groups provides readiness for the understanding of addition and subtraction operations which are introduced later. Procedures for teaching children how to analyze groups are discussed in Chapter 4.

General Procedures in Kindergarten, Grade 1, and Grade 2

The importance of using manipulative materials. To understand the meaning of the operations of addition and subtraction, it is very important for the child to have sufficient experience through manipulating materials to enable him to understand what is taking place when groups are combined, separated, or compared. By manipulating counters which he is able to perceive, he is aided in forming concepts regarding how the abstract number relationships are used. When he uses words or written symbols to express what was done with the groups of counters, he is aided in understanding how abstract number relationships may be expressed by words or by symbols. The knowledge of how to use number symbols to write down the arithmetic processes is essential but this instruction should follow, or accompany, rather than precede, the manipulation of materials to illustrate each particular process. Numerous suggestions for using manipulative materials to illustrate each step in arithmetic are given in various places throughout the following chapters.

The importance of recognizing number relationships in social settings. While the pupils are making progress in learning the uses of the decimal number system, the teacher should ensure that frequent opportunities are provided for them to recognize number situations in their environment, and to use the arithmetic they have learned by applying it in social settings.

Throughout the pupil's daily activities, his attention should be directed to the various number situations which arise. For instance, a first grade pupil can use number to find a certain page in his book during a reading lesson. Questions referring to the number of pages which have been read, or are still to be read, direct his attention to numbers. Questions regarding the number of objects shown in a picture in his reading book give him an opportunity to recognize and express number ideas. Experiences of this kind are available throughout all his daily activities and they assist him to "carry over" what he learned in arithmetic to various social applications. This incidental use of arithmetic contributes, in turn, to a wider and deeper understanding of the number relationships themselves, and consequently to a better understanding of the number system which he is learning to use.

The need for learning to read and to write number symbols. To enable the child to make effective use of workbooks, duplicated material, or chalkboard problems, it is necessary for him to learn to use written symbols for the numbers and to be able to read and write certain quantitative words which are in his vocabulary. The importance of teaching the child to read verbal problems needs particular emphasis because while it is true that there is a close connection between reading arithmetic material and reading other material, there are also differences which should be recognized. Quantitative words take on a greater importance, and sometimes even a different shade of meaning, when used in verbal arithmetic problems.

The teacher should dictate simple problems which the children can solve by using manipulative material alone. She should then show them how to write down, with arithmetic symbols, what was illustrated when they used the materials. Later the children should be allowed to use manipulative material to solve simple verbal problems which have been written on the chalkboard, shown in duplicated material, or found in workbooks. In each instance, they should write down what was done, as this helps them make a connection between visualizing the solution and expressing it in arithmetic symbols.

Teaching pupils to work from written verbal problems strengthens their understanding of arithmetic symbols and it also frees the teacher for short periods of time to work with the slower pupils while the remainder of the group is occupied with the written work.

The pupils should be taught from the first how to work systematically on verbal problems. They should first try to visualize the problem, using manipulative materials to help them if necessary. Then they should decide upon the process which is required. Next, using any manipulative materials which are needed, they determine the answer. Finally, they use arithmetic symbols to write down what was done.

As the pupils gain skill and understanding they may drop the use of manipulative materials in situations where they feel that the materials are not needed. They should be helped then to understand that when certain basic facts in addition and subtraction have been learned, counting is no longer necessary in certain problems because they can work by using the basic facts instead of the materials. At this stage, it is desirable for the teacher to use various games and practice exercises to encourage the children to gain skill in using the basic facts. These procedures are discussed in greater detail in chapters 7 and 8.

Developing Readiness for the Arithmetic Introduced at Higher Grade Levels

In the first grade, a pupil may solve through counting procedures a certain problem which involves the putting together of groups, while at the third grade level he might solve the same problem by using the basic facts which he has learned, and by using the standard algorism for the addition process. When he is solving the problem by counting, he could be said to be using an immature procedure, but when he is using the basic facts in the accepted manner he is applying a mature procedure.

Developing an understanding of the four fundamental operations of addition, subtraction, multiplication, and division as these operations apply to whole numbers and to fractions makes up a large part of the work in arithmetic expected of children during the third, fourth, and fifth grades. At these grade levels, the children are expected to understand and to be able to use procedures in their arithmetic computations which are more mature than counting. They learn the basic facts and use them in solving problems, and they are expected to use the customary procedures for manipulating the numerals and other symbols.

Although children are expected to begin to use some mature procedures before they enter the third grade, the individual differences among the children make it unreasonable to expect all to be equally ready at the same time. The differences among the arithmetic programs of various schools throughout kindergarten and the first grade, also result in the children attaining varying degrees of readiness for learning the mature procedures. As readiness for arithmetic is very important to the child, he should be prepared through various informal and incidental arithmetical experiences which enable him to build a background of information pertaining to number relationships. The teacher should ascertain which of her pupils are ready for the more formal phases of arithmetic instruction by evaluating their knowledge and abilities as indicated throughout their work in the first grade. She should make allowances for the individual differences of the children by carefully grouping them as they are introduced to various phases of arithmetic which are new to them. Evaluation procedures and grouping procedures are discussed in Chapter 14.

During the early grades, the pupil is introduced to the formal procedures for using the fundamental processes of addition, subtraction, multiplication, and division. He begins to learn the basic facts in each of these processes. His knowledge of place-value notation is extended gradually to where he can understand the customary algorisms for carrying out these processes. Suggestions for teaching children how to use common procedures in arithmetic are given in Part II of this book.

The concepts of the fractions "one-half," "one-third," and "one-fourth," which were developed earlier are extended in the second and third grades by developing the meaning of other unit fractions such as one-fifth, one-sixth, one-eighth and so on. The pupil then is introduced to the concept of a fraction of a group, such as one-half of twelve, and to the relationship between fractions and the division process. When the pupils are ready, they may be introduced to fractions other than unit fractions, such as $\frac{3}{4}$, $\frac{3}{5}$, $\frac{5}{6}$, and others. This latter step may be delayed for certain children if the remainder of the second and third grade program in arithmetic seems to be unreasonably heavy for them. The extension of concepts of fractions is discussed in chapters 9 and 10.

By extending the concepts of measurement which were learned in earlier grades, the second and third grade pupil learns new interrelationships among standard measures. The children consolidate what they have learned earlier by making numerous applications of measurement to social situations. This phase of the program is discussed in Chapter 12.

Throughout the second grade, particular attention should be given to problem-solving, and to the development of the pupils' abilities in this respect. Procedures for developing problem-solving abilities are discussed in Chapter 13.

Suggested Learning Activities

1. Interview a first grade teacher and discuss with her the variety of readiness for number work she found in her class at the beginning of the term. What variations were most conspicuous?
2. Explain the statement, ". . . number and the number systems are abstract."
3. Tell why it is not sufficient for a teacher to follow a ready-made arithmetic teaching sequence in kindergarten, and the first and second grades. Which ability group of pupils, high achievers, medium achievers, or low achievers, would be least penalized if a teacher followed a ready-made sequence?
4. Interview a kindergarten teacher and ask about the range of understanding of number concepts in her class at the beginning of the term. What were some of the understandings of the most able pupils which were not understood by the least able?
5. Give five simple problems appropriate to the first grade which a teacher might dictate to children for solution using manipulative materials.
6. Describe three probable incidental experiences at kindergarten level through which the children may learn concepts of quantity.

Guided Supplementary Reading

1. On what incidental learning activity in the kindergarten did Campbell capitalize when making a mural map?
2. What principles of planning for grouping does Greco suggest?
3. What do Grossnickle and Brueckner mean when they say that "the modern arithmetic program must be both realistic and functional"?

4. What justification do Hollister and Gunderson give for developing the social aspects of arithmetic?
5. What kinds of arithmetical concepts can be developed with primary blocks as reported by Johnson and Whipple?
6. Leodas writes that the teaching of mathematics comprises what principal objectives?
7. What are the aims of the arithmetic program described by Maloney?
8. What conditions and trends do McSwain and Cooke point to as likely determiners of social change?
9. What did Priore discover about the arithmetic achievement of beginning first graders and what did she conclude?
10. What two ideas expressed by a number does Rosenquist think should be taught in primary grades?
11. Spitzer advocates the "developmental method" in teaching arithmetic. What three changes from the traditional approach does he suggest are necessary?
12. What is Stokes's view with regard to the place of rote counting in concept-learning?
13. According to Wheat to what use does a pupil put his learning of number names, signs, and system?

Suggested Supplementary References

1. CAMPBELL, DOROTHY, "Kindergarteners Learn Arithmetic," *Arithmetic Teacher,* Vol. 5, pp. 137–139, April, 1958.
2. GRECO, A. J., "Group Methods in Primary Grades," *Arithmetic Teacher,* Vol. 4, pp. 28–29, February, 1957.
3. GROSSNICKLE, FOSTER E., AND LEO J. BRUECKNER, *Discovering Meanings in Arithmetic,* Chapter 1. Philadelphia: The John C. Winston Co., 1959.
4. HOLLISTER, GEORGE E., AND AGNES G. GUNDERSON, Teaching *Arithmetic in Grades I and II,* Chapter 1. Boston: D. C. Heath and Co., 1954.
5. JOHNSON, L. V., AND A. S. WHIPPLE, "Arithmetic and Block Work in Primary Grades," *Arithmetic Teacher,* Vol. 6, pp. 306–309, December, 1959.
6. LEODAS, C. J., "First Number Concepts; Cornerstones of Mathematics," *Journal of Educational Sociology,* Vol. 30, pp. 343–345, April, 1957.
7. MALONEY, J. P., "Arithmetic at the Primary Level," *Arithmetic Teacher,* Vol. 4, pp. 112–118, April, 1957.

8. McSwain, E. T., and Ralph J. Cooke, *Understanding and Teaching Arithmetic in the Elementary School,* Chapter 1. New York: Henry Holt and Co., 1958.
9. Priore, A., "Achievement by Pupils Entering the First Grade," *Arithmetic Teacher,* Vol. 4, pp. 55–60, March, 1957.
10. Rosenquist, Lucy L., *Young Children Learn to Use Arithmetic,* Chapter 1. Boston: Ginn and Co., 1949.
11. Spitzer, Herbert F., *The Teaching of Arithmetic,* Third Edition, Chapter 1. Boston: Houghton Mifflin Co., 1961.
12. Stokes, C. Newton, *Teaching the Meanings of Arithmetic,* Chapter 1. New York: Appleton-Century-Crofts, Inc., 1951.
13. Wheat, Harry Grove, *How to Teach Arithmetic,* Introduction. Evanston, Illinois: Row, Peterson and Co., 1951.

CHAPTER 2

Aspects of Child Development Which Affect Learning Arithmetic in the Primary Grades

Extensive studies in the area of child-development have brought about many changes in teachers' attitudes toward what should comprise the content and activities which are best for children in the primary grades. These studies show that while each individual child is different from all others, there are, in general, well defined stages of development through which all children pass.[1] There is good reason to believe that whenever these stages of development are recognized and understood by teachers the effectiveness of the educational procedures is greatly improved. A summary of some of these general characteristics as they affect the learning of arithmetic by children from five to seven years of age is given here. Further references are suggested at the end of this chapter.

While the maturity traits discussed in this chapter are those generally noted in children at the grade levels indicated, it should be emphasized strongly that some children pass through these stages much more rapidly than others. A teacher should expect to

[1] Edward C. Britton and J. Merritt Winans, *Growing from Infancy to Adulthood* (New York: Appleton-Century-Crofts, Inc., 1958), p. 3.

find children at each grade level who may be beyond the stage of development reached by the "average achiever" at each grade level, or who have not yet reached the stage of development described as characteristic for that particular grade level. Gesell points out that each child has a distinctive style or method of growth and that an understanding of each individual child is necessary to determine the best procedures to use for his guidance.[2]

An understanding of the general characteristics which may be expected in many of the pupils at any grade level will help the teacher determine the general procedures and the arithmetical content which probably would be effective and acceptable at a particular grade level. The pedagogical adage, "Know your pupils," applies to teaching arithmetic as much as it does to any other area of the curriculum.

Maturity Traits of Children in Kindergarten Which Have Implications in Learning Arithmetic

Physical characteristics. Although kindergarten children are growing rapidly, averaging an increase of about three inches in height and about seven pounds in weight in a year, their initial spurt of growth during infancy has slowed down considerably.[3] The coordination of their smaller muscles, though far from complete, is improving. Their eyes are not fully developed, and their vision is rather "far-sighted" and not well adapted to noting small differences at close range. They are not comfortable if they have to sit in one position for more than a short length of time. They wish to move about and to change their positions frequently.

Kindergarten teachers who recognize these characteristics do not require the pupils to remain seated for more than a short period, nor do they require them to work for long periods with small materials which require the coordination of the smaller mus-

[2] Arnold Gesell and Frances L. Ilg, *Child Development* (New York: Harper and Brothers, 1949), p. 43.

[3] Ernest H. Watson and George H. Lowrey, *Growth and Development of Children* (Chicago: The Yearbook Publishers, revised edition, 1954), p. 44.

cles. It would be unnecessarily tiring, for instance, for children at this age to be using pencils and paper to copy numerals or to be counting small objects or manipulating small materials in a situation which requires good coordination.

Emotional characteristics. Kindergarten children are easily upset emotionally and are soon frustrated when they try to do tasks which are beyond their abilities. They like to get started at a task immediately without waiting a long time to have the manner of carrying it out explained by the teacher. They like to show others what they can do, and enjoy receiving individual attention from the teacher. Although their attention span is short, it can be increased by using material in which they are interested. When the kindergarten child sees new material he wishes to use it immediately rather than to think about it or talk about it.

These emotional characteristics imply that an incidental approach to arithmetic, rather than a direct approach, should characterize most of the work at this grade level. The teacher should plan to introduce the arithmetical concepts by directing the children's attention to number situations in connection with the things they are doing and in which they are interested, and not in a separate period where the children have to study number relationships directly. Quantitative words should be introduced as a natural part of the children's vocabulary. Number words should be introduced in connection with their use in carrying on the children's normal activities.

The teacher should be ready to give individual help and to show interest in each child's accomplishments. Group activities should frequently involve counting experiences and the clarification of quantitative vocabulary in connection with the related activities.

Social characteristics. Although the social characteristics of kindergarten children are connected rather indirectly with their learning arithmetic, they are among the most important of all the factors which a kindergarten teacher must consider in planning the total educational program of the child.[4] During this period the

[4] Clarice Dechent Wills and William H. Stegman, *Living in the Kindergarten* (Chicago: Follett Publishing Co., 1950), p. 82.

child is learning rapidly, through his daily experiences, how he should react to other people who are outside of his family. He must learn to modify his behavior so that he can participate as a member of a social group. He must learn to use the degree of emotional control which will enable him to function in a group learning situation. He is learning the degree of consideration he may expect from others as well as the type of behavior others expect from him.

At this age level the kindergarten child is gradually becoming less self-centered and he begins to enjoy playing with other children and forming brief friendships. Usually he likes to please the teacher, and consequently he will respond quickly to her praise or criticism. He tends to be physically aggressive in asserting his own rights, but he can be taught to share and to take turns. Number concepts may be useful to him both in sharing and in taking turns, and any indirect application of number in these respects may have a usefulness for him which he understands.

At this age level, the child participates with others in songs and finger plays where rote counting up to ten, or rational counting using small numbers, are involved.

Intellectual characteristics. The child's intellectual characteristics are particularly important in his development of concepts regarding number. Studies of the language of children and of the quantitative concepts they have formed during their preschool years indicate that they have made a good start on developing quantitative concepts before they come to school.[5] Concepts of time and space, and the ability to count rationally, are rather limited and, as in the case of many of the child's other concepts, they may be very inaccurate or erroneous.

The kindergarten child is interested in the specific information he can get through his sensory experiences and he shows considerable curiosity about natural objects. His language ability has usually developed to the place where he can express himself adequately for his purpose. It is through the child's language that the

[5] W. A. Brownell, *Arithmetic in Grades I and II,* Duke University Research Studies in Education, No. 6 (Durham: Duke University Press, 1941), p. 18; Sina M. Mott, "Number Concepts of Small Children," *The Mathematics Teacher* (November, 1945), p. 51.

kindergarten teacher is able to evaluate the progress he has made in developing quantitative concepts.

As the child's number concepts have developed gradually from his quantitative concepts, and as these quantitative concepts have been formed along with, and as a part of, the child's other concepts, the process by which a child forms early concepts becomes one of interest in teaching arithmetic.

The formation of number concepts. Although the exact mental process by which a child forms concepts has not been determined definitely, psychologists agree that the sensations which a child has received since his infancy from his environment have been identified first as patterns, or percepts, and that these percepts, when given a more generalized meaning, form concepts or understandings. For example, when an infant is subjected to many stimuli through his various sense organs, these unrelated stimuli have no meaning for him at first. As he identifies a pattern of related stimuli, a percept is formed by the pattern being recognized or perceived. Russell states that the percepts of children may be classified into at least nine types: percepts of form, space, time, movement, weight, number, and as social percepts, aesthetic percepts, and humor percepts.[6]

Some of the percepts, particularly those of form, space, and movement, are evident in children at a very early age, while others, such as those of time, weight, and number, cannot be identified until much later.

As a percept takes on meaning, a concept is developed through a process of generalization in which similarities and differences in the percept patterns are recognized. When the child attaches language labels to these concepts, he is able to use them to make further generalizations and to develop new concepts. The child's memory and mental images play an active part in the formation of new concepts and in the refinement of previous concepts.

Quantitative concepts and number concepts. When planning an arithmetic program, it is helpful for a primary teacher, especially

[6] David H. Russell, *Children's Thinking* (Boston: Ginn and Company, 1956), p. 117.

a kindergarten teacher or a first grade teacher, to make a distinction between a "quantitative" concept and a "number" concept. In the early grades, a child's progress in arithmetic may be judged by his ability to develop quantitative concepts and vocabulary as well as by his ability to form number concepts. As used here, the term "quantitative concept" will indicate any concept which denotes quantity or magnitude. It is used in its broad sense and will include the smaller subset of number concepts. The term "number concept" will refer only to those quantitative concepts to which number names may be attached. Mathematically, one could say that the number concepts are thus being considered as a proper subset of the more inclusive set of quantitative concepts.

The child's early quantitative concepts may be identified by examining the vocabulary of the child when he first enters school. As the child learns language, it may be noted that some of his concepts are those having reference to quantity or magnitude. Words such as "big," "little," "tall," "short," "high," "low," "heavy," and "light" express ideas of quantity or magnitude without any definite amount being specified, and for this reason they are called "indeterminate number concepts" by some writers.

When the child learns the number names, he gradually understands how these number names may be used to express the relationships between quantities more definitely. As the standard units of linear measure, weight, liquid capacity, time, temperature, and money are learned, the child uses the number names along with these standard units to give more exact expression to various concepts of quantity or magnitude.

When the child first comes to school, his understanding of numbers has not been developed in proportion to his understanding of many quantitative words and terms. His idea of counting, at this time, might be confined to repeating the number names, without meaning, to twenty or more, and his use of rational counting might be limited to very small groups.

It should be remembered that the child's quantitative concepts are very important to him. He has developed them in an incidental way with little or no direct instruction, and they deal with things in his immediate environment. From his point of view.

these quantitative concepts are a part of his daily thinking and have an immediate use. Any kindergarten activity which clarifies and extends these concepts to enable him to meet his immediate needs will be readily accepted. Number concepts which go far beyond his needs may not be as readily accepted, although he may make some effort to learn them in order to please the teacher or for some other indirect purpose.

Although children make considerable progress in forming quantitative concepts during their preschool years, it is after they enter school that they make rapid growth in forming number concepts. MacLatchy reported a study of 2300 children entering the first grade in which eight per cent of the children could count by rote to one hundred while eight per cent could not count to ten.[7] These wide differences might be explained partially by the fact that, at first, many children have little need for counting, unless it is to please adults. The number names through five, and words meaning "many," which are closely connected to groups as he perceives them, meet most of his immediate needs. The child learns that adults wish him to learn the number names for some reason, and he learns these sounds by rote without paying particular attention to their meaning. Learning these number names in their proper sequence is, however, a very important beginning in understanding number.

Classroom procedures to help children to learn to count and to develop their early number concepts are discussed in Chapter 4.

Maturity Traits of Children in Grade 1 Which Have Implications in Learning Arithmetic

Physical characteristics. The average child in grade one continues his growth at about the same rate that was noted during kindergarten. His weight increases about five pounds and his height about two and a half inches during the year. His lack of muscular coordination results from a tendency for him to over-

[7] Josephine MacLatchy, "Seeing and Understanding in Number," *Elementary School Journal,* 45:144–152.

extend himself in motor behavior and go to extremes. He still finds it difficult to use his small muscles to complete tasks requiring precision or good coordination. Using a pencil properly still presents a problem, and reversals of letters or numerals are common.

At this age level, he is very active. He accompanies mental effort with physical activity which may be observed in his wriggling, chewing, swinging his legs, and unnecessary physical tenseness. A result of this tenseness is that he tires easily if he has to concentrate for more than a few minutes.

Work in arithmetic should be arranged so that he can manipulate materials and move around to some extent rather than be of a type which requires him to sit in one position and use a pencil for very long at any one time.

Emotional characteristics. The abundance of new learnings which the grade one child is expected to grasp and the variety of concepts to which he is exposed, puts him under a certain amount of strain and nervous tension. The relative difficulty of the learning, when compared to his ability and experience, makes him very aware of his limitations, and rather fearful of losing the security he feels in being loved by parents and his teacher. At this age level, he is very sensitive to criticism, and he seeks praise and reassurance. As he often finds that the tasks required of him are somewhat beyond his ability, he is easily frustrated and this may show itself in indecision and difficulty in making up his mind and also in temper manifestations. At the same time, he is very proud of any small accomplishments because these give him a feeling of success and security.

The arithmetic at this level should be very carefully graded so that the steps are small and easily surmounted. Individual attention and flexible grouping procedures are essential for providing for individual differences. Familiar concepts should be used in new situations or new concepts in familiar situations so that the child is not frustrated by too many new patterns of learning at any one time. The work should be graded to his ability in such a way that he feels successful at each step without an unreasonable amount of difficulty. The grade one teacher should be quick to give praise for small accomplishments and should replace negative criticism with positive suggestions.

Social characteristics. The child at this age level tends to compare his accomplishments with those of others in his group, and he measures his success in terms of what others do. His desire for security and for the approval of his parents and teacher makes it seem to him to be very important for him not to fail in his efforts to compete with other children. For this reason, the teacher should avoid using motivating procedures which are individually competitive. The teacher should choose those motivating procedures in which the group as a whole get credit for doing well, or where the child gets credit for improving himself irrespective of the accomplishments of the other children.

Intellectual characteristics. Although a great deal of the arithmetic which the child learns in grade one should be taught through its incidental use in connection with his other activities, it is desirable to start using a short period of about twenty or twenty-five minutes each day in which the child studies arithmetic directly. The various aspects of number which he has been experiencing in connection with other activities can now be brought together in this period and the child can be given help in organizing his information. Those concepts which he has experienced in the area of arithmetic during his other activities may now be reorganized into an understandable group of number relationships. For instance, a lesson dealing with linear measure helps him see the relationships between various standard units and their use, or a review of his number concepts helps him to clarify his thinking regarding number relationships. Brownell[8] has shown that after children at this grade level have learned to count and to analyze small numbers they are capable of grasping the meaning of addition or subtraction when small numbers are used. They are able to express these processes by means of written symbols and to understand their use in solving simple problems.

[8] W. A. Brownell, *Arithmetic in Grades I and II.* Duke University Research Studies in Education, No. 6 (Durham: Duke University Press, 1941), pp. 79–80.

The child's concepts of quantitative terms may also be extended during short arithmetic periods. The relationships among many of the standard units of time, money, linear measure, liquid capacity, temperature, and weight can be understood and the symbols needed to express these relationships in writing can be learned.

A danger to be avoided here is that of attempting to expand the pupil's concepts of abstract number relationships too rapidly, as he might be left with a verbalization of the relationships rather than with a real understanding of their nature.

As concepts of quantitative relationships are organized into more inclusive patterns during an arithmetic period, the child should have abundant experience in using them in connection with appropriate social settings during his daily activities. At this grade level there should be a very close connection maintained between what the child is learning in the arithmetic period and its application in social settings which are familiar to him.

Maturity Traits of Children in Grade 2 Which Have Implications in Learning Arithmetic

Physical characteristics. The growth of the child in grade 2 continues at about the same rate as it did in grade 1, averaging a gain of about six pounds in weight and an increase of a little over two inches in height.[9] At this age level, the child has improved his muscular coordination considerably over what it was a year earlier. He can handle tools or implements which require the use of his smaller muscles with a reasonable precision which is adequate for his normal tasks. He is usually active, although at times he may go to extremes of inactivity. He likes to work at tasks until he feels that he has mastered them. Since he can maintain a sitting position for a longer time without discomfort, the teacher may provide more arithmetic activities requiring writing. As noted above, the teacher should ensure that the child has time to make corrections in his work, as children at this age level show persistence in correcting their errors and altering their work until they feel that it is right.

[9] Watson and Lowrey, *Growth and Development of Children,* p. 44.

At this level, the child likes to manipulate materials and to talk about what he has done. The teacher should provide manipulative materials during the arithmetic period with which the child can illustrate problems and show how to solve them. Counters are particularly helpful in illustrating addition and the different subtraction situations.

Emotional characteristics. By the second grade the child usually has quieted down somewhat in his emotional reactions and is usually ready to do more listening and thinking. His moods may be changeable, but usually he is ready to concentrate on his work until he brings it to a satisfactory conclusion. He is able to reach logical conclusions and he accepts an explanation of why some solutions to problems are more efficient than others.

The arithmetic period may be increased in length and the written expression of arithmetic solutions be given more attention. The incidental uses of arithmetic in daily activities should still be a major source of arithmetic learning.

As in the previous year, the child is very sensitive to the praise or criticism of the teacher. The pupil usually is fond of his teacher and needs to feel that the teacher is interested in him and in his success, but now he is becoming more aware of what others think of him. While the pupils are completing their written work, the teacher should take every opportunity to work with them individually and to show an interest in the progress of each one.

Intellectual characteristics. The average achiever at this grade level has a mental ability which enables him to reason logically in solving simple arithmetic problems where counting is required. He has been introduced to concepts of linear measure, weight, time, liquid capacity, temperature, and money in connection with his experiences outside of school, and he is ready for school experiences which will help him to organize and to extend his information in these areas.

At this grade level, the child can read simple material and his written work is improving. He makes fewer reversals and is becoming self-critical. He is willing to work at rather mechanical tasks and continue with one type of activity until he has completed it. He usually likes oral arithmetic. He is interested in construction at this grade level and this type of activity provides many opportunities for using arithmetic.

By the second grade, many children are becoming very interested in money and in saving it and thinking about how to spend it. They are able to tell time to the minute and to learn the names of the months and seasons. Their concepts of space relationships develop rapidly at this grade level, although they may have difficulty in orienting themselves in order to recognize how these space relationships appear to other people. They show their interest in comparative size by their more realistic drawings.

The teacher can make good use of arithmetic charts or chalkboard drawings at this grade level in illustrating arithmetic concepts and in showing the relationships between standard units of measurement.

Grade 2 pupils often like to work individually and to use workbooks or duplicated materials to some extent. They should be given sufficient time to make changes in their work. These pupils are anxious to have their work checked immediately upon its completion, and sometimes this may be arranged by providing them with the correct answers and allowing them to check their own work.

Motivation in Learning Arithmetic in the Primary Grades

At the first and second grade levels, children have a natural curiosity which directs their attention to those things in which the other children and the teacher appear to be interested. For this reason, the teacher should try to maintain within the class an attitude of interested curiosity toward number activities and she should avoid any procedures which will make the arithmetic period seem tedious or a necessary chore.

Motivation arising from the child's need to understand his environment. During the kindergarten period, the child's number experiences are closely connected with his other activities, and the motivation to use arithmetic sometimes grows out of his need to use number in order to express and to understand his other social experiences. In various instances he wishes to count in order to answer the question "How many?" and thus he extends his knowledge of the cardinal use of numbers. When he uses numbers to identify certain things which have been numbered, such as the pages in his books, the schoolrooms, streets, or houses, he is learning the ordinal use of numbers.

During grade 1 and grade 2, the child finds an increasing need for numbers in order to understand and use measurement concepts, especially in connection with construction activities, social studies activities, and science activities.

Motivation arising from the child's sense of accomplishment. When the teacher begins to direct the child's attention to arithmetic as something which needs to be understood for its own value, as in instances where numbers are being analyzed during a readiness activity for learning addition and subtraction, the need for this learning may not seem to the child to be immediate. The teacher then should consider the various factors which concern the motivation of the child for this type of material.

The nature of the subject matter in arithmetic is such that it enables the teacher to introduce the pupil to new concepts by very easy steps, and the feeling of accomplishment a child experiences as he recognizes that he has mastered any small step is in itself a motivating factor. There seems to be a puzzle element in some types of work which appeals to many children. Children in grade 1 will work industriously at a task such as fitting together the pieces of a simple jig-saw puzzle, and show evidences of satisfaction in successfully accomplishing the task. When pupils are using manipulative materials to answer questions concerning arithmetic they often show a similar type of interest and satisfaction.

A teacher should be sensitive to this feeling of accomplishment which the child experiences when he learns a new step in arithmetic, and she should foster it with encouraging comments. This will help to create a positive emotional tone toward arithmetic as something interesting and as an activity in which the child feels that he can win some measure of recognition from his teacher and his peers.

The importance of adjusting the difficulty of the step to the child's ability. In order to enable the child to feel successful in learning arithmetic, the teacher should endeavor to adjust the difficulty of the steps when she is developing each new concept so that the child is able to learn each small step rather quickly. She should try also to make provision for adequate time to give help to individual pupils at frequent intervals. In some instances, a few minutes of individual help from the teacher will do more to assist a pupil in overcoming a difficulty than a much longer time spent in a group-learning situation. Where there are wide differences of ability found among the pupils of a single class, some type of grouping procedure, particularly in connection with practice exercises, is essential in order to maintain good motivation. Procedures for evaluating and providing for individual differences are discussed in Chapter 14.

Motivation increased by using a variety of activities. A child's interest in arithmetic tends to be increased when his teacher uses a variety of activities in connection with arithmetic. Often a new skill may be made more interesting by varying the type of practice which may be required to fix it. Varying the applications for a particular skill emphasizes its importance and tends to increase interest, as does directing the child's attention to the various ways he may use the new skill in his environment.

Motivation increased by using arithmetic games. Games of various kinds are interesting to most children. When practice or drill procedures are needed the teacher often may stimulate the child's interest by putting the required practice into some game situation. To the pupil the game may seem more important than the arithmetic itself, but he will feel a need for learning the number skills in order to participate in the game.

Where a reasonable amount of speed in responding is desirable in connection with using some particular arithmetic skill, this speed may itself be made part of the game by timing the response or arranging a relay type of activity where several rows of pupils participate. The feeling of working with others which a child derives from participating in a group game is itself a motivating factor.

Another advantage of using arithmetic games with children is that it provides the teacher with additional opportunities to evaluate the pupils' accomplishments and to identify their needs. For this reason an arithmetic game should be chosen to give pupils experience at the level on which they need the new practice, or on which they need review. An arithmetic game may have little or no value for a particular group of pupils if the level of the skills used in the game is much below the point where the pupils really need the practice. For instance, a counting game which might be very helpful to kindergarten or grade 1 pupils might be a waste of time for pupils in grade 2 who have already mastered the counting skills.

In some instances an arithmetic game may be of such a nature that a pupil does not learn very much from it while it is in progress, but it may still provide good motivation for the child to learn arithmetic so that he might participate in the game the next time that it is played. A game provides the child with an immediate use for any arithmetic he already knows and for the new concepts he is developing. He thus experiences more satisfaction in learning arithmetic which will be used almost daily in a game than in learning arithmetic for use at some indefinite time in the future. For this reason, a teacher might find that using a game for a very short period of time each day is just as valuable for motivation as continuing it for longer periods. Once the pupils have learned how to play a certain game, it is probably well to use it along with other similar games for only short periods so that interest in it will not be lost.

Selecting arithmetic games. As noted above, probably the most important factor to be considered when selecting an arithmetic game is that it should be a game which requires the exercise of arithmetic skills at the level at which the pupils need the practice. Unless the game provides the type of experience needed, its value is decreased. The levels at which various types of games could be considered to be helpful, both for developing a new concept or for review purposes, are as follows:

Counting games. Games of this type would be suitable at the levels of rote counting, enumeration or rational counting, counting by two's, five's, or ten's, and so on. Games in which the pupils determine the next number in a sequence, a missing number in a sequence, or the number of times a ball is bounced or an object tapped, are examples of counting games.

Number recognition games. Included in this class would be those games in which pupils are required to identify a group of objects, to recognize the number in a group, or to respond to a numeral or to a verbal question by selecting a certain group of objects.

Games involving the recognition and use of place value would be suitable for pupils while they are learning number notation.

Games involving measurement. Many games may be devised so that pupils are required to identify or to use measuring instruments, and which involve concepts of time, weight, linear measure, liquid capacity, temperature, or money.

Number analysis games. Games in which a number is thought of as being made up of smaller numbers are helpful at the level where readiness for understanding addition and substraction is being developed.

Addition and subtraction games. At the second grade level, the addition and subtraction games should be those which test the meaning of addition and subtraction rather than the memorization of basic facts. Prior to the third grade level, children may be permitted to count in order to determine their answers, as the emphasis should be upon understanding the meaning of addition and subtraction rather than upon the memorization of basic facts.

Although relay type group games may be used where the teacher wishes to stress the speed of response in some particular skill, it is suggested that the speed factor should not be emphasized prior to the third grade. The emphasis should be upon understanding and accuracy, and the pupils given as much time as is reasonable for the level of work being done. For instance, one relay team should be considered to have been as successful as another team if both had the same number of answers correct, irrespective of the time taken to complete the task. This emphasis upon understanding and accuracy encourages the children to think more carefully about their answers. The overexcitement which children sometimes experience during a speed relay game usually does not contribute to a good learning situation.

Examples of various types of games suitable for practicing arithmetic skills and problem solving may be found in the references listed at the end of this chapter.

A consideration of the aspects of child development which affect the learning of arithmetic in the primary grades will reveal the need for some systematic organization of the program so that the psychological factors operating at each stage of the child's development are taken into account. The information which the child has derived from out-of-school experiences should not be ignored; on the contrary it should be utilized through giving the child help in identifying the interrelationships among his various experiences, thus clarifying and extending his previous concepts. At the same time, the organization of the program should be such that each aspect of arithmetic which is important at the lower grade levels should be examined systematically. The teacher should not assume without checking that the pupil has had any given arithmetical experience, or that the pupil's concepts are adequate as a basis for further work. Above the kindergarten level, any approach to arithmetic which is entirely incidental is likely to leave the child with inadequate concepts and with gaps in his knowledge which will retard his further progress. Thus a carefully developed and systematic organization of arithmetic in kindergarten, grade 1 and grade 2, which is planned to make provision for individual differences among the group of pupils concerned, becomes of considerable importance in enabling each child to achieve to the limit of his ability.

Suggested Learning Activities

1. Observe a kindergarten child in a classroom situation for one hour and note the time by the clock as his attention passes from one activity or interest to another. What is his average attention span?
2. Equipped with a handful of counters (plastic discs, buttons, checkers, or the like) test three first graders individually somewhat as follows:

   Count these markers. (Have eleven markers in a pile.)
   Show me seven markers.
   Pick out six white markers and three black ones.
   From this row of markers show me the third one, and the fifth one.
   Here are two piles of markers. Which has more?
3. Interview three second graders about their understanding of common units of measure. Ask such questions or make such requests as:

   How much does this brick weigh? (Let children lift brick.)
   With this piece of chalk draw a line three feet long.
   How many inches from your elbow to the tip of your finger?
   How many pints of water will it take to fill this jar?
4. List arithmetic activities probable in a second grade construction of a grocery store.
5. Observe a teacher at work with a kindergarten, first, or second grade class for thirty minutes and note the number and kinds of encouragement given individuals and the group.
6. Improvise a game suitable for children of kindergarten, or first or second grade which provides practice in an arithmetic skill or understanding likely to be taught at that level. What are its good features? Its weaknesses?

Guided Supplementary Reading

1. How did Ambrosius use a familiar Christmas verse to teach arithmetic?
2. What is overlooked when arithmetic definitions and rules are put in rhyme or verse?
3. For whom does Dumas suggest games using concrete materials will be easier to learn than games requiring only mental processes?
4. How does a teacher's attitude toward the study of arithmetic affect children's learning of it?

5. According to Gunderson, what is the key word that characterizes today's arithmetic?
6. What does Harding recommend should be the nature of arithmetic activities in the kindergarten? (Part 2, Section 1.)
7. Describe ways in which a classroom store can be used in the teaching of arithmetic.
8. What two important axioms regarding the teaching of mathematics are put forth by Jones?
9. What is Knowles' point of view with regard to motivation in mathematics?
10. What is the effect of rote teaching of arithmetic and poor teachers' attitude as reported by Ratanakul?
11. Spencer and Brydegaard make a strong case for readiness in the mathematics program. What considerations do they list as essential?
12. What purpose is to be served by the kinds of drill techniques suggested in the article by Vaughn?

Suggested Supplementary References

1. AMBROSIUS, D. S., " 'Twas the Night Before Christmas (in the First Grade)," *Arithmetic Teacher,* Vol. 5, pp. 317–318, December, 1958.
2. DESSART, D. J., AND J. A. BROWN, "Arithmetic in Verse," *Arithmetic Teacher,* Vol. 5, pp. 273–274, November, 1958.
3. DUMAS, ENOCH, *Arithmetic Games.* San Francisco: Fearon Publishers, 1960.
4. FEHR, H. F., "Note on Philosophy of Teaching Arithmetic," *Arithmetic Teacher,* Vol. 3, p. 31, February, 1956.
5. GUNDERSON, A. G., "Arithmetic for Today's Six- and Seven-Year-Olds," *Arithmetic Teacher,* Vol. 2, pp. 95–101, November, 1955.
6. HARDING, L. W., AND OTHERS, *Arithmetic for Child Development,* Part 1, Section 1 and Part 2, Sections 1, 2, 3. Dubuque, Iowa: W. C. Brown Company, Inc., 1959.
7. HESS, C., "Opening Day Sale!" *Grade Teacher,* Vol. 78, p. 22, December, 1960.
8. JONES, PHILLIP S., "The Growth and Development of Mathematical Ideas in Children," *The Growth of Mathematical Ideas,* Twenty-fourth Yearbook. Washington, D.C.: The National Council of Teachers of Mathematics, 1959.
9. KNOWLES, L., "Make Them Take, or Make Them Want Mathematics?" *Grade Teacher,* Vol. 78, p. 10, October, 1960.

10. RATANAKUL, S., "Learning Arithmetic from Kindergarten to Grade Six," *Arithmetic Teacher,* Vol. 2, p. 129, November, 1955.
11. SPENCER, PETER L., AND MARGUERITE BRYDEGAARD, *Building Mathematical Concepts in the Elementary School,* Chapter 2. New York: Henry Holt and Co., 1952.
12. VAUGHN, W. D., "Some Drill Techniques for Arithmetic," *Mathematics Teacher,* Vol. 50, pp. 436–437, October, 1957.

CHAPTER 3

Organizing the Arithmetic Program in Kindergarten, Grade 1, and Grade 2

The classroom procedures used by a primary teacher should depend upon the characteristics and abilities of her pupils and also upon the mathematical concepts and skills in computation which she thinks it desirable for them to learn.[1] This content should be selected in the light of what is needed at the particular time to meet the needs of the children's daily life and also with a view to a long-range plan which will develop the readiness and preparation needed by the pupils when they enter the intermediate grades. Having considered some of the characteristics of primary grade children in the previous chapter, we shall examine more closely the content we hope these children will learn during their time in kindergarten and in the first and second grades. An effective plan for organizing the arithmetic content and the sequence of experiences of the children, so that

[1] Agnes G. Gunderson, "Arithmetic for Today's Six- and Seven-Year-Olds," *Arithmetic Teacher,* 2:95–101, November, 1955, and Morris Pincus, "Enrichment in Arithmetic for the Primary Grades," *Arithmetic Teacher,* 6:186–190, October, 1959.

the psychological factors in each situation are given due consideration, is of primary importance. The development of such a plan soon becomes one of concern to a primary teacher, as it presents the many difficulties which are inherent in any teaching situation requiring a balanced consideration of the various needs of a particular group of children.[2]

The Need for an Effective Organization of Content

After a teacher has determined the arithmetic content which is suitable for the group of children she is teaching, she must decide upon the sequence in which the arithmetic topics should be introduced, and she must also select suitable teaching techniques to enable the children to clarify their former concepts and develop new concepts.

A brief consideration of our own daily activities and experiences will soon convince us that concepts of magnitude and number enter into all phases of daily living. Whenever we consider the magnitude of objects, we are dealing with quantitative concepts. These concepts, along with our number concepts, function extensively in our daily thinking. The concepts of magnitude and of number which children develop incidentally [3] in connection with their daily activities are so extensive that it might be thought unnecessary to go much beyond clarifying the quantitative concepts which the children meet in the various areas of the school curriculum and in their daily lives. In the kindergarten this incidental approach to arithmetic is sometimes sufficient, although direct teaching is desirable in connection with counting experiences and in teaching the children to read the numerals for small numbers.

As the child moves through grade 1 and grade 2, the scope of these incidental contacts with the broader quantitative concepts and also with many specific number concepts increases very rapidly. The problem of helping him to organize a mass of un-

[2] Gunderson, *op. cit.*

[3] O. L. Davis, Jr., Barbara Carper, and Carolyn Crigler, "The Growth of Pre-School Children's Familiarity with Measurements," *Arithmetic Teacher*, 6:186–190, October, 1959.

related facts then emerges and this problem becomes more demanding as the child progresses.

It is quite possible, if given enough time, that a child with good mental ability could organize this information for himself. There is a danger, however, that unless he is given the help which will enable him to organize his number information efficiently, he might move into the third grade and later into the intermediate grades without the readiness in concepts and skills which is needed to accomplish successfully the new and relatively difficult tasks required of him.

If we examine carefully the large amount of quantitative information which the children usually accumulate by the end of the second grade from their daily activities in the home, school, and community,[4] and if we consider, at the same time, the arithmetic which children are expected to learn in the intermediate grades, we are able to identify certain "threads" around which the child's quantitative experiences may be organized. It may be difficult to identify clearly the point at which these "threads" begin because they originate during the child's preschool years, but as he progresses through kindergarten they become more distinct. By the time he reaches the first grade, these "threads" have developed to the place where they form a good basis for a plan on which to organize his program in arithmetic.

Planning Sequences of Arithmetic Topics in the Lower Grades

Organizing content around "threads" of activity. When children reach the intermediate and upper grades, their teacher may get suggestions for an effective sequence in which to introduce new arithmetic topics by examining the logical nature of the subject matter itself. For instance, lessons concerning the meaning of

[4] Esther Swenson, "Arithmetic for Preschool and Primary-Grade Children," in *Report of the Society's Committee on Arithmetic,* Fiftieth Yearbook of the National Society for the Study of Education (Chicago: University of Chicago Press, 1951), pp. 53–75.

fractions should precede those concerned with the addition of like fractions, and these lessons, in turn, should precede lessons dealing with unlike fractions. The nature of the content of the arithmetic taught at the upper grade levels lends itself to a logical sequence of steps where each step leads on to an understanding of the next step.

In the kindergarten, grade 1, and grade 2, a clearly defined logical sequence is not as apparent, because here the child may be considered to be following not one but many "threads" of arithmetic activity. It is true that along any one "thread" a fairly clear sequence may be established. For instance, with regard to developing an understanding of number and the number system, we could think of a "thread" starting from counting and continuing to the analysis of small groups and then on through addition and subtraction, and at higher grade levels, continuing through the multiplication and division of whole numbers to other number concepts. The concept of fractions [5] could provide another "thread" which later, in the higher grades, extends to ideas of using decimal fractions and per cent. The "thread" of an aspect of measurement, such as the concept of time, could likewise be thought of as starting from a lesson topic such as recognizing the purpose and uses of clocks, and then being extended during other lessons to telling time to the hour, the half hour, and then to five-minute or minute intervals. Understanding the meaning of many other time concepts, such as those connected with the use of the calendar or holiday dates, would also be developed at appropriate places within the particular sequence which deals with the concept of time.

Other "threads," easily identified, are concerned with each of the various measurement concepts [6] of weight, liquid capacity, linear measure, and temperature. Concepts of monetary values would provide another "thread" as would those concepts concerning the identification of forms and shapes.

In the lower grades where these concepts are first developed, the organization of the program should be such that these "threads" may be followed concurrently, because they often merge and in-

[5] Agnes G. Gunderson and Ethel Gunderson, "Fraction Concepts Held by Young Children," *Arithmetic Teacher,* 4:168–174, October, 1957.
[6] O. L. Davis, Jr., Barbara Carper, and Carolyn Crigler, *op. cit.*

tertwine. In other words, the concepts developed in one "thread" of activity help explain or extend concepts in other "threads." For instance, the concept of fractions is used in connection with telling time, but it is used also in all the other areas of measurement. The concepts involved in learning the number system itself, such as those of counting or learning the place value of numerals, are used in writing numerals, and also used in connection with each of the threads dealing with types of measurement.

Figure 1.1 provides a diagramatic representation of these threads or sequences of concept development, around which arithmetic content may be organized in the primary grades. The diagram indicates that counting activities in the kindergarten lead into the analysis of small groups in the first and second grades. This, in turn, provides readiness for understanding the meaning of addition and subtraction. Addition may be used later to introduce multiplication, while subtraction, along with fraction concepts, provides part of the readiness for understanding division. From an understanding of small numbers and how to read them in grade 1, pupils proceed to the understanding and use of place value in calculations concerning the fundamental operations of addition, subtraction, multiplication, and division of whole numbers in grade 3. Fraction concepts provide readiness for understanding decimal fractions and per cent in the upper grades. The various threads leading to the development of concepts of money, time, weight, linear measure, temperature, and liquid capacity, may be identified also and used in organizing arithmetic content in those areas.

Developing concepts in the various areas concurrently. Although the child should follow the logical sequence apparent in each of these "threads," it would not be suitable to try to develop one of these areas completely and then start another area. Concepts which come later in the sequence of each area often are more difficult than the early concepts in the sequences of other areas. The teacher should plan to introduce and develop the concepts in all areas more or less concurrently. For instance, in the kindergarten, a small beginning may be made with the child in all of the areas of measurement in so far as he meets these concepts incidentally in his usual daily activities. In grade 1 and grade 2, the further development

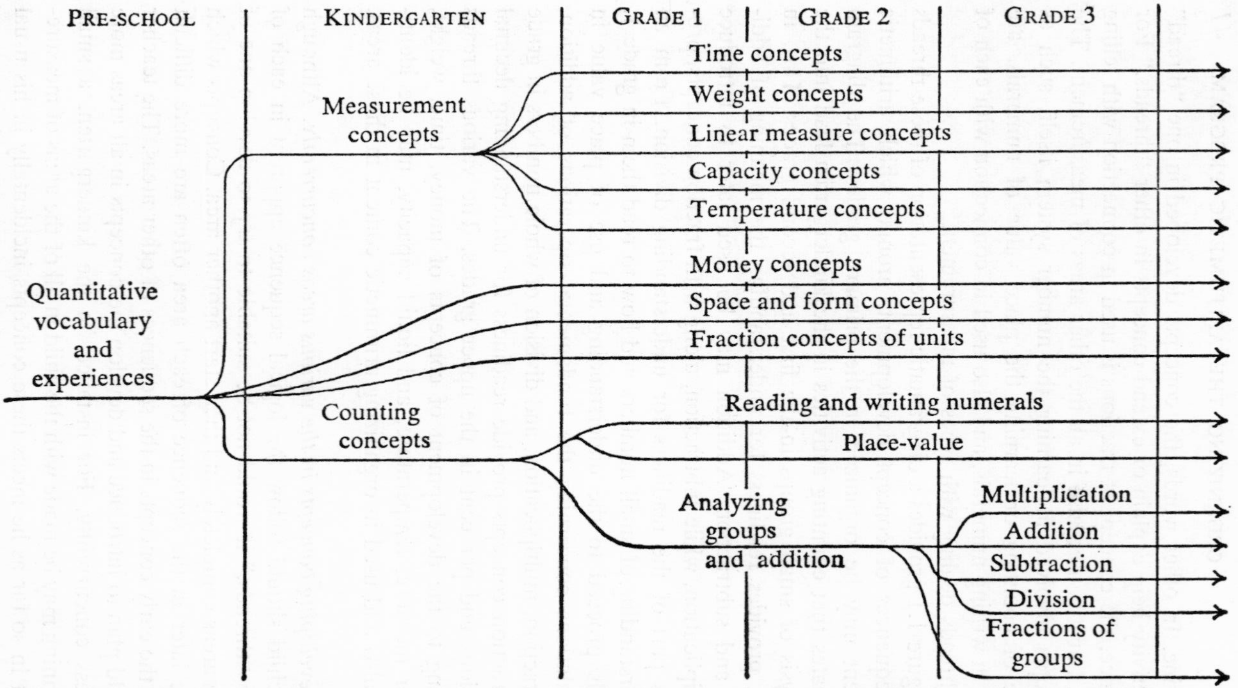

Figure 1.1 Diagram to indicate how the arithmetic program in the primary grades might be organized as "threads" of arithmetic activity.

of all of the areas continues but here he is given direct help, during an arithmetic period, to aid him to understand the interrelationships within each area. During these grades, his understanding of the number system, which is gradually being developed through counting experiences and analyzing small groups, increases and deepens his understanding of all of the areas of measurement.

The importance of the child's using the concepts from each of the areas of arithmetic in connection with various aspects of his daily activities should be emphasized in the primary grades.[7] Whenever an opportunity arises which enables a child to use concepts of measurement or other number concepts in any area of the curriculum, he is strengthening his understanding of arithmetic and its uses.

In the next two chapters a step-by-step sequence for introducing and developing the major arithmetical concepts found in each "thread" of activity is discussed. Although the procedures for the development of each "thread" in the arithmetic program are described separately, it must be understood that the classroom activities should be organized so that the "threads" are followed more or less concurrently.

Before proceeding to a discussion of the details in the sequence in each area of the arithmetic program, it is desirable to consider carefully two other very important phases of the teacher's work because they determine to a considerable extent the effectiveness of the arithmetic program in kindergarten and the first and second grades. These are: (1) the procedures used to encourage pupils to develop their quantitative vocabularies, and (2) procedures for utilizing the arithmetical situations arising throughout school activities.

Developing Quantitative Vocabulary

The teacher's task of helping children develop vocabulary begins from the time they first enter kindergarten. The vocabulary which the child can use himself is smaller than the vocabulary he understands when his teacher talks to him. He could be said to have a "speaking" vocabulary as well as a "listening" vocabulary.

[7] Swenson, *op. cit.*

The development of both of these vocabularies is necessary and is one of the important tasks of the kindergarten teacher.[8] The child's listening vocabulary is closely related to his understanding of new concepts, and determines among other things his readiness for reading.[9] His speaking vocabulary forms a basis for his work in oral expression and in written expression.[10]

Many of the words which the pupil needs to understand and to learn to use correctly are words involving quantitative relationships or space relationships of some description. The following words are examples only, and the lists are not mutually exclusive as the use of the word determines its placement.

Words Usually Implying Quantitative Concepts

few	young	count
many	old	enough
more	heavy	equal
less	light	most

Words Usually Implying Space Concepts

full	beside	under
empty	between	over
right	after	near
left	around	middle

Learning these words and the many other words which express quantitative relationships or space relationships should be thought of as an important part of arithmetic in kindergarten, grade 1, and grade 2.

Sequence in which new words are introduced. As may be noted in the examples listed above, some words involve more difficult concepts than others. While no definite order must be followed, it

[8] Josephine C. Foster and Neith E. Headley, "Language in the Kindergarten," Chap. 17 of *Education in the Kindergarten* (New York: American Book Co., 1948), pp. 289–303.

[9] David H. Russell, "Building Meaning Vocabularies," chapter 9 of *Children Learn to Read,* 2d edition (Boston: Ginn and Company, 1961), pp. 261–292.

[10] Mildred A. Dawson, "Language in the Learning Process," Chap. 1 of *Teaching Language in the Grades* (New York: World Book Co., 1951), pp. 3–13.

is well to observe the general principle of moving from the simple to the more complex concepts. In planning a sequence for developing the vocabulary of a child, it is important for the teacher to know which concepts are already familiar to him [11] because another general principle, that of working from the known to the unknown, implies that we build new concepts, whether simple or complex, upon our former experiences. The teacher should determine, through questions, discussions, and general observation, which of the common words involving quantitative or space relationships are known by the children. She should then use her judgment in deciding upon which new words her pupils are ready to learn.

A good procedure to use when developing children's vocabularies is to take advantage of some situation in which the kindergarten children are naturally interested and then bring in new words in such a way that the words are understood from the context or are explained so that they fit naturally into the discussion. Rather than "talking down" to the children by using only the words they already understand, the teacher should frequently bring in new words, and then ensure that the new words are understood. This is a natural way for the child to develop his vocabulary, as he is accustomed to learning new words by hearing them used by adults and the children around him.

Stories and songs in which numbers and quantitative words are used also help the children to understand the meaning of the quantitative terms as they use them in various contexts. Flannel board stories are especially interesting to kindergarten children. In such an activity the teacher places objects upon the flannel board to illustrate a story as she tells it or reads it aloud. These stories afford many opportunities to use quantitative expressions and are particularly valuable as they permit the children to see the number relationships illustrated by the material at the same time that they hear them expressed verbally.

While the children are still in kindergarten, they are ready to hear and use many words which refer to different phases of measurement. At this grade level, some of the instruments commonly

[11] Corwin E. Bjonerud, "Arithmetic Concepts Possessed by the Preschool Child," *Arithmetic Teacher,* 7:347–350, November, 1960.

used in measurement may be identified, such as clocks, watches, calendars, egg-timers, rulers, yardsticks, scales, thermometers, and quart measures. Some of the measurement units may be used also in connection with the social studies, reading, or with activities other than arithmetic. The kindergarten child will probably hear the following units mentioned while he is in school or at home: hour, day, month, year, pound, pint, quart, dollar, penny, nickel, dime, as well as many others.

Words indicating shapes such as "circle," "round," "square," "half-circle," are sometimes used in connection with games or while using modeling clay or in paper-cutting. The word "half" is used often, and "quarter," or "fourth," may be used occasionally.[12]

Although the concepts implied by words of this kind are often too difficult to be understood completely by a child at the kindergarten level, he is at least introduced to the concept by hearing the word used correctly in a context which is familiar to him.

As noted above, there is no definite order in which these words must be introduced. The teacher should make use of opportunities to introduce, use, or clarify quantitative expressions which arise during the normal kindergarten activities. A question such as, "What is the shape of your ball?" directs the attention of the child to the particular relationship which the teacher wishes him to note, and gives him practice in using or thinking of the term in a context which either introduces or clarifies the quantitative concepts.

While working with any group of kindergarten children, the teacher will observe that some are much more advanced than others in their understanding and use of quantitative terms. When the brighter children are able to understand and use new terms, the teacher should encourage them to do so. There is no need to wait for everyone in the group to be ready for a term before it is introduced, as the slower children will learn from hearing the word used by other children as well as by hearing the teacher use it.

[12] California Bureau of Elementary Education. "The Development of Arithmetical Ideas in Young Children," Chap. 17 in *Teachers Guide to Education in Early Childhood* (Sacramento: California State Department of Education, 1956).

Utilizing Arithmetical Situations in Daily Activities

Although the importance of encouraging children to make use of arithmetic in their daily activities has been mentioned, more thought should be given to the value of this phase of the arithmetic program.

Using a daily arithmetic period. In kindergarten, all the arithmetic with the exception of counting experiences may be planned so that quantitative concepts are developed in connection with the normal daily activities, and consequently no daily separate period for the direct study of arithmetic should be necessary for this grade level.[13] In grades 1 and 2, although the basis for much of the arithmetic may be provided through the pupils' daily activities, a short daily period for the direct study of arithmetic is very helpful. The purpose of this daily period should be to help the pupils clarify and organize the quantitative concepts they have been learning and to extend their number concepts by directing their attention to the many number relationships in their environment. During this daily period, the pupils are introduced to the manner in which numerals and other arithmetic symbols are used to express number ideas. The teacher is also provided with an opportunity to evaluate further the capabilities of the children so that the program may be regulated to suit their needs and their abilities. Through the observation of the children's responses and reactions, the teacher is able to plan further activities which will make up the most effective program for this particular group.

By the time the pupils reach the third grade, they are ready both physically and psychologically to spend more time daily on the direct study of arithmetic. A tendency to be avoided at this time is that of confining the use of arithmetic to this daily period only, neglecting to help the children to use their new and more extended arithmetical understandings throughout all daily activities wherever they might apply.

Directing attention to arithmetical relationships. Although arithmetical relationships and concepts of quantity are found in nearly

[13] *Ibid.*, pp. 540–541.

every area of the school program, these relationships and concepts may not be recognized by the pupils unless the teacher directs attention to them. Many opportunities to consider measurement units or the uses of measurement are available daily. For example, when the teacher suggests a certain size for the objects made during construction work and makes suggestions for their accurate placement, the pupil's attention is directed to number as it is used in measurement. In the social studies while the pupils are studying the local community or environment the considerations of distance and units of time, weight, capacity, or money, provide practice in arithmetic.[14] In health education, utilizing standard tables of height and weight, or considering the nature and quantity of various foods, provide some number experiences. In physical education, the scoring, timing, or measuring of distances provides opportunities for the pupils to use numbers. When a group of children form smaller groups to make up relay teams, one meaning of division is being exemplified. Even while planning a school party or picnic, number concepts may be used in making decisions regarding the quantities of various supplies which are needed. Science activities often involve the keeping of records, and considerations of weight, distance, capacity, and other number concepts. Study trips also provide numerous occasions where number can be used during the planning and also during the follow-up of the trip while the pupils are reporting and organizing the information gained from their experiences.[15]

As noted above, while opportunities are present for the pupil to use his arithmetical concepts in some way throughout all his daily activities, these opportunities may be overlooked quite easily and consequently neglected unless the teacher consciously directs the attention of the pupils to the various arithmetical relationships which are involved in each experience. Whenever the teacher is planning activities in any area of the primary school curriculum, she should be alert for the possibilities within the activity to extend the pupils' number concepts.

Using mature levels of computation. It should be noted that the

[14] Enoch Dumas, *Arithmetic Learning Activities* (San Francisco: Fearon Publishers, 1957), pp. 6–26.

[15] John U. Michaelis, "Using Community Resources," *Social Studies for Children in a Democracy* (Englewood Cliffs, N.J.: Prentice-Hall, Inc., 1950).

level of maturity at which the pupil functions in handling the arithmetic in his daily activities is important. While the pupil is learning to count, he can be expected to solve his problems on the counting level only. Once he has learned to use addition and subtraction facts, he should be encouraged to use the addition and subtraction processes instead of counting. After the pupil has learned the meaning and use of multiplication and division, he should be encouraged to use these processes where they are applicable. For instance, there may be a tendency for a child who has learned the purposes of multiplication to revert to addition or counting during his daily activities in a situation where multiplication would be a more mature way for solving certain problems in measurement. He may feel much more familiar with the counting or addition procedures because he had used them formerly in similar situations. Once the pupil has learned how to multiply, the teacher should encourage him to use this more efficient procedure when it is suitable for solving a problem.

More will be said on the importance of using arithmetic in social settings in Chapter 14 where problem solving is discussed. It should be stressed that one of the most effective ways of securing "carry-over" from the arithmetic period to problem solving in social settings is for the teacher to encourage the pupils to recognize number situations in their various activities and to encourage them to use a suitable level of arithmetical thinking in solving their daily problems.

Principles Basic to the Effective Organization of the Arithmetic Program in Kindergarten, Grade 1, and Grade 2

Although many rather detailed suggestions for selecting content and for presenting the material will be found in the next two chapters, the teacher should not overlook the very valuable suggestions often found in local courses of study, teachers' guides, and the teachers' manuals which accompany pupils' textbooks and workbooks.

One principle emphasized here as basic to the effective organization of the arithmetic program in the primary grades may be stated as follows: Providing that the teacher is competent, she should be given the freedom needed to organize the arithmetic program to meet the individual needs of the particular group of primary grade children she is teaching so that this program will be organized with full consideration given to the arithmetic concepts these particular children need and can assimilate at that time, as well as to what they are expected to accomplish in succeeding grades.

A second principle emphasized is that the arithmetic program in kindergarten, grade 1, and grade 2 should be developed carefully and systematically, although advantage should be taken also of incidental arithmetic experiences.

A third principle is that careful consideration should be given to factors of child development which will contribute to the most effective learning in each situation.

As will be noted in succeeding chapters, organizing the most effective arithmetic program for a particular group of children in the early grades is no easy task. It will provide a worthy challenge to the competent primary grade teacher.

Suggested Learning Activities

1. Interview parents of three children of either kindergarten or first grade level and list all the out-of-school quantity or magnitude communication needs the adults can recall arising in the youngsters' daily life during the past week. Identify those needs calling for words of comparison, for indefinite number concepts, for counting, and for measuring.
2. Examine word lists at the back of a set of your choice of preprimers, primers, and first readers to note words expressing quantity. Do the same for words expressing space concepts. How many do you find of each?
3. Make a list of stories, poems, and songs (appropriate to a primary grade of your choice) which contain quantitative terms.
4. Select a science activity appropriate to the first grade and suggest arithmetic learnings which could well be included.

Guided Supplementary Reading

1. On what basis does Brownell conclude that systematic arithmetic instruction should begin in the first grade?

2. What are the implications of the Buswell-John study of children's arithmetic vocabularies?
3. What value does Curtin see to having a special arithmetic period as opposed to complete integration with social studies and science?
4. What conclusions from research evidence support the "meaning theory" in teaching arithmetic?
5. What constitutes a good program in primary arithmetic as seen by Deans?
6. Under what headings does Dumas suggest arithmetic activities which can be planned as outgrowths of a primary social studies unit on the home?
7. Why is research of the type pursued by Feldhusen and Klausmeir valuable to educators?
8. What five facets of the arithmetic program do Grossnickle and Brueckner identify?
9. For what reasons does Hollister suggest that teachers carefully assess the arithmetic knowledge of school beginners?
10. How can counting boys and girls present each day be used to teach vocabulary?
11. What were Miller's findings regarding how much time per day was being spent on teaching arithmetic?
12. What does Pieters mean by "the strategic moment" in teaching arithmetic at primary levels?
13. What advice does Risden have for parents of pre-school children?
14. How does Rosenquist propose that pupils learn to understand the meaning of a process?
15. What general kinds of experiences in arithmetic does Smith recommend for kindergarten children?

Suggested Supplementary References

1. BROWNELL, W. A., AND OTHERS, "Start in the First Grade," *Research in the Three R's,* pp. 401–406. New York: Harper and Brothers, 1958.
2. BUSWELL, G. T., AND L. JOHN, "Children's Knowledge of Arithmetic Vocabulary," *Research in the Three R's,* pp. 408–410. New York: Harper and Brothers, 1958.
3. CURTIN, J., "Arithmetic in the Total School Program," *Arithmetic Teacher,* Vol. 4, pp. 235–239, December, 1957.
4. DAWSON, D. T., AND A. K. RUDDELL, "Case for the Meaning Theory in Teaching Arithmetic," *Elementary School Journal,* Vol. 55, pp. 393–399, March, 1955.

5. DEANS, E., "Arithmetic in the Primary Grades," *National Elementary Principal,* Vol. 39, pp. 22–28, October, 1959.
6. DUMAS, ENOCH, *Arithmetic Learning Activities.* San Francisco: Fearon Publishers, 1957.
7. FELDHUSEN, J. F., AND H. J. KLAUSMEIER, "Achievement in Counting and Addition," *Elementary School Journal,* Vol. 59, pp. 388–393, April, 1959.
8. GROSSNICKLE, FOSTER E., AND LEO J. BRUECKNER, *Discovering Meanings in Arithmetic,* Chapter 3. Philadelphia: The John C. Winston Co., 1959.
9. HOLLISTER, G. E., "Some First Graders Count Down," *Education,* Vol. 79, pp. 272–275, January, 1959.
10. INSTEBO, E., "How Many Children Are Here Today?" *Arithmetic Teacher,* Vol. 2, p. 161, December, 1955.
11. MILLER, G. H., "How Much Time for Arithmetic?" *Arithmetic Teacher,* Vol. 5, pp. 256–259, November, 1958.
12. PIETERS, M. B., "Utilizing the Strategic Moment in Arithmetic," *Arithmetic Teacher,* Vol. 5, pp. 311–314, December, 1958.
13. RISDEN, G. A., "Andy Can Count to 100," *American Childhood,* Vol. 43, pp. 35–36, September, 1957.
14. ROSENQUIST, LUCY L., *Young Children Learn to Use Arithmetic,* Chapter 1. Boston: Ginn and Co., 1949.
15. SMITH, L. K., "Arithmetic in the Kindergarten," *Instructor,* Vol. 67, p. 34, November, 1957.
16. SOWARDS, G. W., "Organization of the Curriculum; Arithmetic," *Review of Educational Research,* Vol. 29, p. 151, April, 1959.

CHAPTER 4

Developing Concepts of Number and the Decimal Numeration System

Before continuing with a discussion of procedures for introducing numbers to children, it is desirable to identify certain mathematical concepts and terms which later will enable us to define more precisely the number ideas we wish children to develop.

The term "set" is used to refer to any well defined collection of elements. These elements might be concrete, as when we speak of the set of children who are twelve years old, or the set of desks in a certain classroom. The elements of a set might be abstract in nature, as when we speak of the set of counting numbers greater than five, or the set of fractions equivalent to ¾. Set concepts and symbolism are discussed in Chapter 6 and again in Chapter 15.

One set may be said to be "mapped into" a second set when each member of it is matched with one or more members of the second set. Each member of the second set is said to be an "image" of the member with which it is matched in the first set. For example, one may use his fingers to record the balls and strikes in a baseball game; one finger on the left hand for each ball and one finger on the right hand for each strike. In each instance there is a one-to-one mapping between the set of balls or strikes and the set of fingers on each hand because there is a single image, a finger, in the second set for each element, a strike, in the first set. It should be noted, as in Figure 4.1, that in a one-to-one mapping

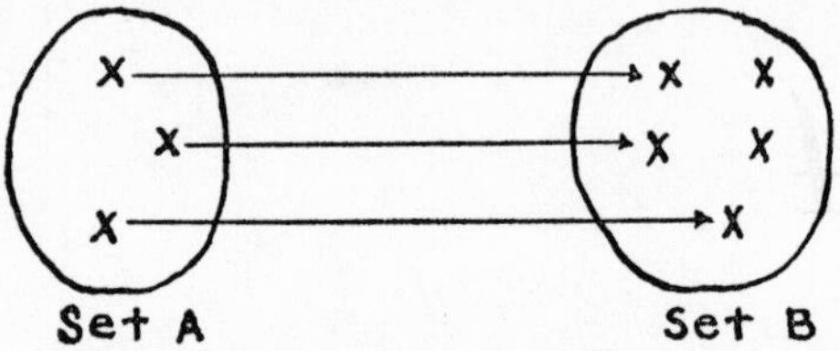

Figure 4.1 A diagram of a one-to-one mapping of set *A* into set *B*. An example here might be a set of three strikes mapped into a set of five fingers.

there may be some elements in the second set which are not images of elements in the first set. This would be the case in instances where the second set has more elements than the first set.

One might have more than one item of one set mapped into the items of the second set, as in the case of table settings. There may be seven items (napkin, fork, plate, knife, spoon, saucer, cup) for each person, and this could be called a seven-to-one matching. Figure 4.2 shows a diagram of a seven-to-one matching.

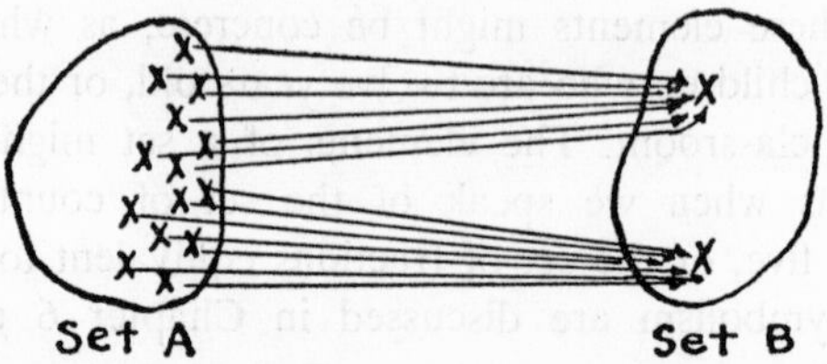

Figure 4.2 A diagram of a seven-to-one mapping of set *A* into set *B*.

In some instances there may be a one-to-one mapping which is "reversible" as it assigns each member of the first set to one and only one member of the second set, and at the same time assigns each member of the second set to one and only one member of the first set, as illustrated in Figure 4.3. Such is the case when students are assigned to seats. We say then that the set of

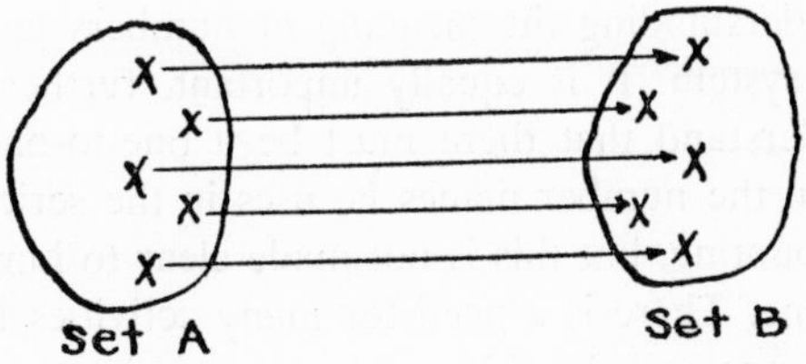

Figure 4.3 A diagram showing one-to-one correspondence between two sets. This is a one-to-one mapping of set *A* into set *B* and a one-to-one mapping of set *B* into set *A*. This is called a reversible mapping and it indicates that the two sets have the same cardinal number associated with them.

students and the set of seats occupied by them are in one-to-one correspondence, because in this instance there is a reversible one-to-one mapping.

When two sets are in one-to-one correspondence, the two sets are said to have the same *cardinal* number. In the language of mathematics, we may think of the number five as being the number property which is common to all sets which may be put into one-to-one correspondence with a standard set, or model set, of five elements.

Dantzig [1] has pointed out that in order to devise a counting process our set of models must be arranged in an ordered sequence. Our series of number names, "one," "two," "three," "four," and so on, and their ordered sequence identifies the arrangement of the set of models for us. By thinking of each number name in the series as standing for the cardinal number which is one more than the cardinal number represented by the preceding name in the ordered series, we are equipped with a device which permits us to find how many objects are in a group by matching each object being counted with a number name in our series in a one-to-one correspondence. The last number name used in this way will indicate the number of objects in the group being counted.

We must recognize the fact that it is important for a child to memorize the sequence of number names because we know that a knowledge of this sequence is needed to provide him with a

[1] Tobias Dantzig, *Number, the Language of Science* (New York: The Macmillan Company, revised edition, 1954), p. 8.

basis for understanding the meaning of numbers and the decimal numeration system. It is equally important, furthermore, for the child to understand that there must be a one-to-one correspondence between the number names he uses in the series and the objects he is counting, but this is not made clear to him through rote counting alone. There is a need for many activities in which he is given experience in using his number names in counting concrete objects. It is through this type of experience that he gradually forms a concept of the standard set, or model group, which is represented by each number name, and until this is accomplished there is no other way for him to understand the meaning of a number name. Counting experiences are very important for the child in kindergarten, and the teacher should not assume that a pupil will "pick up" the required concepts through his own efforts without help.

Introducing Numbers to Children

Using counting experiences. In Chapter 2 we noted that the child's early concepts of number were developed as he learned to count by rote, and that these number concepts were formed along with rather vague quantitative concepts. At first, the child learns the number names only as a series of sounds. During his preschool years he learns by rote that certain sounds, such as "one," "two," "three," follow one another in a certain order. He learns that adults call these sounds "numbers" but at first these names have no particular meaning for him.

When children first attend school, most of them can count by rote to some extent.[2] Rote counting is necessary to children as an early step in their introduction to numbers. The children should be led to understand that, in the particular order of number names which they are learning by rote, each number name following "one" will indicate a group, or set of elements, which is larger by one than the set named by the preceding number name in the series. They learn, for instance, that in the series of number names which they have memorized, "six" succeeds "five" because "six" is associated with a set of elements which is one more than the set

[2] G. E. Hollister and Agnes Gunderson, *Teaching Arithmetic in Grades I and II* (Boston: D. C. Heath and Co., 1954), pp. 51–58.

of elements associated with "five." In mathematical language this might be stated more explicitly by saying that the counting numbers possess the property that each number has a *successor,* defined as "one more than the number."

After learning the order of the number names by rote, the next step is that of learning how to use the counting series in order to determine how many objects there are in a group. An important objective of the teacher, at this stage, is to help the pupils to understand that the last name used in counting the objects, in a one-to-one correspondence, is used also to indicate the total number of objects in a group, or to answer the question, "How many are there in the group?" It is well for the teacher to follow each counting experience with the question, "How many are there?" until the pupils understand that an important reason for counting is to determine how many objects there are in a group. Requiring the children to repeat the number names aloud, either individually or in chorus, while the teacher or a pupil touches each of the objects in a group or moves it toward the first object counted, helps the pupils to understand the connection between the series of number names and the group of objects being counted. This process of counting to find how many there are in a group by matching the number names with the objects being counted is called "rational counting" or sometimes "enumeration" and is basic to an understanding of most other arithmetical concepts.

There are numerous opportunities for counting activities in the kindergarten. The number of children in the whole class or the number of those in groups engaged in various activities may be found by counting. The supplies of crayons, scissors, or blocks needed for some activity may be counted. The teacher may ask the children to count to find how many chairs are needed or how many bottles of milk are required for lunch. Simple games may bring in counting activities, as do some songs and stories. Since the children at this age level like counting objects, the teacher will have no difficulty in finding counting activities for them at any time of the day.

Understanding the meaning of the number names. As a child gains experience in rational counting, he begins to note that he can distinguish one small group from another through counting, and that some groups have either the same or a different number of objects in them. In other words, he finds that he can identify the size of a certain group by using a number name. Through counting groups of objects he begins to associate each number with a group of a certain size. For instance, after counting many groups containing the same number of objects, such as four books, four children, four items of food, or a group of dissimilar objects such as a ball, a boy, a bat, and a dog, he begins to associate the word "four" with the numerousness of any group of four objects, and he is forming a concept of a model group which is represented by the number name "four." This association of a number with the numerousness of a group of a certain size is what was referred to above as the *cardinal* use of number. The number four has become for him the number property of all sets which may be put into one-to-one correspondence with a model set of four elements, and he has grasped the meaning of the number four.

Through further experiences with groups, the child learns that each model group, or set, represented by his counting sequence of number names is one more than the set represented by the previous number name in the sequence which he learned by rote. As he grasps this idea, he is able to count out any number of objects he wishes by starting from one and building a group by increasing it by ones until he has a group representing the number he wants. He can count out a given number of objects from a larger group when he is asked to do so.

At this stage, it is good teaching practice to give each child ten or twelve cardboard discs, tickets, or other objects which he can manipulate easily. The pupil may then count out small groups on his desk when the teacher says the number names. The teacher may also ask the pupils to complete simple tasks which will require them to count out groups. For instance, they may be asked to put a certain number of discs to one side of their desks or to arrange groups in various positions. The teacher should observe which pupils understand the directions and are able to follow them, and which pupils need more help. Words and phrases connoting space relationships such as, "above," "near," "at the side of," "top," "bottom," or "middle," may be combined also with number relationships in this type of practice by giving directions such as, "Put *five* discs *near* the *center* of your desk."

As the children become more experienced in counting, the teacher will notice that they begin to recognize the number of objects in a small group of five or less without having to count the objects individually. This is a normal stage in concept development, and the teacher should encourage the pupils to "think" the number of objects in a small group as long as they wish to do so, providing that they are accurate when answering. This ability to recognize the number of objects in a small group without actually counting the objects indicates that the pupil's perceptual ability has developed to the place where he can recognize a simple pattern as the model group, or standard set, which he connects with a certain number name.[3]

The pupil is now ready to understand that by using his knowledge of counting he has a new way for comparing groups. At first, before he could count rationally, he could compare two groups only by matching each object in one group with an object in the other group in a one-to-one correspondence. For instance, he could match each of the pupils at a table with a single crayon until all were supplied with crayons. Now, with his counting ability, he can count the number of pupils at a table and know how many crayons he would need to supply all of the pupils. Counting will begin to take on a new usefulness and meaning for him. He will find it an easier way of meeting some of his daily tasks, and the teacher should encourage him to use counting to deal with these common situations.

Analyzing Groups to Provide Readiness for Learning Addition and Subtraction

When using the customary algorisms of addition and subtraction at higher grade levels, the child needs to learn to use the basic addition facts and the basic subtraction facts. Although the answers to many problems may be found by counting, the teacher wishes the pupils to understand that once the addition facts and subtraction facts have been learned, it is more efficient to use these

[3] Dan T. Dawson, "Number Grouping as a Function of Complexity," *Elementary School Journal,* 54:35–43, September, 1953; and Edwina Deans, "In the Classroom," *Arithmetic Teacher,* 7:367–372, November, 1960.

facts, along with the process of addition or subtraction, than it is to use counting to find answers to problems. By the time the pupils reach the third grade, they should understand that once the basic facts have been learned they can work more quickly and with fewer mistakes than would be the case if they tried to solve all their problems by counting.

In the first grade, the children are not expected to memorize many of the basic facts. The emphasis in this grade is placed more upon having the children understand the meaning of addition and subtraction, that is, what takes place when we perform these operations upon numbers.

In order for the children to understand these operations it is necessary first for them to see how we may think of any whole number, other than zero and one, as being made up of two or more other numbers. This step, which begins when a child learns that there are various ways of breaking a group into two or more groups, is sometimes called "analyzing groups" and through the analysis of groups the child learns how the basic facts are formed. This knowledge, in turn, helps him to understand how basic facts are used in addition and subtraction, and is thus a readiness stage for learning these operations.

It is quite likely that the child in grade 1 will memorize voluntarily some of the easier basic facts simply because he uses them so often that he can visualize them and remember them without difficulty. This is particularly true in the case of some of the "doubles" and also for basic facts where the number one is added to, or subtracted from, another small number. The teacher need not put undue stress upon memorizing the basic facts at first, but she should give the children considerable practice in analyzing small groups, so that they may understand how the basic facts are derived and how they may be used to solve problems in addition and subtraction. Analyzing groups also provides readiness for understanding the operations of multiplication and division.

Good teaching practice at this grade level again includes the use of a variety of manipulative materials by the pupils. The teacher wishes the pupils first to perceive how a group of objects may be made up of two smaller groups, and then to understand that, in somewhat the same way, a whole number, other than zero or one, may be thought of as being made up of two smaller numbers. Finally, she wishes the pupils to see how the process is recorded by using numerals. The distinction between adding numbers and combining groups of objects need not be stressed at this early stage but should be emphasized later. The distinction should be clear, of course, to the teacher.[4] By keeping in mind the distinction between abstract numbers and the numerals and objects used to represent them, the teacher will be inclined to use more precise language in her explanations, and this, in turn, should help the pupils gradually to develop clearer concepts.

A teaching procedure for analyzing groups. The procedure used by a teacher during a lesson to show children in grade 1 how the number seven could be better understood by analyzing a group of seven objects might be as follows:

STEP 1. Provide each child with seven counters, such as cardboard discs, and with a pencil and paper.

STEP 2. Through questions, lead the children to manipulate and "discover" the ways in which the group of seven discs could be made up of two smaller groups, such as one and six, two and five, and three and four.

STEP 3. Have each child record what he has done with the counters by requiring him to write the number symbols for each of the groups which he has formed, as $2 + 5 = 7$, and also as $5 + 2 = 7$.

STEP 4. Use the flannel board to show the same groupings and write the number symbols on the chalkboard. Pupils will check their work and discuss the manner in which the symbols were used to express the number situations.

STEP 5. Evaluate the child's learning through questions and observations of his use of the material. Determine whether or not he understands that seven may be thought of as being made up of two and five, and of other combinations. He should see that this may be written as $2 + 5 = 7$ or as $5 + 2 = 7$ so that readiness will be provided for his understanding the commutative nature of addition when this

[4] Wayne Peterson, "A Case in Point," *Arithmetic Teacher,* 8:10–13, January, 1961.

property is emphasized as a principle or "law" at a later time.

STEP 6. Have the children note other arrangements of subgroups which make up the whole group. For instance, they should note that the subgroups could be arranged to show $3 + 3 + 1 = 7$, $2 + 2 + 2 + 1 = 7$, $3 + 2 + 2 = 7$.

By following a procedure similar to that suggested for analyzing a group of seven, the pupils should analyze groups representing all the numbers from two through eighteen. The teacher should proceed slowly through groups up to that representing ten to ensure that the pupils understand the nature of the process, and work with the numbers above ten only after the pupils have demonstrated that they have a firm grasp on the meaning of the smaller numbers.

After some groups have been analyzed, the pupils should review simultaneously the groups representing some of the even numbers, and be led to discover that any group representing an even number may be formed by two subgroups of the same size, and that a group representing an even number may be formed of subgroups each of which is two.

Particular attention should be given to groups which may be formed by a number of equal subgroups, for example, six as formed by two groups of three or by three groups of two. This provides readiness for understanding multiplication.

The numbers four, nine, and sixteen should be noted particularly as being represented by groups which may be arranged in subgroups in such a way that the number of subgroups is the same as the number of objects in each subgroup. For example, a group of nine may be formed by three groups of three objects.

Although the symbols $2 + 5 = 7$ are used also to indicate an addition process, the emphasis at first is not upon the addition process but simply upon having the pupils understand that a group of seven may be thought of as being made up of smaller subgroups. Through experiences of the kind noted above, the pupils will come to understand that just as groups may be combined to make a larger group, so numbers may be added to make another number. At this level, the plus sign may be read as "and" while the sign for equality is read as "are" or as "make." When the pupils understand the meaning of addition and subtraction, the plus sign should be read as "plus" while the sign for equality should be read as "equals" and the subtraction sign read as "minus." Appropriate vocabulary such as "sum" and "difference" may be introduced then.

The concept that the operation of subtraction is the inverse of that of addition need not be stressed at first, although the idea is introduced to the child by being exemplified in various instances as he manipulates the groups of counters during the time he is analyzing groups. A procedure for developing generalizations pertaining to inverse operations will be discussed in Chapter 7.

Reading and writing number symbols. The language of arithmetic is expressed through symbols which have been passed down to us through the centuries. Some aspects of arithmetic and of other branches of mathematics which children learn involve the manipulation of these symbols in accordance with certain principles. A danger which must be avoided carefully at any grade level is that of having children use these symbols without fully understanding their meaning or the significance of the number operations indicated by them. Some of the most important changes in the teaching of arithmetic during the past two decades have been brought about through teachers becoming aware of the importance of giving meaning to arithmetic. Brownell,[5] Wheat,[6] Brueckner and Grossnickle,[7] and many others have exerted considerable influence in securing an emphasis upon the "meaning approach" to arithmetic which is accepted widely today by authorities in the field of elementary school arithmetic.[8] Children who understand number and number operations are usually more interested, learn new processes more quickly, retain with less drill, and more readily make applications of what they have learned.

To someone who has taught children in kindergarten and the

[5] W. A. Brownell, "The Place of Meaning in Teaching Arithmetic," *Elementary School Journal,* 47:256–265, January, 1947.

[6] Harry G. Wheat, *How to Teach Arithmetic* (Evanston, Illinois: Row, Peterson and Company, 1951).

[7] Leo J. Brueckner and Foster E. Grossnickle, *How to Make Arithmetic Meaningful* (Philadelphia: John C. Winston Co., 1947).

[8] Dan T. Dawson and Arden K. Ruddell, "The Case for the Meaning Theory in Teaching Arithmetic," *Elementary School Journal,* 55:393–399, March, 1955.

first grade, the difficulty of having children at these grade levels distinguish clearly the difference between a symbol or numeral, such as "5" and the number for which it stands may seem almost insurmountable. The number five is an abstract relationship which the child cannot perceive directly but can recognize only as something which pertains to a group of a certain size. The symbol, or numeral, "5" is something that he can see, and he all too readily accepts the symbol as being the number itself, rather than thinking of the numeral as a symbol which stands for the number.

It is not surprising then that the child may give more thought to the symbols of arithmetic than to the numbers they represent, until any distinction between a numeral, or number symbol, and the number it represents may be lacking entirely. Arithmetic may become for him a rather mechanical manipulation of symbols in accordance with certain rules but without his having a clear understanding of the number situations the numerals are intended to express.

One basic teaching procedure which tends to enable the child to make a distinction between a numeral and the number relationship itself is to require him to make use of a variety of manipulative materials, particularly counters such as discs, tickets, or other objects, while he is solving a problem, and then to help him to understand that he may use numerals to express the number relationships in the situation as demonstrated with the materials.[9] In this way, his attention is directed first toward the number situation illustrated with the materials, and secondly toward the symbolic representation of these situations. It is suggested that the teacher should precede the use of numerals with an illustration of how the number relationships in a given problem may be represented by counters or by diagrams until the point is reached where the teacher is assured that the pupils understand the meaning of the numerals and why they are using them in each situation.[10]

During the first grade, most children are ready to learn how to read and to write the numerals from one to one hundred or more.

[9] Gertrude Hildreth, "Principles of Learning Applied to Arithmetic," *Arithmetic Teacher,* 1:1–5, October, 1954.

[10] Edwina Deans, "In the Classroom," *Arithmetic Teacher,* 7:303–308, October, 1960; and Edwina Deans, "In the Classroom," *Arithmetic Teacher,* 7:367–372, November, 1960.

At first, they should be shown how to form the numerals from one to ten. The place at which to start each numeral and the direction of the strokes should be made very clear to them. While they are learning to write numerals, it is helpful for the children to have a wall chart available for reference, such as is shown in Figure 4.4.

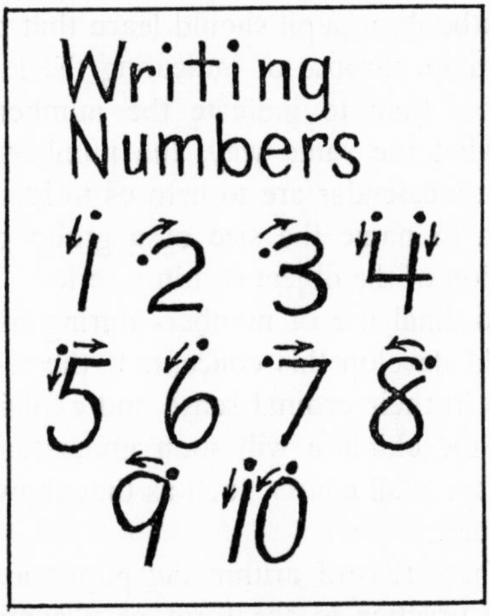

Figure 4.4 Wall chart useful for children as a reference while they are learning to form the numerals. Note that at this stage the children may refer to the numerals as "numbers."[11] The distinction between "number" and "numeral" should be made as soon as the children are ready to understand it.[12]

Children at this grade level normally make many reversals of both numerals and letters until they have succeeded in memorizing the shapes of these symbols.

The need for learning the ordinal use of numbers. During his daily school activities, a child in grade 1 should learn the ordinal use of numbers, such as "first," "second," "third," and so on. He should learn that these numbers are not being used to indicate the

[11] John R. Clark, "Number, Numeral, and Operation," *Arithmetic Teacher,* 7:222–225, May, 1960.
[12] Wayne Peterson, "A Case in Point," *Arithmetic Teacher,* 8:10–13, January, 1961.

size of a group nor the total number of objects in a group, as is the case when he uses cardinal numbers. The numbers have an ordinal use when they are employed to identify some particular element within a series. Numerals such as "1," "2," "3" and number words such as "one," "two," "three," and so on, may also have an ordinal use. For instance, when finding a certain page in his reading textbook, a pupil should learn that the page number is there for the main purpose of indicating the location of a particular page rather than to indicate the number of pages in a group. In somewhat the same way, the numbers on houses, on street signs, or on a calendar are to help us to identify a particular thing rather than to name the size of a group of objects. They indicate the position of the object within a series.

The frequent ordinal use of numbers during his daily activities will help the child develop this concept. If the teacher frequently will use numbers in their ordinal sense and explain their meaning when necessary, the children will soon understand their purpose and use in this way. Wall charts, such as that shown in Figure 4.5, may be of assistance.

Here, as in other areas of arithmetic, pupils may be motivated by arranging the practice in the form of a game. A "game" as

Figure 4.5 Wall chart indicating the use of ordinal numbers.

simple as asking the pupils if they can find the third, fifth, or eighth page in their textbook will help provide some practice, and a resourceful teacher will devise many ways for keeping the practice or drill aspect of arithmetic from becoming tedious for the pupils.[13]

Learning How the Value of a Numeral Is Determined by the Position of Its Digits

When the child is ready to learn how to write the numerals for the numbers greater than nine, he should be introduced to the concept of "place value." He should be shown how the number ten has particular importance in our number system because we name numbers and also write the numerals in such a way that the number of tens, or power of ten, is indicated. For example, the number name "twenty-two" and the numeral "22" refer to a set of elements which could be thought of as being grouped as 2 tens and 2 ones. There are, of course, many other ways in which the elements of a set could be grouped, but we want the child to learn that in naming the numbers or in writing the numerals for them the groups of ten take on a special significance.

This concept may be illustrated by requiring the children to manipulate small objects, such as tickets or small sticks, and to group them into bundles of so many tens and so many ones. They should note then that when we write a numeral or say a number name we are indicating the groups of tens and ones. At this stage of learning, each time the children group the objects into bundles of ten, they should write the numeral indicated by the arrangement, as this will help them clarify their concepts of place value. This procedure is illustrated in Figure 4.6.

The teacher also may require the children to use "Everybody show cards" for further practice. Each pupil should have a card holder and two sets of ten cards each, with each set containing the numerals from zero through nine. After each child has arranged certain objects into groups of ten, he should write the numeral on his paper and also place the cards in the holder to indicate the

[13] Morris Pincus, "Enrichment in Arithmetic for the Primary Grades," *Arithmetic Teacher,* 7:412–413, 417, December, 1960.

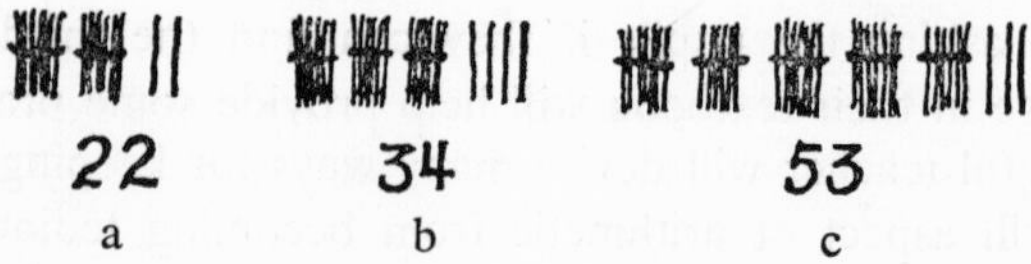

Figure 4.6 Illustrating the use of bundles of ten sticks and writing the appropriate numeral in order to develop the concept of the place value of digits.

number, as illustrated in Figure 4.7. On the command, "Everybody show," the children hold up their cards, facing the teacher, who is able thus to tell at a glance whether or not the children have the right answer.

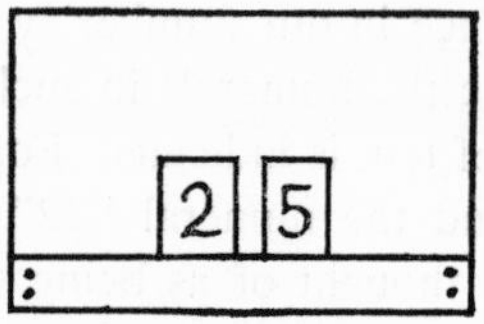

Figure 4.7 Illustrating the arrangement of digits in a numeral by using "Everybody show cards."

The children may also use both place-value pocket-charts and place-value boxes to illustrate the concept of place value, by putting bundles of tickets or strips of colored construction paper into the pockets, as shown in Figure 4.8.

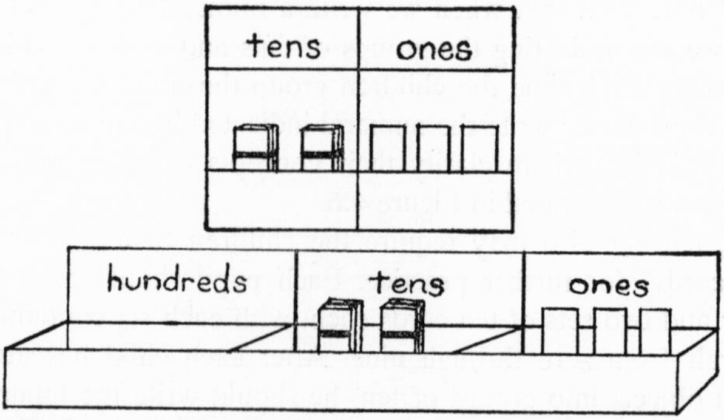

Figure 4.8 Arrangements of tickets in a place-value pocket-chart and a place-value box to illustrate the meaning of the numeral "23."

Wall charts may be prepared similar to those shown in Figure 4.9, and the pupils encouraged to discuss them. They should

1	2	3	4	5	6	7	8	9	10
11	12	13	14	15	16	17	18	19	20
21	22	23	24	25	26	27	28	29	30
31	32	33	34	35	36	37	38	39	40
41	42	43	44	45	46	47	48	49	50
51	52	53	54	55	56	57	58	59	60
61	62	63	64	65	66	67	68	69	70
71	72	73	74	75	76	77	78	79	80
81	82	83	84	85	86	87	88	89	90
91	92	93	94	95	96	97	98	99	100

1	11	21	31	41	51	61	71	81	91
2	12	22	32	42	52	62	72	82	92
3	13	23	33	43	53	63	73	83	93
4	14	24	34	44	54	64	74	84	94
5	15	25	35	45	55	65	75	85	95
6	16	26	36	46	56	66	76	86	96
7	17	27	37	47	57	67	77	87	97
8	18	28	38	48	58	68	78	88	98
9	19	29	39	49	59	69	79	89	99
10	20	30	40	50	60	70	80	90	100

Figure 4.9 Charts showing arrangements of numerals from 1 to 100.

note how the numerals may be arranged in a certain order on each of the charts, and how these numerals indicate the number of tens and ones for each number.

The "hundred board," shown in Figure 4.10, may be used in

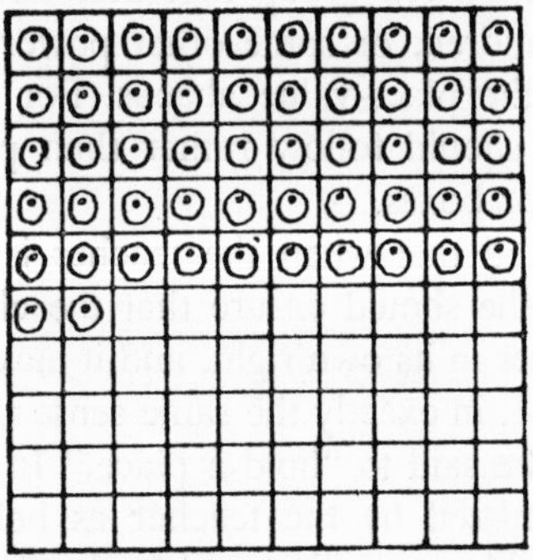

Figure 4.10 Discs arranged on a "hundred board" to illustrate how the number "52" may be thought of as 5 groups of ten and 2 ones.

various ways by a resourceful teacher to strengthen further the children's concepts of place value. For instance, with fifty-two discs on the board, the pupils could note that there are five groups of ten plus two more discs, and that the numeral indicating this number, "52," also indicates that there are 5 tens and 2 ones.

A "place-value abacus" is shown in Figure 4.11, and it may

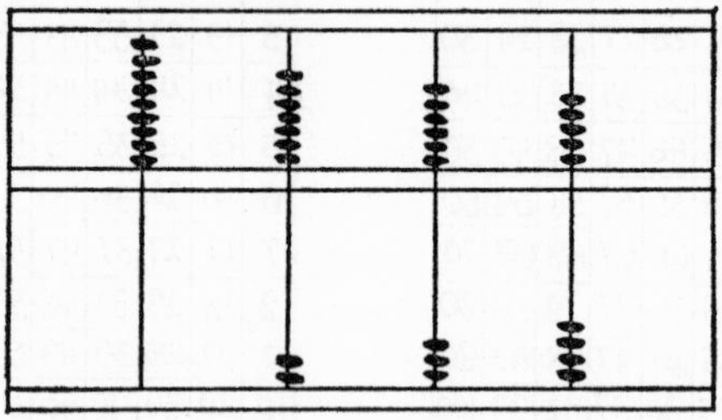

Figure 4.11 Arrangement on a "place-value abacus" to illustrate how the number "234" may be thought of as 2 hundreds, 3 tens, and 4 ones.

be used to illustrate the concept of place value in yet another way. In this instance, the pupils may see that a number such as 234 may be indicated by 2 beads in the hundreds' place, 3 beads in the tens' place, and 4 beads in the ones' place. When using an abacus, we do not "bundle" a ten group together, but we let one bead represent ten, a hundred, or some other power of ten, according to its position on the place-value abacus. For these reasons, the use of the abacus should follow rather than precede the use of place-value charts or boxes.

It should be noted that when the teacher is discussing "zero" with the children, she should ensure that the children understand that zero is a number in its own right, and it may "hold a place" in a numeral, therefore, in exactly the same sense that any other digit in a numeral may be said to "hold a place." In other words, zero should not be dismissed by the teacher as being "just a placeholder." [14] The use of zero is discussed further in Chapter 6.

The concept of place value and how the position of a digit in a numeral changes the value of the numeral is extended further as the child progresses through higher grade levels. This concept is

[14] Carl N. Shuster, "Teaching the Digit Zero," *Arithmetic Teacher,* 4:13–14, January, 1957.

introduced in grade 1, but it is basic later to an understanding of the nature of the various algorisms used in the fundamental operations of addition, subtraction, multiplication, and division of whole numbers. Still later, the concept of place value is needed to understand the system of notation used in decimal fractions. Introducing the concept of place value to elementary school children, and then employing this concept to help them to understand the nature of the algorisms they use in arithmetic, has been one of the important features of the "meaning approach" which has been stressed in recent years. In Chapter 15 it will be shown how the concept of place value may be used at higher grade levels to introduce children to systems of numeration where bases other than ten are employed, and thus enrich their program in arithmetic through deepening their understanding of various numeration systems.[15]

Developing the Meaning of Addition and Subtraction

The concepts of addition and subtraction formed by a child in the primary grades are very different from those developed later when he gains more insight into mathematics. In the primary grades, he may think of the addition of three and four in terms of combining a group of three objects with a group of four objects and finding the size of this larger group of objects which he can see and count.

A few years later, as his mathematical understandings develop, he may come to think of the addition of three and four in more precise mathematical terms as a binary operation performed on two numbers in a set and which results in a unique number in the same set. This concept is discussed in Chapter 6. At this point, he may be thinking in terms of the natural numbers as a set of abstract elements which need not be connected directly with objects, and where the nature of the operation itself is a matter of definition.

As his concept of the meaning of addition develops, he will find that it may be extended to include number systems other than the

[15] Patricia Spross, "Enrichment for Understanding," *Arithmetic Teacher,* 7:404–408, December, 1960; and J. Fred Weaver, "Enriching the Elementary School Mathematics Program for More Capable Children," *Journal of Education,* 142:1–40, October, 1959.

natural number system. He may come to think of addition in terms of a union of disjoint sets of elements, and which has an application in instances where these elements are something other than numbers. Disjoint sets are those sets which have no member in common.

Before the child leaves the primary grades, his idea of the operations of addition and subtraction as these are applied to numbers represented by small groups of objects should be quite clear. As the children analyze small groups, they are perceiving continuously the way two or more groups of objects may be put together to make up a larger group, and thus they are being prepared for the concept of how the addition of numbers is applied to solving problems in social settings where groups are considered to be combined. They see also how a large group of objects may be broken into two or more smaller groups, and thus are being made ready for understanding how the subtraction of numbers is applied to problems in social settings where groups are considered to be broken up or compared.

The curricula suggested in certain foreign countries, as well as some curricula used in this country, indicate that the average achievers in the second grade, as well as some children in the first grade, are psychologically capable of understanding the operations of addition and subtraction of whole numbers and of using numerals correctly to express these concepts. A teacher need not hesitate to introduce the concepts of addition and subtraction and to provide pupils with the appropriate activities to learn these operations as soon as the pupils are ready. Reasons for delaying the introduction of addition and subtraction are usually related to the priorities which need to be given to reading and to other areas of the curriculum.

There is some evidence to indicate, however, that children lose little by having the more normal presentation of addition and subtraction delayed for a few months, as their increased maturity enables them to learn rather quickly the content which might have been introduced earlier.[16] In instances where the pupils' success in

[16] J. S. Taylor, "Omitting Arithmetic in the First Year," *Educational Administration and Supervision,* 2:87–93, 1916; and Clifford Woody, "When Shall Systematic Instruction in Arithmetic Begin?" *Educational Method,* 16:165–66, January, 1937.

reading, language, and other areas of the curriculum permits the necessary time to be made available for teaching more arithmetic, the teacher may have the children advance to the next steps in learning addition and subtraction as outlined in Chapter 7.

As the pupils analyze small numbers in grade 1, they are provided also with readiness for understanding subtraction. The operation of subtraction may be considered to be the "inverse" of that of addition in that it "undoes" what was "done" by addition. In the addition of natural numbers, we are finding a number which is made up of two known numbers, while in the subtraction of natural numbers we are finding one of two numbers which were used to make up a known number, and thus, through subtraction, we are finding a number which constitutes the difference between two known numbers. This concept is illustrated in Figure 4.12.

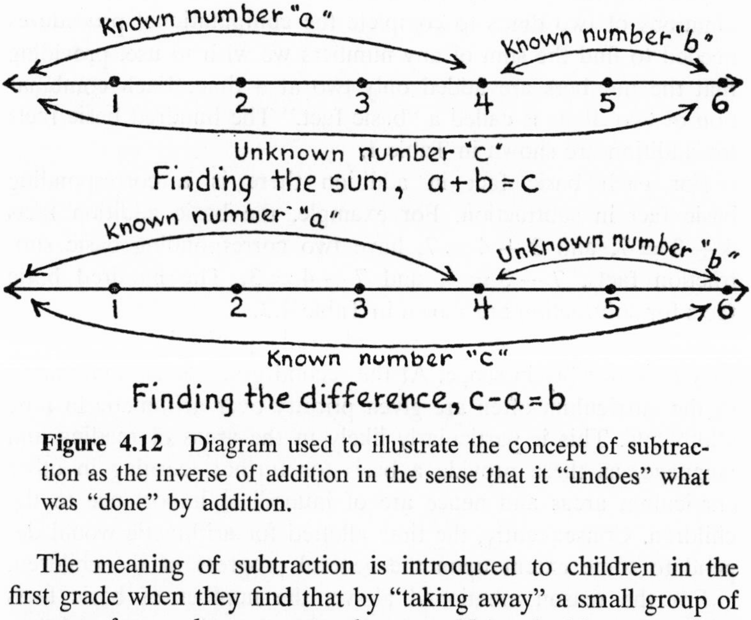

Figure 4.12 Diagram used to illustrate the concept of subtraction as the inverse of addition in the sense that it "undoes" what was "done" by addition.

The meaning of subtraction is introduced to children in the first grade when they find that by "taking away" a small group of counters from a larger group, they are able to find how many are left. A difficulty which children might have at a later time while solving problems is that they might come to think of subtraction as connected only with a situation in which a group is "taken away" from another group. This difficulty may be avoided by the teacher's showing them at a later time that in solving problems in social settings there are certain subtraction situations, such as when groups are being compared, where objects are not taken away, or removed, from a group. The types of subtraction situations which pupils will meet eventually while solving problems in social settings will be discussed later.

Learning the Basic Facts of Addition and Subtraction

In order to use the computational procedures for addition and subtraction easily and accurately and without counting, children will find it necessary to memorize a number of "basic facts." In arithmetic, only the digits 0, 1, 2, 3, 4, 5, 6, 7, 8, or 9 are used in any one place of any numeral representing a whole number. It is possible, therefore, by learning the sum of each of these combinations of two digits to complete the computational procedures needed to find the sum of any numbers we wish to use, providing that the numbers are added only two at a time. Each combination of two digits is called a "basic fact." The hundred basic facts for addition are shown in Table I.

For each basic fact in addition there is a corresponding basic fact in subtraction. For example, the basic addition facts $4 + 3 = 7$, and $3 + 4 = 7$, have two corresponding basic subtraction facts, $7 - 3 = 4$, and $7 - 4 = 3$. The hundred basic facts for subtraction are shown in Table 4.2.

Arithmetic programs for second grade pupils in this country vary considerably in scope. At the second grade level, some areas of the curriculum often are given priority over arithmetic in time allotments. This is particularly likely in the areas of reading and language, as these provide a basis for further learning in other curriculum areas and hence are of immediate importance to the children. Consequently, the time allotted for arithmetic would depend to some extent upon the general progress of the children.

For the reason mentioned above, the number of basic facts which any group of children in the second grade are expected to memorize should be left to the discretion of the teacher. It is suggested that for average achievers, learning the forty-five basic facts in addition which are encircled in Table 4.1 and then forty-five

Table 4.1

Basic Facts of Addition

0	1	2	3	4	5	6	7	8	9
0	0	0	0	0	0	0	0	0	0
0	1	2	3	4	5	6	7	8	9
0	1	2	3	4	5	6	7	8	9
1	1	1	1	1	1	1	1	1	1
1	2	3	4	5	6	7	8	9	10
0	1	2	3	4	5	6	7	8	9
2	2	2	2	2	2	2	2	2	2
2	3	4	5	6	7	8	9	10	11
0	1	2	3	4	5	6	7	8	9
3	3	3	3	3	3	3	3	3	3
3	4	5	6	7	8	9	10	11	12
0	1	2	3	4	5	6	7	8	9
4	4	4	4	4	4	4	4	4	4
4	5	6	7	8	9	10	11	12	13
0	1	2	3	4	5	6	7	8	9
5	5	5	5	5	5	5	5	5	5
5	6	7	8	9	10	11	12	13	14
0	1	2	3	4	5	6	7	8	9
6	6	6	6	6	6	6	6	6	6
6	7	8	9	10	11	12	13	14	15
0	1	2	3	4	5	6	7	8	9
7	7	7	7	7	7	7	7	7	7
7	8	9	10	11	12	13	14	15	16
0	1	2	3	4	5	6	7	8	9
8	8	8	8	8	8	8	8	8	8
8	9	10	11	12	13	14	15	16	17
0	1	2	3	4	5	6	7	8	9
9	9	9	9	9	9	9	9	9	9
9	10	11	12	13	14	15	16	17	18

Table 4.2

Basic Facts of Subtraction

0 0 0	1 0 1	2 0 2	3 0 3	4 0 4	5 0 5	6 0 6	7 0 7	8 0 8	9 0 9
1 1 0	2 1 1	3 1 2	4 1 3	5 1 4	6 1 5	7 1 6	8 1 7	9 1 8	10 1 9
2 2 0	3 2 1	4 2 2	5 2 3	6 2 4	7 2 5	8 2 6	9 2 7	10 2 8	11 2 9
3 3 0	4 3 1	5 3 2	6 3 3	7 3 4	8 3 5	9 3 6	10 3 7	11 3 8	12 3 9
4 4 0	5 4 1	6 4 2	7 4 3	8 4 4	9 4 5	10 4 6	11 4 7	12 4 8	13 4 9
5 5 0	6 5 1	7 5 2	8 5 3	9 5 4	10 5 5	11 5 6	12 5 7	13 5 8	14 5 9
6 6 0	7 6 1	8 6 2	9 6 3	10 6 4	11 6 5	12 6 6	13 6 7	14 6 8	15 6 9
7 7 0	8 7 1	9 7 2	10 7 3	11 7 4	12 7 5	13 7 6	14 7 7	15 7 8	16 7 9
8 8 0	9 8 1	10 8 2	11 8 3	12 8 4	13 8 5	14 8 6	15 8 7	16 8 8	17 8 9
9 9 0	10 9 1	11 9 2	12 9 3	13 9 4	14 9 5	15 9 6	16 9 7	17 9 8	18 9 9

subtraction facts encircled in Table 4.2 should be considered a suitable load. These would include the basic facts with sums of ten or less and the corresponding subtraction facts, with the "zero facts" being excluded. The remaining basic facts would be learned in the third grade.

This suggestion does not imply that pupils in the second grade should never use the facts with sums greater than ten. Where pupils are using counting procedures to find a sum or a difference, they have no difficulty in finding the answers to addition problems where numbers greater than ten are required. What is emphasized here is that second grade pupils need not be required to *memorize* the basic facts with sums above ten. During the time they are in grade 2 and grade 3, average achievers might be expected to memorize the hundred basic addition facts and the corresponding subtraction facts.

As pointed out in Chapter 2, how much should be expected of any particular group of pupils depends upon several interrelated factors. All areas of the curriculum must be considered. It takes considerable skill and insight on the part of the primary teacher to determine correctly how to adjust the emphasis in the various subject matter areas so that the best learning situation may be obtained.

The task of memorizing the basic facts of addition and subtraction is a formidable one for some children. Studies have been made to determine the order in which these basic facts are most easily learned. Thiele concluded that when children were encouraged to use generalizations in learning basic facts, better results were obtained than when generalizations were not stressed.[17] Other studies have indicated that when children understand the relationships involved and are encouraged to use generalizations in connection with mastering the basic facts, the learning is facilitated.

The procedure recommended most widely to teachers at the present time is that of having the children learn the basic facts by "families," sometimes called "related facts." All the addition and subtraction facts which the children can illustrate with any given

[17] C. L. Thiele, *The Contribution of Generalization to the Learning of the Addition Facts,* Contributions to Education, No. 763 (New York: Bureau of Publications, Teachers College, Columbia University, 1938), p. 76.

group of eighteen or fewer counters would represent a "family" for that group. For example, the "family of seven" would be made up of the following addition and subtraction facts.

0	7	6	1	5	2	4	3
7	0	1	6	2	5	3	4
7	7	7	7	7	7	7	7

7	7	7	7	7	7	7	7
−7	−0	−1	−6	−2	−5	−3	−4
0	7	6	1	5	2	4	3

By using seven counters, any of the basic facts for the "family of seven" could be discovered by the children as they manipulate the counters in various ways. For example, they find that a group of seven may be made up of groups of three and four, and that the difference between seven and four is three while the difference between seven and three is four, as shown in Figure 4.13.

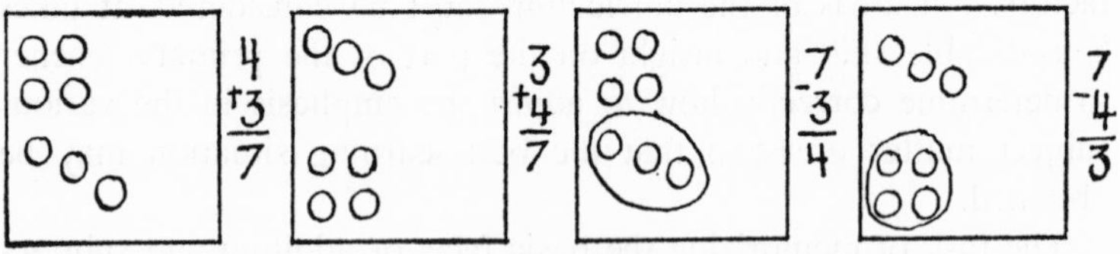

Figure 4.13

"Perception cards" may also be used to illustrate the basic facts of the "family of seven" as shown in Figure 4.14.

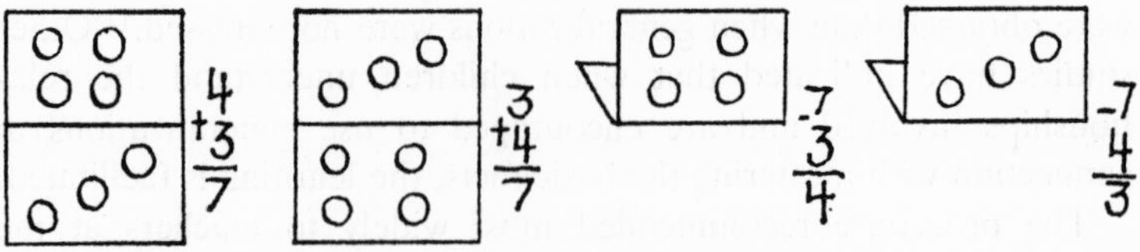

Figure 4.14

During the early stages of learning the basic facts, the pupils should be encouraged to use various procedures for determining each basic fact. At first, the pupils may have to count in order to determine the fact. They may also use a known fact to determine an unknown fact, as when they use their knowledge that three and three make six in order to reason that three and four must make seven because it would be one more than six. The family of eighteen would represent the largest family that the children would need to learn because $9 + 9 = 18$ is the largest basic addition fact.

Since the teacher wishes the pupils to memorize the facts eventually so that they can respond to them instantaneously, considerable practice is necessary. Often the motivation for this practice may be provided through using the facts in number games, or by using flash cards or some other devices such as those described later.

To encourage children to make the effort required to learn the basic facts, a teacher should remind them from time to time that the facts will be very useful to them once the facts have been learned. After any family of basic facts has been studied and the facts discovered by the children, the teacher should spend four or five minutes daily helping pupils practice using the facts. A short daily review of the facts will help emphasize their importance, and will also provide the spaced review which contributes to effective learning.

By using the facts in games or with practice devices the work is made more interesting for the pupils. The individual differences among the children make it necessary for some to spend more time than others in order to learn the basic facts. Some devices should be provided to encourage the children to work individually on this task. Practice may be encouraged through the use of various devices such as the following.

Flash cards. These cards may be used by the teacher with a group of children to play some arithmetic game. Flash cards for individual use may resemble those in Figure 4.15. The pupils are

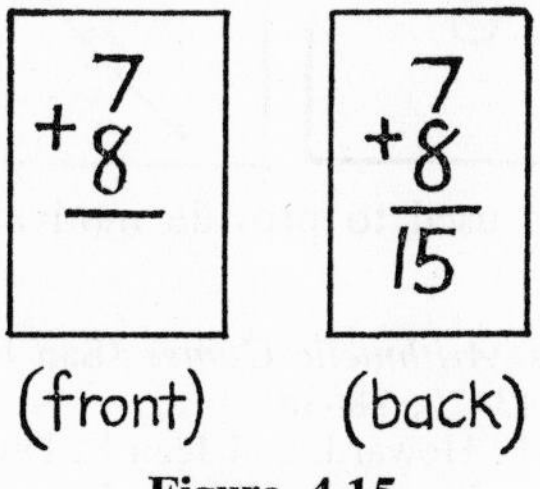

Figure 4.15

encouraged to test themselves, and then practice those facts of which they are unsure.

Spinners. Figure 4.16 illustrates a type of spinner which might be used by groups in games or by individual pupils. The window indicates the fact which must be recalled and the answer is shown through the window in the back of the spinner.

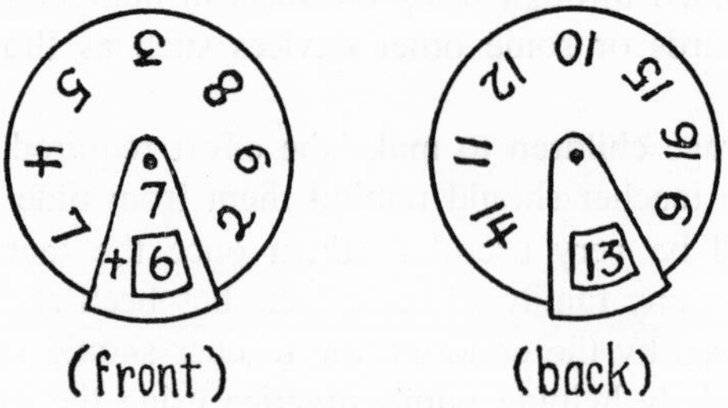

Figure 4.16

Chart devices. Figure 4.17 shows types of charts which may be used by small groups of pupils for practicing basic facts.[18]

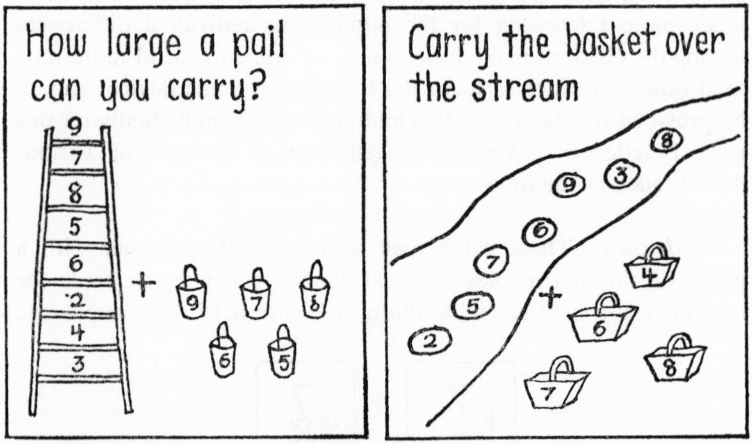

Figure 4.17 Charts used to provide motivation for practicing basic facts.[19]

[18] Also see Enoch Dumas, *Arithmetic Games* (San Francisco: Fearon Publishers, Inc., 1960), pp. 13–20, 28–38.
[19] Enoch Dumas, Charles F. Howard, and Jean E. Dumas, *Arithmetic Charts Handbook* (San Francisco: Fearon Publishers, Inc., 1960), p. 35.

Using Manipulative Materials

The importance of using manipulative materials. One of the most noticeable changes which has taken place in the teaching of arithmetic during the past decade is concerned with the increased use of manipulative materials in the classroom. A visitor to a modern classroom cannot fail to notice that the teacher continually makes use of manipulative devices to help children visualize number concepts. The teacher uses various devices daily to illustrate the meaning of number, the place value of numbers, the meaning of the fundamental processes, and to develop the meaning of the various measurement concepts. A visitor would notice that charts illustrating arithmetical concepts are used liberally, as well as motion-picture films and filmstrips. He would see also that the children individually use counters and other manipulative materials during many of the arithmetic periods.

This increased use of manipulative materials by the teacher and the pupils in the elementary school results from the growing recognition of the value of this material. The emphasis which is now given to the need for children to understand the meaning of number, and also to the importance of their "discovering" arithmetical relationships, has led to a search for more efficient ways of helping children visualize the abstract relationships of numbers.

As a teacher increasingly uses manipulative materials to illustrate number concepts, she will find another value beyond that of helping children visualize number relationships. She will find that the children become more interested in arithmetic, and that for this reason the arithmetic period will become more productive. Children seem to have a natural interest in manipulating objects in various ways. Their task in arithmetic becomes one of "seeing how something works," and their natural curiosity becomes a valuable motivating factor in any arithmetic lesson. In addition to these other advantages, the use of manipulative materials provides the variety in any arithmetic lesson which children in the elementary school grades need. The variety of activities found in manipulating objects, in looking at charts or filmstrips, in listening to the teacher, in answering questions or in writing responses, helps hold the children's attention to the work being done throughout the arithmetic period.

A teacher need not fear that an abundance of manipulative materials will somehow prevent the child from working at a higher or more abstract level at a later time. She will find that a child readily abandons the use of counters, place-value charts, and other materials as soon as he completely understands how to use the number symbols and efficient number processes. This is particularly the case when a child is told that it is more efficient to employ arithmetic symbols alone, without the material, as soon as he understands the way the numerals should be used. Even after the pupils can use certain number processes at an abstract level, it is desirable for them to have manipulative materials available in order for them to see how their answer in a given situation seems reasonable, or as is sometimes said, to enable them to "prove" their answers.

A child who continues to count on his fingers in order to solve a problem which could be answered more efficiently by using addition will find that it is much faster to use addition facts than it is to count, once the facts have been understood and memorized, but until he has learned the particular addition facts needed for the solution of the problem he has no resource other than that of counting. Timed drills and games help with motivating efficient procedures.

Another important value of having the children use manipulative materials in the primary grades is that it enables the teacher to evaluate the progress of individual pupils quite readily. As the pupils manipulate counters or other objects on their desks, the teacher can move among them and see at a glance the procedure being used and the progress being made. This is particularly helpful in kindergarten and the first grade because mistakes and misunderstandings may be corrected as soon as they occur, and the lesson paced according to the progress of the pupils. A slow pupil who successfully accomplishes a task can be identified immediately, and often may be given some recognition by being called upon to explain to the remainder of the class how he solved the problem.

Using "counters." The term "counters" or "markers" refers to any small objects which the pupils can manipulate easily. Often counters refer to discs or squares of rather heavy cardboard which are approximately an inch in width. Milk bottle tops, tongue depressors, popsicle sticks, macaroni "shells," and many other objects are used. A teacher should select something which is handled easily, which will not roll or make much noise if dropped, and which is safe for children to use. A small paper or plastic bag holding ten or twelve counters should be made available to each child in the lower primary grades.

From the time a child begins to write number symbols, or numerals, he should have a pencil and paper available whenever he is using manipulative counters and be required to write with numerals an expression of what he does each time with the counters. For instance, in the first grade while he is analyzing small groups and when he uses counters to find that three counters and four counters may be grouped to show seven counters, he should learn also, at the same time, how to write the expression $3 + 4 = 7$, and $4 + 3 = 7$, in both horizontal and vertical form. This will help him to clarify his understanding of the relationship between groups of concrete objects, the symbol which stands for the number, and the number itself which is abstract. The teacher thus helps the child grasp an abstract concept by using concrete materials and symbols which can be perceived.

After a child has manipulated the counters to illustrate a particular idea, and has written the expression in symbols, the teacher should use a flannel board to illustrate the same situation. This enables the pupil to check his work with regard to the procedure used as well as to check his answer.

The pegboard. A pegboard is used in connection with activities designed to develop counting during kindergarten or while analyzing small groups in the first or second grades.

Counting-wires. Beads or clothespins on a piece of heavy wire can be used during counting experiences in kindergarten or while analyzing small groups in the first or second grades.

Hundred board and discs. The hundred board may be used to develop the concept of the importance of ten in our system of numeration, and to illustrate the meaning of numerals for numbers greater than ten, as shown in Figure 4.10.

Place-value devices. The place-value abacus and place-value chart have uses other than those already mentioned for children in the lower primary grades. A place-value wall chart may be used by the teacher for demonstrating regrouping procedures in algorisms being taught to children in the intermediate grades. These uses will be described in later chapters in connection with teaching children the meaning of the fundamental processes. In grade 1 each child should have a card at his desk marked to enable him to use groups of tickets (stiff colored paper cut into strips about the size of theatre tickets) to illustrate the meaning of numerals, as shown in Figure 4.18.

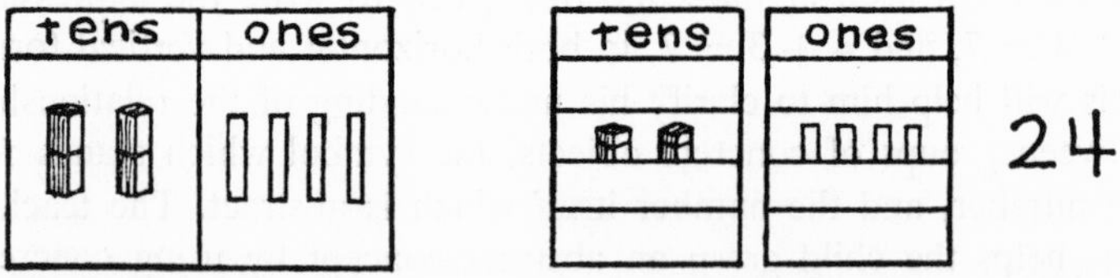

Pupil's place-value card | Teacher's place-value wall charts | Chalkboard

Figure 4.18 Illustrating the combined use of pupils' place-value cards, the teacher's place-value wall chart, and the chalkboard to indicate how the numeral "24" may be thought of as representing 2 tens and 4 ones.

The number line. A drawing such as that shown in Figure 4.19 is called a number line. On a drawing representing a line, some point is taken as an origin and to the right of this, at a convenient distance, a dot is placed. The distance between the origin and this dot to the right represents the unit length. Zero is associated with the origin, and the positive integers are associated with other dots placed at intervals equal to the unit length along the drawing to the right of zero, as shown in Figure 4.19. Points to the left of zero are associated with negative numbers.

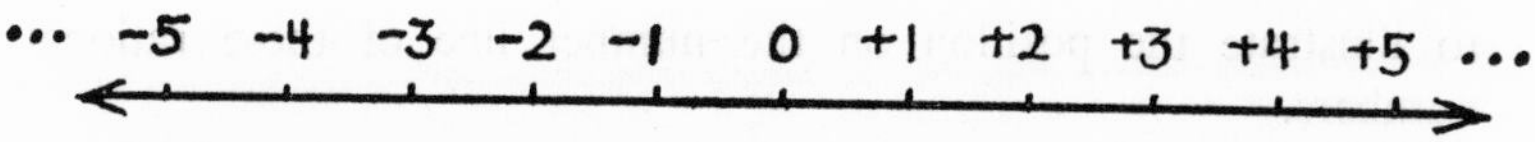

Figure 4.19 Integers associated with points on a drawing of the number line.

Prior to the time children study negative numbers, only that segment of the number line which contains points associated with the whole numbers is used, as shown in Figure 4.20. Later, seg-

Figure 4.20 A segment of the number line indicating only the points associated with whole numbers, and suitable for use in primary grades.

ments of the number line to indicate certain rational numbers may be used, as described below, and at still higher grade levels when irrational numbers are introduced, the segment of the line which shows a point associated with $\sqrt{2}$ may be used.

One of the concepts which children should learn early in the primary grades is that numbers may be *ordered,* or placed in a certain relationship to each other on the number line so that any given number represented on the line will be larger than any number represented on the line to the left of this given number. Thus 5 is associated with a point to the right of the point associated with 4, 3, or any smaller number. When children are introduced to negative numbers at higher grade levels, they will see that points associated with negative numbers are represented on the number line to the left of zero. Thus as −5 is less than −4 it is associated with a point to the left of −4.

When rational numbers are introduced, a drawing of a segment of the number line, such as shown in Figure 4.21, may be used

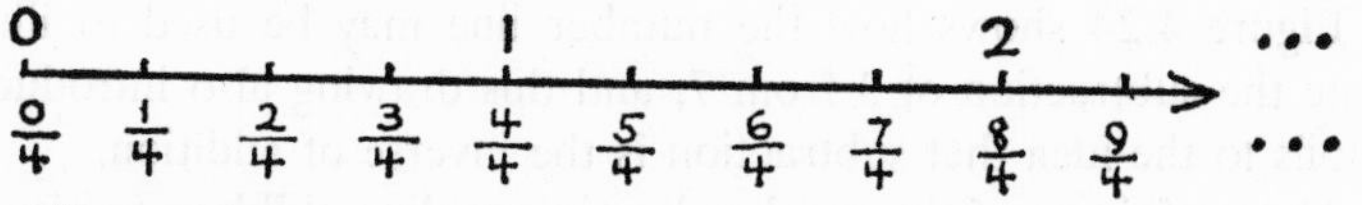

Figure 4.21 A segment of the number line to illustrate the relative position of certain rational numbers.

to illustrate the position on the number line of these rational numbers.

When pupils are studying rational numbers, a drawing such as that in Figure 4.22 will illustrate the concept that a point, such

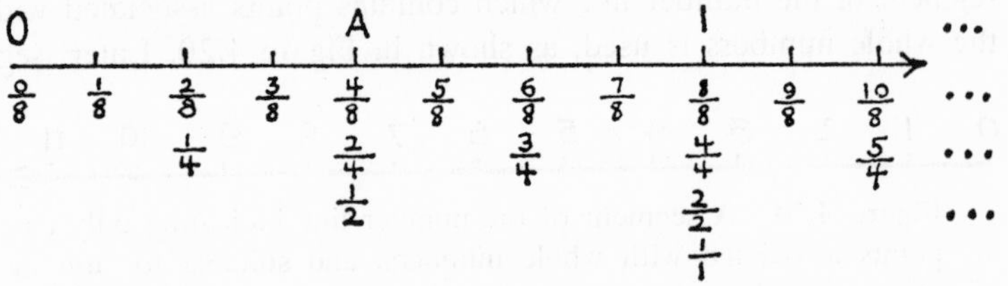

Figure 4.22 A segment of a number line to illustrate the concept that equivalent fractions refer to the same rational number.

as *A*, might be associated with many equivalent fractions, in fact with infinitely many of them. This will help pupils understand that each of a set of equivalent fractions, such as ½, 2/4, 3/6, 4/8, and so on, refers to the same rational number.

Certain operations on numbers may also be illustrated by using drawings of the number line. The operation of addition on whole numbers may be illustrated by using brackets, arrows, or some other device, as shown in Figure 4.23, which shows how the number line could be used to indicate the addition of 4 and 3.

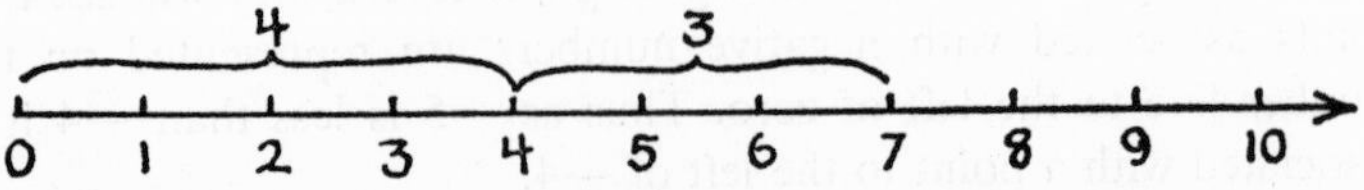

Figure 4.23 A segment of the number line used to illustrate the addition of 4 and 3.

Figure 4.24 shows how the number line may be used to illustrate the subtraction of 3 from 7, and this drawing also introduces pupils to the idea that subtraction is the inverse of addition.

The usefulness of the number line in enabling children to visualize many important properties of number and the operations on numbers should be recognized by each teacher in the primary

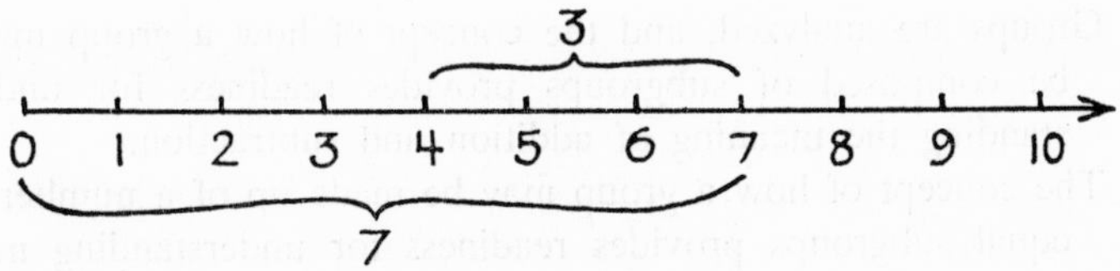

Figure 4.24 A segment of the number line used to illustrate the subtraction of 3 from 7.

grades. By becoming acquainted with the concept of a number line in the primary grades, children are being prepared for the time when the concept will be extended by using it to illustrate more advanced concepts, such as the concept of a coordinate plane, at higher grade levels.

The uses of the number line to clarify concepts of the multiplication and division of whole numbers and of rational numbers, as well as the introduction to the concept of irrational numbers, are discussed in later chapters.

Beginning Steps in Developing Concepts of Numbers and the Operations on Them

It might be helpful at this point to summarize the steps through which children pass as they develop concepts of number as far as these have been identified in this chapter. These steps are as follows:

1. The child becomes aware of the numerousness of the elements in a situation, and uses expressions such as "many" or "a lot of" to indicate this awareness.
2. The child uses one-to-one correspondence to determine the equivalence or nonequivalence of groups, and uses expressions such as "more than" or "less than" to indicate nonequivalence.
3. Rote counting is followed by rational counting and the child becomes aware of the cardinal use of numbers as this use is associated with groups.
4. The ordinal use of numbers to identify a particular thing in a series is introduced.

5. Groups are analyzed, and the concept of how a group might be composed of subgroups provides readiness for understanding the meaning of addition and subtraction.
6. The concept of how a group may be made up of a number of equal subgroups provides readiness for understanding multiplication and division.
7. Addition is associated with the concept of how groups may be combined into larger groups.
8. Subtraction is associated with the concept of how groups may be broken into subgroups and also with how groups may be compared.
9. The basic facts of addition and subtraction are illustrated and learned.
10. The commutative property of addition is noted.
11. The concept of subtraction being the inverse of addition is introduced.
12. Concepts of how numerals are used to express number concepts are developed concurrently with other number concepts as they are needed.

Suggested Learning Activities

1. Give an example of one-to-one mapping of one set into another but which does not show one-to-one correspondence.
2. Give an example of a pair of sets such that each element of one set is matched with two elements of the second set.
3. In a classroom election a set of tally marks on the chalkboard is mapped into a set of votes cast for a particular candidate. This is an example of elements of one set matched with elements of another set in one-to-one correspondence. Give two other examples.
4. Make a list of incidental counting needs, in or out of school, which might be encountered by first graders.
5. Make a place-value pocket chart and plan a lesson using it with children of first or second grade. Excellent construction directions will be found in Frances Ceccarini and Wilbur H. Dutton, *Making Instructional Aids and Independent Seat Work in Arithmetic* (Published by the authors, Box 25342, West Los Angeles 25, Calif., 1955), pages 7–14.
6. Make a list of incidental addition and subtraction needs likely to be

encountered by second graders in day-to-day activities both in and out of school.

7. Make a set of "Perception Cards" for the "family of eight" and plan an activity for their use.

Guided Supplementary Reading

1. Using the number line described by Ashlock, how would you help children of a second or third grade class understand 7 + 6?
2. Banks shows how by using one-to-one correspondence one may determine whether a given set contains more than, less than or the same number of elements as another set without resorting to counting, adding, or subtracting. What example does he use?
3. What value is attached to learning the correct vocabulary of arithmetic?
4. To what is Buckingham referring when he writes about "the rational domain"?
5. What suggestions does Clark make regarding the use of workbooks in the first grade?
6. What advantage does Clark ascribe to discovery in learning arithmetic?
7. What organization plan does Clendenon suggest when teaching basic number facts to children in large classes?
8. What teaching aid was used by Drasin in teaching recognition of groups at the "semi-concrete level"?
9. What arithmetic does Eads think has little value at the kindergarten level?
10. What does Eads suggest about the time required for children to learn arithmetic facts?
11. What conclusion does Fisher reach regarding the meanings of certain mathematical terms?
12. How do Gibb, Jones, and Junge differentiate among the names "integers," "whole numbers," "cardinal numbers," and "natural numbers"?
13. What caution does Harding emphasize regarding the use of artificial devices in arithmetic instruction?
14. What items does Harston suggest may be used to develop meaningful arithmetic concepts in the first grade?
15. What use does Hausdoerffer suggest for the "number fence"?
16. What justification does Hertz make for using more than one kind of teaching device?

17. By what means did Holinger help a "non-learner" attach meaning to number symbols?
18. What teaching aid do Hollister and Gunderson recommend for teaching children the decimal nature of our numeration system?
19. What device does Jones suggest be used for developing understanding of primary numbers?
20. Why does Sister Mary Jovita advocate teaching ordinal numbers before cardinal counting?
21. In what way does Larsen differentiate between "concrete" and "abstract" numbers?
22. What does Logsdon mean when he says, "A class of elements is said to be *closed* under a given operation . . ."?
23. What device for arithmetic self-help is suggested by Mahoney?
24. What arithmetic concepts does Sister Teresa Margaret suggest be taught in kindergarten?
25. What results did Meddleton find in his experiment with systematic practice in learning number combinations as compared with the usual drill and practice and review program?
26. According to Oesterle, when should zero facts be introduced?
27. What point of view does Peterson take regarding the uses of the words "numeral" and "number"?
28. How does Riess suggest that the fingers be used in developing number concepts?
29. What advantage does Risden claim for "structuring the basic facts?"
30. Schaaf names five words synonymous with *set.* What are they? Why does he not include the word "group"?
31. On what premise does Stern base her arguments in favor of the use of models and devices in teaching arithmetic?
32. Swain shows that in our everyday conversation we identify sets and subsets. What parts of speech are basic to this process?
33. What advantage does Wheat attribute to good teaching of counting?

Suggested Supplementary References

1. ASHLOCK, ROBERT B., "The Number Line in the Primary Grades," *Arithmetic Teacher,* Vol. 8, pp. 75–76, February, 1961.
2. BANKS, J. HOUSTON, *Learning and Teaching Arithmetic,* Chapter 4, Boston: Allyn and Bacon, Inc., 1959.
3. BISHOP, R. W., "Learning the Language," *Texas Outlook,* Vol. 42, p. 22, June, 1958.

4. BUCKINGHAM, BURDETTE R., *Elementary Arithmetic,* Chapter 1. Boston: Ginn and Co., 1953.

5. CLARK, A., "Experiments in Primary Grades," *Arithmetic Teacher,* Vol. 6, pp. 203–205, October, 1959.

6. CLARK, CAROLINE HATTON, "To Tell—or Not to Tell," *Arithmetic Teacher,* Vol. 5, pp. 65–68, March, 1958.

7. CLENDENON, EARL, "Efficiency in Teaching Basic Facts," *Arithmetic Teacher,* Vol. 6, pp. 144–147, April, 1959.

8. DRASIN, LILLIAN P., "Forgotten Level; Semi-Concrete Materials," *Arithmetic Teacher,* Vol. 4, pp. 211–213, November, 1957.

9. EADS, L. K., "Teaching Mathematics in the Kindergarten," *Grade Teacher,* Vol. 76, p. 55, October, 1958.

10. EADS, L. K., "Testing *vs.* Drill on Number Facts," *Grade Teacher,* Vol. 74, p. 46, June, 1957.

11. FISHER, L. R., "Building Concepts of Two in the Arithmetic Vocabulary," *School Science and Mathematics,* Vol. 57, pp. 636–638, November, 1957.

12. GIBB, E. GLENADINE, PHILLIP S. JONES, and CHARLOTTE W. JUNGE, "Number and Operation," *The Growth of Mathematical Ideas, Twenty-fourth Yearbook,* Washington, D.C.: National Council of Teachers of Mathematics, 1959.

13. HARDING, LOWRY W., *Arithmetic for Child Development,* Part 3. Dubuque, Iowa: Wm. C. Brown Co., 1959.

14. HARSTON, H. T., "Meaningful Arithmetic in the First Grade," *Instructor,* Vol. 65, p. 74, September, 1955.

15. HAUSDOERFFER, W. H., "Introducing Our Number System in the Primary Grades," *Arithmetic Teacher,* Vol. 4, pp. 61–63, March, 1957.

16. HERTZ, PAULINE, "Manipulative Devices in the Lower Grades," *Arithmetic Teacher,* Vol. 4, pp. 214–216, November, 1957.

17. HOLINGER, DOROTHY, "Helping the Non-Learner in Grade One," *Arithmetic Teacher,* Vol. 5, pp. 15–24, February, 1958.

18. HOLLISTER, GEORGE E., AND AGNES G. GUNDERSON, *Teaching Arithmetic in Grades I and II,* Chapter 2. Boston: D. C. Heath and Co., 1954.

19. JONES, K. B., "Building Number Concepts in the Primary Grades," *American Childhood,* Vol. 41, p. 11, February, 1956.

20. JOVITA, SISTER MARY, "To the Teacher of the First-Grade Arithmetic," *Catholic School Journal,* Vol. 57, pp. 234–236, September, 1957.

21. LARSEN, HAROLD D., *Arithmetic for Colleges,* Chapter 1. New York: The Macmillan Co., 1958.

22. LOGSDON, MAYME I., *A Mathematician Explains,* Chapter 2. Chicago: The University of Chicago Press, 1956.
23. MAHONEY, A., "Number Combinations for Slow Learners," *Instructor,* Vol. 67, p. 68, September, 1957.
24. MARGARET, SISTER TERESA, "Use of Numbers in Kindergarten," *Catholic School Journal,* Vol. 58, pp. 35–36, December, 1958.
25. MEDDLETON, I. G., "Experimental Investigation into the Systematic Teaching of Number Combinations in Arithmetic," *British Journal of Educational Psychology,* Vol. 26, pp. 117–127, June, 1956.
26. OESTERLE, R. A., "What About Those Zero Facts?" *Arithmetic Teacher,* Vol. 6, pp. 109–111, March, 1959.
27. PETERSON, WAYNE, "A Case in Point," *Arithmetic Teacher,* Vol. 8, pp. 10–13, January, 1961.
28. RIESS, A. P., "Pre-First Grade Arithmetic," *Arithmetic Teacher,* Vol. 4, pp. 50–54, March, 1957.
29. RISDEN, G., "Structuring the Basic Facts," *Education,* Vol. 79, pp. 276–279, January, 1959.
30. SCHAAF, WILLIAM L., *Basic Concepts of Elementary Mathematics,* Chapter 1. New York: John Wiley and Sons, Inc., 1960.
31. STERN, CATHERINE, "Concrete Devices of Structural Arithmetic," *Arithmetic Teacher,* Vol. 5, pp. 119–130, April, 1958.
32. SWAIN, ROBERT L., *Understanding Arithmetic,* Chapter 2. New York: Rinehart and Co., Inc., 1957.
33. WHEAT, HARRY GROVE, *How to Teach Arithmetic,* Chapter 1. Evanston, Illinois: Row, Peterson and Co. 1951.

CHAPTER 5

Developing Concepts of Measurement, of Money, and of Fractions

Measurement Concepts Form an Important Part of Arithmetic

An interesting and important part of the child's arithmetic experiences is related to learning how measurements are made with regard to time, length, weight, liquid capacity, and temperature. As the child proceeds through kindergarten and the first and second grades, he increasingly comes into contact with the vocabulary and concepts of measurement in his daily activities at home and in the community, and in order to understand his environment he will experience a growing need for information about measurement. Some of the out-of-school arithmetic with which he comes into contact is concerned with the purchases he sees made at the market and with the measurements of household supplies, and so an understanding of the uses of measurement and the uses of money takes on an increasing importance for him.

It should be noted, moreover, that whenever the children use measurement concepts, other number concepts are being employed at the same time and thus they find further use for the knowledge of number they already possess. For instance, the first and possibly only need the child in kindergarten or first grade will have for using fractions will be in connection with some measurement concept. The children will learn many quantitative words such as "dozen," and "couple," which are used commonly in connection with measurement ideas. They will learn many words such as "bushel," "gallon," "hour," and "degree" which are peculiar to certain areas of measurement because they refer to units of measurement themselves. The meaning of these words may be clarified best through using them in measurement activities.

Measurement concepts extend early number concepts. An extension of the child's concept of number is begun when he learns about measurement because he now begins to understand how numbers may be used to indicate the relationship between a certain quantity or magnitude being measured and a given unit. Up to this point, the child has been associating numbers with sets of discrete objects. Now, by applying a known unit to an unknown quantity and determining the number of units, he is enabled to associate a given quantity or magnitude with some number. This has immediate practical value for him because he now can use numbers to aid him in describing the properties of things, such as length, weight, or capacity. Through discussions, he can be led to understand how this information is of value in the adult world in connection with buying, selling, constructing, and in many other ways.

Another concept which is new to the child is introduced when he learns about measurement. He learns that the numbers arising from measurement situations represent only approximately the real measurements.[1] For example, he finds that when a measurement is reported as three inches, it means that the real measurement

[1] Joseph N. Payne and Robert C. Seber, "Measurement and Approximation," *The Growth of Mathematical Ideas,* Twenty-Fourth Yearbook of the National Council of Teachers of Mathematics (Washington: National Council of Teachers of Mathematics, 1959), p. 197.

is closer to three inches than it is to either two inches or to four inches. If the measurement is reported as $3\frac{3}{8}$ inches, it means that it is closer to $3\frac{3}{8}$ inches than to either $3\frac{2}{8}$ inches or to $3\frac{4}{8}$ inches. He learns that while a measurement may be reported to a thousandth of an inch, or with even greater precision, the number is still an approximate representation of the physical quality being measured. The number reported lies between two limits and is thus not defined sharply. This concept is extended at higher grade levels, and leads to the concepts of precision, accuracy, error of measurement, tolerance, tolerance interval, and to how to carry out computations with numbers arising from approximations. Procedures for extending concepts of measurement at higher grade levels are discussed in Chapter 12.

Another concept which is introduced to the pupil is that there is a variety of standard units in use, that the original selection of these units was of an arbitrary nature, and that their meaning depends upon how they are defined.[2] He is thus introduced to the fundamental role of definitions and the arbitrary nature of definitions in mathematics.

General Procedures for Introducing Measurement Concepts

A good general procedure for introducing measurement concepts is that of having the children consider measurement problems in a social setting, and then allowing them to manipulate the measuring instruments which are commonly used, such as the ruler, household scales, or containers of unit capacity for liquids. Through discovering experimentally the relationships between a series of measurement units, such as pints, quarts, and gallons, the children gain experience in using the measuring units and also gain an understanding of their meaning. At times, measurement information which might seem to be obvious to the teacher is misunderstood by some of the children and must be clarified.[3]

[2] *Ibid.*, p. 197.

[3] Davis, O. L., Jr., Barbara Carper, and Carolyn Crigler, "The Growth of Pre-School Children's Familiarity with Measurements," *Arithmetic Teacher*, 6:186–190, October, 1959.

For instance, the teacher may need to explain to the children that a measurement unit of capacity, such as a quart, refers to how much the container holds rather than to the container itself, or the teacher may need to help the pupils understand that the container would have to be filled completely, or up to a given mark, in order to measure out one quart.

The teacher should use a variety of measuring devices in connection with each type of measurement. For instance, the children should perceive that a quart container could have various shapes and the quantity of the contents still remain the same. They should make use of cylindrical quart measures, as well as milk cartons of rectangular cross-section. When learning about units of weight, for instance, they should note that the contents of a cylindrical can of coffee or a rectangular prism of butter might each weigh one pound, and that certain characteristics, such as shape, are irrelevant when weight alone is being considered.

Measurement activities in the kindergarten. Measurement activities in the kindergarten usually grow out of, and are combined with, other activities. As the children pursue some activity which is interesting to them, the teacher should direct their attention to the measurement aspects of the situation, and supply them with the vocabulary needed to express these relationships in suitable ways. For example, while the children are using blocks or boxes to build a playhouse, a wall, or a bridge, and also during periods of class discussion of the objects constructed, the teacher could direct their attention to the length, width, or height of their work by counting the blocks or other objects used in the construction, and also by using a ruler or yardstick.

In kindergarten, the children may watch the teacher while she uses a ruler to measure the length of some of their construction work, and they could count with her as she determines the length by repeatedly applying the ruler along each part being measured. When the children first see the teacher using some measuring instrument, such as a ruler, scales, or thermometer, they may learn little beyond the name of the instrument being used and the general procedure and purpose for using it. Through repeated observations, they gradually perceive more details about how the instrument is used and how the final measurement is determined. When the point is reached in grade 1 or grade 2 where the children themselves are able to start using instruments in simple measurement situations, practice becomes the most important factor in enabling them gradually to gain skill in using the instruments with increasing degrees of precision.

Measurement activities in grade 1. During the first grade, as in the kindergarten, measurement activities often grow out of, and are combined with, other types of activities, but at this grade level a daily period is provided for more direct work on some particular aspect of arithmetic. Usually the topics studied in this daily period are those dealing with the number system, as outlined in an earlier chapter. Periodically the arithmetic period should be used to direct the children's attention toward some aspect of measurement. In such periods, the teacher evaluates what the pupils have learned concerning the area of measurement in question, and then helps them to clarify, organize, and extend their information through discussions and further experimentation with measuring instruments.

As the time which is devoted to the pupils' individual seatwork activities is extended in the first grade, the importance of the individual work being selected to reinforce the group work is increased. The pupils should be supplied with workbooks, duplicated worksheets, or other material which will provide them with practice related to the measurement activities discussed during the group work, and provide practice in reading measurement terms and in expressing measurement situations in writing.

During the first grade, pupils learn the names of several common measuring instruments and learn their purpose. They should note that some instruments, such as the ruler or quart container, are used in the direct measurement of a magnitude, while in the case of some other instruments, such as a thermometer, or car speedometer, the results are indicated on a scale of some type.

At first, the pupils may employ units other than standard units when making comparisons. They might determine the width of some object in the classroom in terms of the length of their pencils or in terms of their outstretched arms. Through discussion, they then may be led to realize the advantages of using standard units. The various types of standard units and their suitability for certain purposes then should be explored.

Children in the first and second grades may be encouraged to make estimates of measures in various instances by asking them to state the numbers between which they think the real measure of an object lies. For instance, they might estimate that the teacher's desk is more than three feet but less than six feet long. Making estimates, such as this, will help provide them with readiness for understanding that the number recorded in a measurement is only an approximation of the real measure.

At this grade level, pupils may work individually or in small groups on the preparation of classroom charts which summarize measurement information which the pupils have discovered through firsthand experience with measurement instruments. This is not too difficult for them when the chart is to be constructed by pasting pictures or materials on tagboard. Charts such as that shown in Figure 5.1 help pupils summarize and review information regarding units of measurement.

Measurement activities in grade 2. During the second grade, as in the first grade and the kindergarten, many measurement activities grow out of, or are combined with other activities. At this grade level, the teacher may require more arithmetical thinking from the pupils than was the case in the earlier grades. By suggesting that the pupils frequently use measuring instruments in connection with their other activities, the teacher encourages them to make measurement a natural part of many activities. For instance, in construction work, a certain size might be suggested for objects being made, or the teacher might suggest that the most suitable position for certain elements of their construction work could be located best by measurement. During a study trip, the vocabulary dealing with various aspects of measurement could be extended by requiring the children to note rather carefully what is being observed and then to express themselves with more precision. During a study trip to a bakery, the weight of various sizes of loaves of bread could be noted, or the

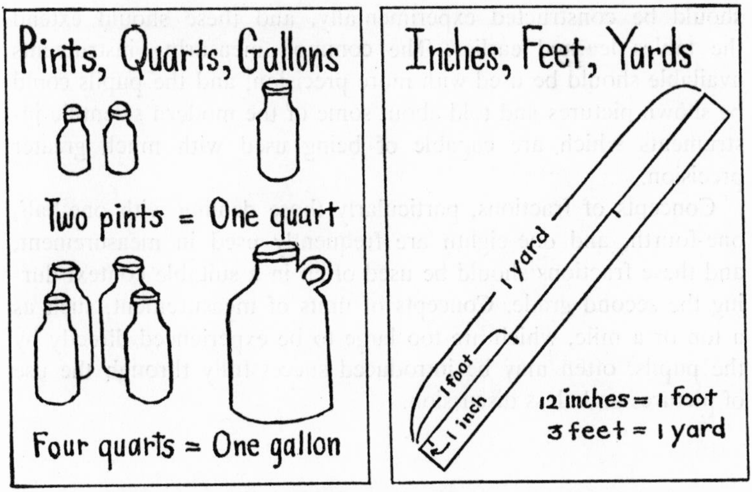

Figure 5.1 Charts prepared for pupils in order to summarize measurement information. Firsthand experience should precede the preparation of charts.[4]

types of scales which automatically weigh flour and other ingredients could be discussed in such a way that concepts of measurement are being introduced and extended.

In grade 2, as in grade 1, a daily short period for arithmetic in which pupils study directly various aspects of the subject is desirable. Periodically, this time should be devoted to studying some area of measurement and to giving the pupils practice in using measuring instruments. In grade 2, pupils may become very interested in weighing various objects on household scales and comparing them in various ways. If the teacher should ask the pupils to bring various types of rocks, wood, or other materials into the classroom, she will find that the pupils are very interested in weighing them while they are studying other characteristics of the material.

During grade 2, the pupils should review their earlier work in measurement, and then should extend their vocabularies by learning about new units of measurement. Tables of measurement

[4] Enoch Dumas, Charles F. Howard, and Jean E. Dumas, *Arithmetic Charts Handbook* (San Francisco: Fearon Publishers, Inc., 1960), pp. 21–23.

should be constructed experimentally, and these should extend the tables learned earlier. The common measuring instruments available should be used with more precision, and the pupils could be shown pictures and told about some of the modern scientific instruments which are capable of being used with much greater precision.

Concepts of fractions, particularly those dealing with one-half, one-fourth, and one-eighth are frequently used in measurement, and these fractions should be used often in a suitable context during the second grade. Concepts of units of measurement, such as a ton or a mile, which are too large to be experienced directly by the pupils, often may be introduced successfully through the use of pictures and class discussion.

A Sequence for Introducing Topics in Areas of Measurement

As noted earlier, the development of concepts in all areas of measurement can be carried on best when these areas are studied concurrently. For instance, in the kindergarten, easy concepts and vocabulary may be introduced which pertain to each of the areas: linear measure, liquid capacity, time, weight, and temperature. In grade 1 these concepts are developed further in all five areas and in grade 2 all of these same areas of measurement are studied again, and the pupils' knowledge increased still more. Although the concept of speed presents some difficulties at first because it involves two types of units, it may be introduced by discussing the purpose of an automobile speedometer and by comparing the usual speeds of different types of vehicles.

Within each of these areas of measurement, a sequence for introducing new topics, with suitable vocabulary, can be determined. An awareness of this sequence will enable the teacher to plan her work systematically. At the kindergarten level, this sequence of topics may be used as a checklist to keep account of the measurement topics which have been introduced incidentally in connection with various daily school activities. In grades 1 and 2, this sequence of topics will serve to suggest suitable topics during some of the short daily arithmetic periods, in addition to its use as a checklist of incidental arithmetic experiences.

It will be noted that the sequences of topics which are given below are not broken at any particular place for each grade level. How far along each sequence of topics the teacher will proceed with a class depends, of course, upon the ability of the pupils and upon the amount of time the teacher considers desirable for the particular group of pupils to spend upon arithmetic.

It should also be noted that it is not necessary for a teacher to follow strictly the order of topics in each sequence. While, in a general way, the order of topics is determined by the principle of moving from the simple to the more complex concepts, each sequence is suggested only as a general guide to the teacher. Measurement topics which are considered to be interesting and helpful to the pupils at a particular time, due to work being done in areas other than arithmetic, might be more appropriate than the topic next indicated in the sequences described below. The spontaneous interest of the children at any particular time provides very strong motivation for learning and should be given consideration by the teacher when planning the sequence for introducing new topics.

The foregoing point of view is similar to that held by many good teachers, namely, that the order of the topics in a pupil's workbook should not determine necessarily the order in which arithmetic topics are introduced. On the contrary, the selection of a workbook assignment should depend upon the topic which has been selected by the teacher as the most suitable for the pupil at a particular time. For this reason, a workbook which has been prepared so that the pages may be removed and used in any order is convenient.

Suggested Sequences of Topics in the Areas of Measurement

CONCEPTS OF TIME	TYPICAL ACTIVITIES
1. There are names for parts of the day such as: day, night,	Class discussion of pictures or daily activities in which the

CONCEPTS OF TIME	TYPICAL ACTIVITIES
evening, morning, noon, sunrise, sunset.	teacher directs the attention of the pupils to the items which will introduce or clarify various concepts of time and increase vocabulary.
2. Clocks are used to keep track of time.	Class discussion in which the teacher uses a cardboard "clock" and the pupils note the position of the hands for certain activities such as when school begins, lunch, recess periods.
3. How a clock is used.	A chart could be prepared to indicate the time certain activities begin. The children use cardboard "clocks" and manipulate the hands to learn to tell time to the hour, and in later sessions, to the half-hour, quarter-hour, and minute intervals. Pupils may prepare charts on which they draw the faces of clocks to indicate suitable times for daily activities.
4. How a calendar is used. The vocabulary would include eventually the days of the week, the months of the year, and the dates of certain days such as Christmas, New Year's, and national holidays.	Children discuss the uses of the calendar to keep track of days of the week, and also in anticipation of certain days such as birthdays and holidays. Pupils prepare a chart to indicate the birthdays of children in the class, as shown in Figure 5.2.

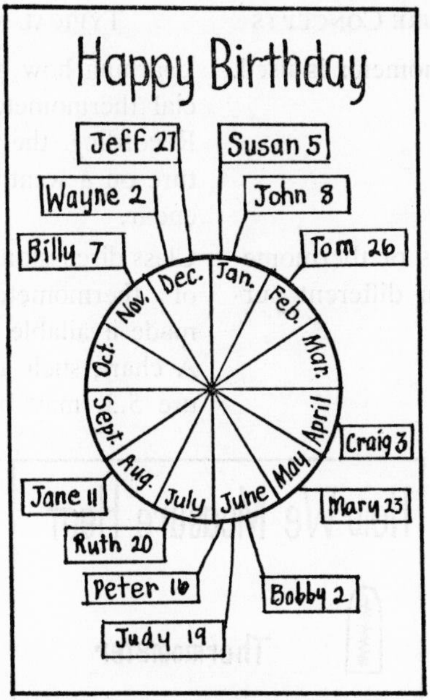

Figure 5.2 Birthday chart.[5]

TEMPERATURE CONCEPTS	TYPICAL ACTIVITIES
1. As we come into contact with the air and objects in our environment, we experience changes of temperature, for which we use words such as cold, colder, warm, warmer, hot.	Class discussion of daily weather. Feeling various objects in the room which seem to vary in temperature.
2. A thermometer is used to indicate temperature.	Class discussion of daily weather. Noting that the liquid stands at a higher level in the thermometer when it is hot than when it is cold.

[5] Enoch Dumas, Charles F. Howard, and Jean E. Dumas, *Arithmetic Charts Handbook* (San Francisco: Fearon Publishers, Inc., 1960), p. 18.

Temperature Concepts	Typical Activities
3. How a thermometer is used.	Learning how a large commercial thermometer is read. Recording the daily temperature on a weather chart or calendar.
4. Various types of thermometers are used for different purposes.	Class discussion of various types of thermometers which are made available or are pictured. A chart, such as shown in Figure 5.3, may be helpful.

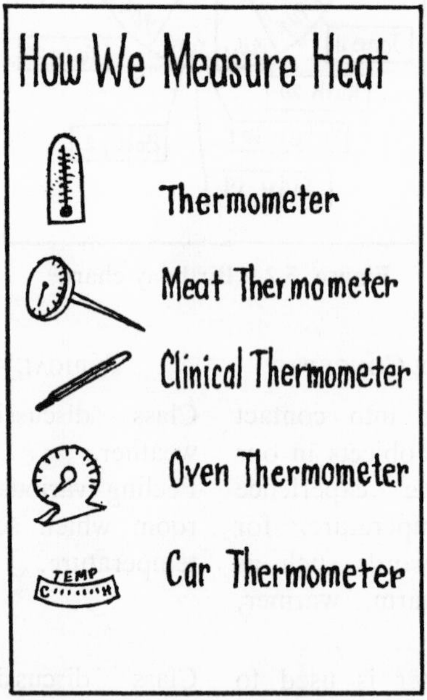

Figure 5.3 Chart showing types of thermometers.[6]

Linear Measurement Concepts	Typical Activities
1. The meaning of words such as long, short, tall, far, near,	Directly comparing the linear aspects of various objects.

[6] *Ibid.*, p. 22.

LINEAR MEASUREMENT CONCEPTS	TYPICAL ACTIVITIES
high, and low, which express linear relationships.	Class discussion of pictures during which the teacher directs the pupils' attention to linear aspects of objects.
2. A ruler or yardstick is used to determine linear relationships with some precision.	The class observes and discusses the manner in which the teacher uses a ruler in connection with some construction activity.
3. How a ruler is used, and the words needed to express linear measure, such as "inch," "foot," and "yard."	Pupils begin to use rulers, with increasing degrees of precision, in their other activities.
4. Various types of measuring instruments, such as tapes, odometers, and altimeters, are used for determining linear relationships.	Class discussion while looking at the instruments or their pictures in connection with reading or other class activities. Watching for measuring instruments during a field trip to a bakery or market.
5. How fractions are used in measurement.	Classroom activities requiring the more precise use of a ruler or other measuring instrument.

CAPACITY CONCEPTS	TYPICAL ACTIVITIES
1. The meaning of common words or phrases pertaining to capacity, such as "full," "empty," "cupful," "spoonful."	Using common expressions of capacity as they are needed in connection with other classroom activities.
2. Certain words such as "pint" or "quart" are used to indicate capacity in terms of a unit.	Classroom activities in which pupils use containers for measuring a pint, quart, half-pint, and a cup.
3. The interrelationships among half-pint, pint, cup, quart, and gallon.	Demonstrations or activities in which the pupils experimen-

TYPICAL ACTIVITIES

tally determine the interrelationships.

The preparation of a chart showing interrelationships among common measures of capacity, as shown in Figure 5.4.

The preparation of tables of capacity after experimentation.

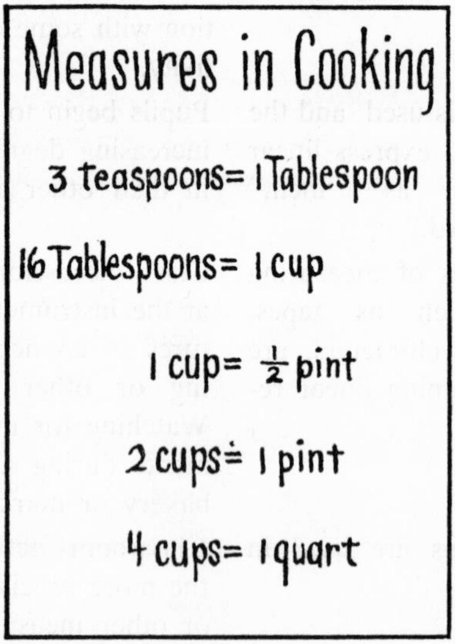

Figure 5.4 Chart showing interrelationships among common measures of capacity.[7]

WEIGHT CONCEPTS	TYPICAL ACTIVITIES
1. The meaning of common words or phrases pertaining to weight such as "heavy," "light," and "weigh."	The use of words pertaining to weight in connection with various classroom activities. Class discussion of how and why the pupils were weighed by the school nurse.

[7] Enoch Dumas, Charles F. Howard, and Jean E. Dumas, *Arithmetic Charts Handbook* (San Francisco: Fearon Publishers, Inc., 1960), p. 23.

WEIGHT CONCEPTS	TYPICAL ACTIVITIES
2. Scales are used to measure weight in terms of a unit of measure.	
3. Food is purchased often by the pound.	Use of the word "pound" in connection with class activities such as "playing store."
4. How scales are used to indicate weight in pounds, and later how scales indicate ounces.	Demonstrations and activities involving the weighing of objects on household scales.
5. Various types of scales are used for various purposes.	Class discussion during the direct observation of various types of scales, or while examining pictures of different types of scales.
6. The relationships between "ounces" and "pounds."	Preparation of a chart showing the relationship between an ounce and a pound after determining the relationships experimentally.

Aids in Developing Measurement Concepts

As mentioned earlier, measurement concepts of length, weight, liquid capacity, temperature, and time should be developed concurrently. For this reason, all of the following measuring devices may be useful at each of the primary grade levels. The way in which these devices could be used would vary throughout each grade level according to the maturation of the children. In kindergarten, the measuring devices may be introduced only to identify them by name, to mention their general use, and to identify the unit with which each is concerned. In the first grade, the uses of the devices may be demonstrated to the extent needed for the children to get a better understanding of their general use. In the second grade, the children begin using some of the measuring devices with some degree of precision.

Linear measurement. Rulers and yardsticks should be available to the pupils at each grade level. The tailor's tape measure and a steel tape measure are helpful to have available when discussing linear measure in the first and second grades. Second grade pupils find a carpenter's steel square and the description of its many uses very interesting.

Pictures of other measuring devices which are not available themselves in the classroom, such as an altimeter, an odometer, or a micrometer, are useful for stimulating discussion at the second grade level.

Weight. Second grade pupils are very interested in using household scales to weigh various objects. Coffee cans which are similar in size and shape, but which contain varying weights of sand, provide practice in using household scales that children at this grade level find interesting.

Children at all primary grade levels are interested in using the school health scales and in discussing their own weights in connection with health lessons.

Pictures showing types of scales used to weigh loaded trucks, or other heavy objects, are useful for discussion purposes. When children learn the meaning of "ounce" their attention should be directed to the weight markings on various food containers in the market.

Liquid capacity. Milk or cream cartons for half-pints, pints, and quarts, as well as milk bottles having these capacities, are useful at the first and second grade levels. A gallon jug, a measuring cup, and a set of measuring spoons also should be available at these grade levels and used by the children when they are learning the interrelationships among the various units of liquid capacity.

Temperature. Both an ordinary weather thermometer and a cooking thermometer should be accessible to children in each of the primary grades. The use of a clinical thermometer should be discussed during health instruction. The pupils' attention should be directed to the thermostat in the classroom and its use should be discussed. Second grade pupils can be taught to read the weather thermometer with some degree of precision.

Time. The schoolroom clock, discarded alarm clocks, cardboard "clocks," and calendars are useful devices for developing concepts of measuring time. Calendar charts, which are constructed with pockets in which children place a card bearing a numeral each day to indicate the date, are useful at all primary grade levels to help develop an understanding of how ordinal numbers are used to identify dates.

Pictures of various types of clocks and sundials are helpful to stimulate discussion among second grade pupils. Other discussion topics concerned with the various automatic timing devices used in modern living should be introduced. The automatic devices used to control the cooking time on electric ranges or the cycles of an automatic washing machine, to control street lights, signs, and traffic signals form interesting discussion topics at the second grade level.

Children in the lower primary grades find egg timers which operate on a sand glass principle very interesting, and these may be used to introduce a discussion of how man used water clocks, sundials, and other ways of telling time before the invention of modern devices.

A watch or clock with a sweep second hand should be discussed by the class and an appreciation of short intervals of time, such as second and minute, should be developed.

Simple timetables, such as those sometimes used for bus schedules, may be brought into the classroom, and the pupils taught how to read them.

A metronome may be introduced in connection with a music lesson and this use of measuring time discussed.

Developing Concepts of Money

Before entering kindergarten, children have observed adults using money in making purchases in markets and elsewhere. Many children have been given a small coin occasionally and allowed to select a piece of candy and pay for it themselves. Through experiences such as these, preschool children make a start in recognizing that money has value and is used as a medium of exchange.

After entering school, children increasingly come into contact with situations involving money. They see that money is used in connection with school collections for milk and for lunches, and also for donations to the Red Cross, the March of Dimes, or other agencies. Early in grade 1 or late in the kindergarten year, the teacher may find that some children are ready to be given some direct instruction about money. At this time, she should work with small groups of children and help them to recognize certain coins. Pennies, nickels, dimes, and quarters will be recognized without much difficulty if the teacher allows the children to examine real coins and discuss them.

As the children progress in their ability to do rational counting in grade 1, and later as they gain the ability to analyze small groups, as discussed in Chapter 4, toy money may be used with increasing frequency as manipulative material. At first the children do not recognize the comparative values of the various coins but use their toy money as they would use any other counters. As soon as the children are ready, the teacher should direct their attention to the comparative values of pennies, nickels, and dimes, and later, to coins of larger denominations and to bills.

The concept of the comparative values of coins may be developed by discussing the coins in terms of what they will buy, and by referring to their value in terms of cents. During this stage of the work, charts may be prepared to show the comparative values of some of the coins, and the children should be allowed to use these charts while "making change" with toy money. A suitable type of chart is shown in Figure 5.5 on page 111.

Social studies activities during the first or second grade in which the pupils "play store" in connection with a unit on the market provide very effective practice in changing money and in recognizing the comparative values of coins. During a study trip to a market, the attention of the children should be directed to how the prices of goods are indicated, and also to how the cash register is used to assist the clerks in making change. When the children

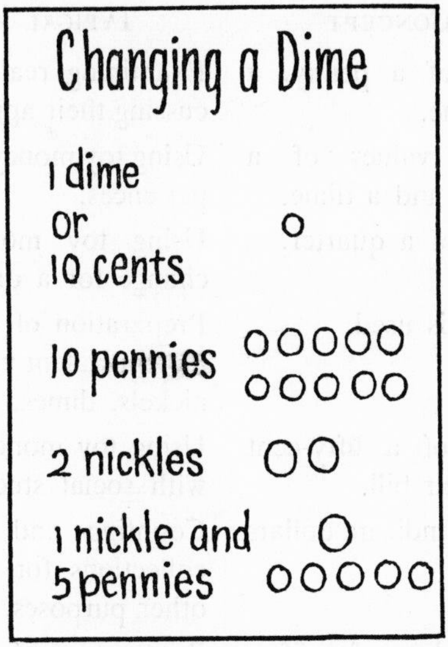

Figure 5.5 Chart showing comparative values of coins.[8]

develop the ability to count money and to understand the comparative values of coins, they may be allowed to count the money collected by the class for milk or for other purposes. They should be shown also how to write the sum of the amount collected, using the dollar sign or the cents sign. When the children begin to use the dollar sign and a decimal point to indicate dollars and cents, it is not necessary for the teacher to try to have them develop the meaning of decimal fractions. It is sufficient to tell them that in this usage the point simply marks off the cents from the dollars.

A Suggested Sequence for Developing Concepts of Money

MONEY CONCEPT	TYPICAL ACTIVITIES
1. Money is used in making purchases.	Class discussion of pictures of people in a market.

[8] *Ibid.*, p. 20.

Money Concept	Typical Activities
2. Recognition of a penny, a nickel, and a dime.	Examining real coins and discussing their appearance.
3. Comparative values of a penny, a nickel, and a dime.	Using toy money in counting experiences.
4. Recognition of a quarter.	Using toy money in making change for a quarter.
5. How change is used.	Preparation of a chart showing the equivalent values of pennies, nickels, dimes, and quarters.
6. Recognition of a fifty-cent piece and a dollar bill.	Using toy money in connection with social studies activities.
7. Signs used to indicate dollars and cents.	Counting and checking class collections for milk, lunch, or other purposes.
8. Equivalent values of a fifty-cent piece and a dollar bill in terms of smaller coins.	Preparation of a chart showing the equivalent values of a dollar bill in terms of smaller coins.
9. Making change when both dollars and cents are involved.	Using toy money.

Aids in Developing Money Concepts

Toy money representing the various coins and bills is useful at the lower primary grade levels. Real money is best for teaching children to recognize coins, but toy money may be used for teaching the comparative value of coins, for learning how to make change, and for use in problem situations involving the meaning of addition or subtraction.

Samples of coins and bills of foreign countries are interesting to children in the second grade. Foreign stamps may be used also to stimulate discussion at this grade level, and to introduce the concept that various foreign countries use different monetary units.

Recognizing Geometric Shapes

At the present time there is little evidence available to indicate which concepts of geometry children should be encouraged to learn in the kindergarten and in the first and second grades. Recent studies indicate, however, that children in the primary grades are capable of understanding some of the elementary concepts of geometry when they are given direct instruction in this area of mathematics.

Traditionally, children have been given sufficient instruction to enable them to recognize some common geometric shapes, such as the circle, the square, the triangle, the rectangle, the cube, the cone, and the sphere, along with the vocabulary needed to express recognition of these shapes. In some instances, the recognition of geometric shapes has been combined with the work in recognizing fractional parts of objects. For instance, when the teacher is illustrating the meaning of halves, fourths, or thirds, and when she wishes to emphasize the idea that fractions need not be identified with circles only, she may use shapes other than circles in diagrams representing fraction concepts.

As the reports of several studies of the concepts held by children when entering kindergarten or the first grade have stated that many children at these grade levels recognize a circle, a triangle, and a square, direct instruction in recognizing common geometric shapes should prove to be helpful at these grade levels. It is suggested that the teacher should determine, through discussions and questions, which geometric shapes are recognized by the children in her class, and then extend the pupils' knowledge to the place where they can recognize other common geometric shapes.

Charts or diagrams similar to those shown in Figure 5.6 could be used as a basis for a discussion, and the attention of the pupils directed to these shapes as they may be noted in connection with objects in the environment.

A workbook [9] recently published and designed for an experimental program to introduce geometry to children in the second grade provides a series of exercises graduated in difficulty which

[9] Newton Hawley and Patrick Suppes, *Geometry for Primary Grades* (San Francisco: Holden-Day, Inc., 1961).

give pupils practice in using compasses, a straightedge, and a pencil in geometric constructions. The children are required to recognize and to construct triangles, quadrilaterals, pentagons, and hexagons. They are introduced to terms such as "line segments," "intersection of lines," "arcs of circles," "radius" and "center of a circle." Among other constructions they are asked to complete the follow-

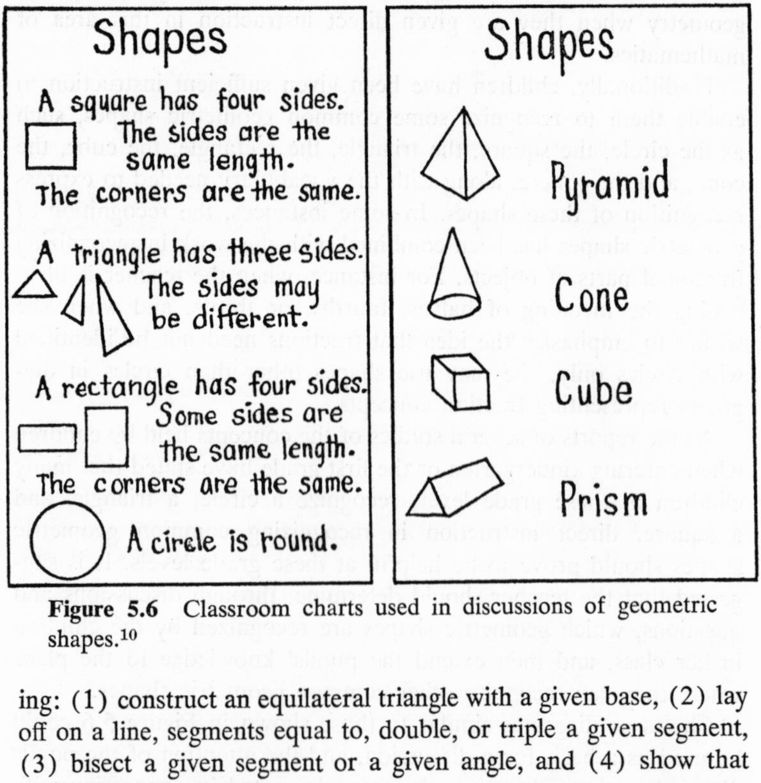

Figure 5.6 Classroom charts used in discussions of geometric shapes.[10]

ing: (1) construct an equilateral triangle with a given base, (2) lay off on a line, segments equal to, double, or triple a given segment, (3) bisect a given segment or a given angle, and (4) show that two angles are equal.

Some conclusions reported by teachers using these workbooks are that the children are interested in the work and that they grasp the concepts which are introduced. The teachers note also that there are some observable gains in the children's ability to

[10] Enoch Dumas, Charles F. Howard, and Jean E. Dumas, *Arithmetic Charts Handbook* (San Francisco: Fearon Publishers, Inc., 1960), p. 26.

read and to follow directions which could be attributed to the nature of the work required of them.

In situations where the teacher assumes that time is available for such activities, there should be no great difficulty in introducing children in the second grade to some of the simpler concepts of geometry which have not been included in traditional programs in this country until the pupils have reached higher grade levels. The teacher's decision as to whether to introduce certain geometrical concepts in the primary grades is not only one of determining whether the children are capable of grasping these concepts, but it is also one of determining the comparative values to the child of these and other activities.

A Fraction as a New Kind of Number

One viewpoint in contemporary mathematics holds that common fractions are numbers which belong to the set of *rational* numbers.[11] Each of the rational numbers may be thought of as a set of equivalent ordered pairs of integers, the numerals for which may be written in the form a/b, where "b" is not replaced by zero, and which are considered to obey certain rules when the operations of addition and multiplication are performed on them. For instance, the set of equivalent fractions $\frac{1}{2}$, $\frac{2}{4}$, $\frac{3}{6}$, $\frac{4}{8}$ and so on, would be a single rational number. The numeral for any one fraction in this set, for example $\frac{1}{2}$ or $\frac{12}{24}$, could be used to designate this particular rational number. Rational numbers are discussed in Chapter 9.[12]

Techniques may be developed in the near future for introducing into the elementary school program the concept of fractions being ordered pairs of integers,[13] but it is suggested here that at present,

[11] John E. Freund, "Fractions," Chapter 9 of *A Modern Introduction to Mathematics* (Englewood Cliffs, N.J.: Prentice-Hall, Inc., 1956), pp. 125–143.

[12] An alternate development of the concept of a rational number holds that a fraction is a symbol which indicates the quotient of two numbers. See, for example, School Mathematics Study Group, *Mathematics for High School, First Course in Algebra, Part I, Revised Edition* (New Haven: Yale University Press, 1961), p. 9.

[13] Henry Van Engen, "Rate Pairs, Fractions, and Rational Numbers," *Arithmetic Teacher,* 7:389–399, December, 1960.

while we are awaiting the results of experiments now being carried on, the traditional procedures which have been used successfully for introducing concepts of fractions to primary grade children should be employed. The traditional approach to developing the children's concepts of fractions is first to have the child think of a fraction as a number used to refer to part of something. Although this restricted concept of a fraction will have to be extended later at higher grade levels, we know that the idea does not present any psychological difficulties which put it beyond the capabilities of most first grade children.

The teacher should be aware of the fact, however, that when a child is introduced to the concept of a fractional part, he is meeting for the first time a kind of number which is new to him. Up to this point, his idea of number has been in terms of natural numbers. His idea of number is thus closely related to the idea of a group of objects. Now, in a fraction, he is introduced to a number which he has difficulty in recognizing as one which conforms to his idea that a number is something pertaining to a group, because he is expected to think of a unit being divided into a number of equal parts and then to consider the relationship between one or more of these parts and the total number of equal parts.

It should be remembered that while this concept is basic to a child's understanding of fractions, it is abstract, and for this reason it is difficult for some children to grasp. The teacher must be very patient in using a variety of materials to illustrate the concept in various ways, and she should not assume that the concept will be grasped quickly, even though the child gives correct answers to questions regarding the concrete material. It is suggested that the teacher should use a questioning procedure, where she tries to draw the information from the class at each step of a lesson. This will assist her in evaluating the children's knowledge, and help her to identify those children who need further help. This questioning procedure also encourages the pupils to think for themselves and tends to increase their motivation.

By the time the child reaches the third grade, he should extend his concept of fractions by learning that a fraction may be used also to express the size of part of a group as well as part of some unit. As this idea is related closely to the idea of division where a group is divided into two or more equal parts, the concept may be developed concurrently with learning the meaning of division.

The Child's Need for Fraction Concepts

Studies of the arithmetic knowledge of children entering school have shown that many children develop some concepts of fractions during their preschool years.[14] These concepts may be incomplete or erroneous in many instances, but the words, "one-half," "one quarter," or "a third," may be part of the child's vocabulary, and he may be able to identify one-half or one-fourth of objects or of diagrams showing various shapes. At first he may not recognize that the parts of the unit must be equivalent in size, but may speak of a "big half," or a "little half." When the pupils begin to grasp the idea that "one-half" refers to one of two equal parts, it may be considered a step forward.

Although "one-half," "one-fourth," and "one-third," and possibly "one-sixth" or "one-eighth" may be the only fractions introduced to children in grades 1 and 2, the various meanings which are attached to these fractional parts are very important for children at these grade levels. During his daily activities the child in grades 1 or 2 will hear these fractions named, or think of their use, in connection with concepts of measurement only. For instance, he will hear time expressed to the half-hour and the quarter-hour. He will also hear instructions involving the use of half a sheet of paper or sharing half of certain material with others. The frequent daily use of "one-half" and "one-fourth" or "a quarter of" makes it desirable for the names of these fractions to be part of his "speaking vocabulary" as well as part of his "listening vocabulary."

As the child progresses in his understanding of measurement, and when he begins to use measuring instruments with more precision, an understanding of "one-half" and, to a lesser extent, "one-fourth," will also be needed with increasing frequency. In grade 2 some children may be able to understand the use of "one-

[14] Corwin E. Bjonerud, "Arithmetic Concepts Possessed by the Preschool Child," *Arithmetic Teacher,* 7:347–350, November, 1960.

eighth," as it is used in connection with making measurements with a ruler.

It should be remembered that a teacher should plan to provide children with some experiences designed to develop readiness for arithmetic at higher grade levels as well as to provide the many experiences which will enable boys and girls to meet the arithmetic needs in connection with the daily activities at their present grade level. At the first and second grade levels, the readiness can be established which will aid the child in understanding fraction concepts which must be developed at higher grade levels. At the lower grade levels, a good understanding of the three fractions, "one-half," "one-fourth," and "one-third," obtained by using them in his daily activities, provides a basis for understanding the more difficult fraction concepts he will meet at successive grade levels.

A further difficulty in grasping fraction concepts is the problem the child has in understanding that while the term "one-half" may refer either to one-half of an orange or to one-half of a watermelon, the half is very much larger when it refers to a watermelon than when it refers to an orange. Thus he finds that the symbol, "½," may be used to refer to either a large or a small quantity. He must grasp the concept that when he is using fractions, the unit concerned must be recognized as an important part of the total situation. While the pupil is in the lower grades and is dealing with fractions of objects which he sees, this difficulty is not as apparent. When he is at a higher grade level and begins to use symbols more extensively to express his number ideas, he is confronted with the difficulty of understanding why the symbol "¼" may refer at times to an even larger quantity than the symbol "½," such as in the instance where "¼" refers to a large unit, such as a large circular disc, and "½" refers to a smaller unit, or smaller disc, as indicated in Figure 5.7.

In order to develop the child's concept that a fraction pertains to some unit or group when applied to concrete situations, the teacher may place a circular disc on the flannel board, and then place upon this whole disc a sector which illustrates the given fraction. By using discs of different sizes, along with suitably sized sectors in each instance, the teacher illustrates how, in one instance, "one-half" may be either larger or smaller than "one-half" in

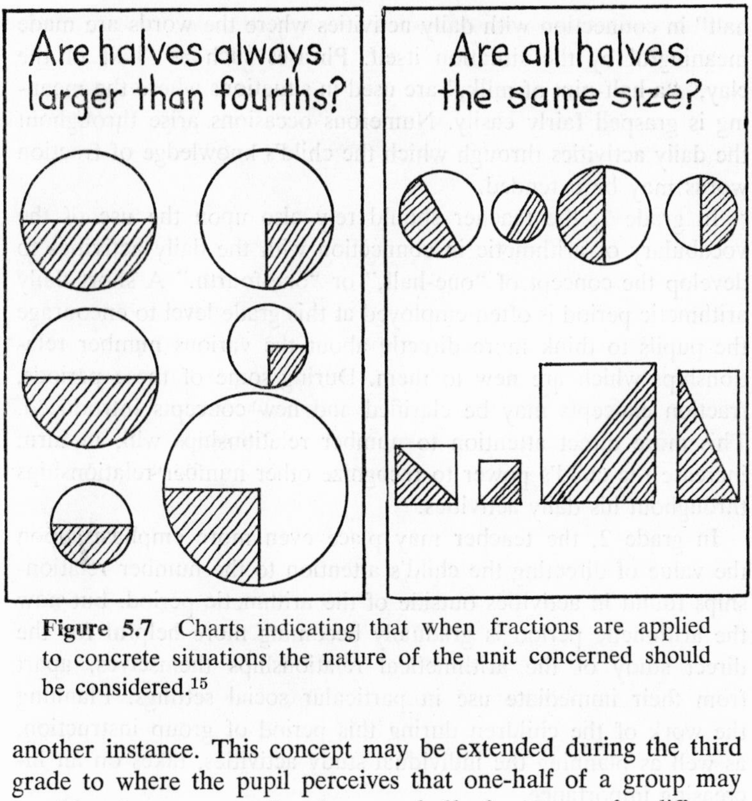

Figure 5.7 Charts indicating that when fractions are applied to concrete situations the nature of the unit concerned should be considered.[15]

another instance. This concept may be extended during the third grade to where the pupil perceives that one-half of a group may be either larger or smaller than one-half of a group of a different size. Wall charts, such as those shown in Figure 5.7, may be helpful in illustrating this concept.

General Procedures for Increasing the Child's Competency in Using Fractions

The general procedure for helping the child understand fractions follows that which is used in other areas of arithmetic. For example, in the kindergarten, the teacher should use the words "one-

[15] Enoch Dumas, Charles F. Howard, and Jean E. Dumas, *Arithmetic Charts Handbook* (San Francisco: Fearon Publishers, Inc., 1960), p. 37.

half" in connection with daily activities where the words are made meaningful by the situation itself. Phrases such as "half of the clay," "a half-pint of milk," are used in situations where the meaning is grasped fairly easily. Numerous occasions arise throughout the daily activities through which the child's knowledge of fraction words may be extended.

In grade 1, the teacher should rely also upon the use of the vocabulary of arithmetic in connection with the daily activities to develop the concept of "one-half," or "one-fourth." A short daily arithmetic period is often employed at this grade level to encourage the pupils to think more directly about the various number relationships which are new to them. During some of these periods, fraction concepts may be clarified and new concepts introduced. This more direct attention to number relationships will, in turn, increase the child's power to recognize other number relationships throughout his daily activities.

In grade 2, the teacher may place even more emphasis upon the value of directing the child's attention to the number relationships found in activities outside of the arithmetic period, but now the arithmetic period is gradually becoming more helpful for the direct study of the arithmetical relationships themselves, apart from their immediate use in particular social settings. Planning the work of the children during this period of group instruction, as well as planning the individual study activities, takes on an increasing importance.

Using manipulative materials to develop concepts of fractions. As noted above, a fraction is a new kind of number for the child to learn. The concept of a fraction as a number to represent part of something rather than to represent a group of objects must be developed carefully, because here the pupil does not use his former counting series in quite the same way as he did when dealing with natural, or counting, numbers.

Although the concepts of square measure are not introduced in the primary grades, the pupil intuitively recognizes large variations in the areas of objects. For this reason, teachers have learned through experience that areas, particularly areas of sectors of circular objects, are helpful in enabling the child to grasp those abstract number relationships which we call "fractions," and to learn how these ideas are expressed in spoken and written symbols. The value of using materials and diagrams to illustrate arithmetical relationships has been emphasized in connection with developing concepts in all areas of arithmetic, but the use of materials and diagrams to help children develop concepts of fractions should receive special emphasis because of the possible areas of confusion which have just been pointed out.

When selecting materials, the teacher should try to make use of objects which provide illustrations of fraction concepts and which, at the same time, are found in the child's home and community environment. This helps provide "carry-over" from the arithmetic lesson in school to the social uses of arithmetic. For example, after an arithmetic lesson where the pupil has used blocks of wood or clay which have been wrapped in butter paper to represent quarter-pounds of butter and placed in a butter carton, he is reminded of arithmetical concepts when he sees quarter-pound blocks of butter being used in his home.

Concurrently with the use of sectors of circular objects or other materials to illustrate fractions, it is well to give the child considerable experience in thinking about fractional relationships in the various aspects of measurement. Through discussions, demonstrations, and direct individual experience, the child should be reminded of how the fractional part "one-half" has been used by him in connection with concepts of time, length, liquid capacity, and other measurements. By using a variety of instances where the pupil may recognize the use of a certain fraction, the teacher is preparing him for the generalized idea which is represented by a phrase such as "one-half" or by the symbol, "$\frac{1}{2}$."

The flannel board. The use of a flannel board by the teacher to illustrate fractions with sectors of circular objects is very helpful to children in the primary grades. In addition to using a flannel board and sectors of circles, a teacher should arrange for each pupil to be supplied individually with a "fraction kit." This kit may consist of a large envelope containing sectors of circles cut from colored construction paper to illustrate halves, thirds, and fourths. Each kit should have at least one complete circular object to represent the unit. At first, sectors being used to represent the fractions should be placed upon this unit, and the pupils should learn that these sectors are always related to some unit. Thus, "one-half" refers to one-half of a whole unit, and is not to be thought of as "one-half" without reference to any unit. This will help the children understand how "one-half" may refer to areas of various sizes depending upon the unit to which it refers.

Cardboard forms to illustrate how squares, rectangles, triangles, and forms other than circles may be divided into halves, thirds, and fourths should be available for use on the flannel board.

The flannel board is probably one of the most helpful aids available for introducing the meaning and the processing of fractions.

Aids to Illustrate Fractions Used in Measurement

Linear measure. A series of sticks cut so that one of them represents a certain length, and others show one-half, one-third, and one-fourth of this length are easily prepared. Dowels one-half inch in diameter are good for this purpose.

Pieces of tape or string which can be folded to illustrate halves and fourths are helpful to represent fractions of lengths.

Weight. Pieces of wood or clay the size and shape of quarter-pound blocks of butter can be wrapped in the wrappings from butter or oleomargarine. These can be weighted so that they will each weigh one-fourth of a pound, and then used along with the household scales to illustrate fractions of weight.

Volume. As mentioned earlier, cream or milk cartons for half-pints and pints help illustrate fractions of capacity. Measuring cups and a set of measuring spoons also should be available for this purpose.

"Pies" made out of layers of cardboard glued together and then cut to illustrate fractional parts are attractive to primary children. If the pie plate is marked off into sectors corresponding to the sectors of the "pie," the relationship between the fractions of the area of the sectors of the plate and the fraction of the volume of the "pie" is easily seen.

Time. The pupils' attention should be directed to how a clock indicates half-hour and quarter-hour periods. A cardboard "clock" can be used to show why we use the fractions "one-half" and "one-quarter" in telling time to the half-hour and quarter-hour.

Money. Pupils may use toy money to see why we sometimes speak of a fifty-cent coin as a "half dollar" or a twenty-five-cent coin as a "quarter."

Dozen. An egg carton containing a dozen "eggs" made of clay or papier-mâché can be used to illustrate fractions of a dozen.

Charts. Charts such as those shown in Figure 5.8 are helpful when summarizing information or when extending concepts so that they will have a more generalized application.

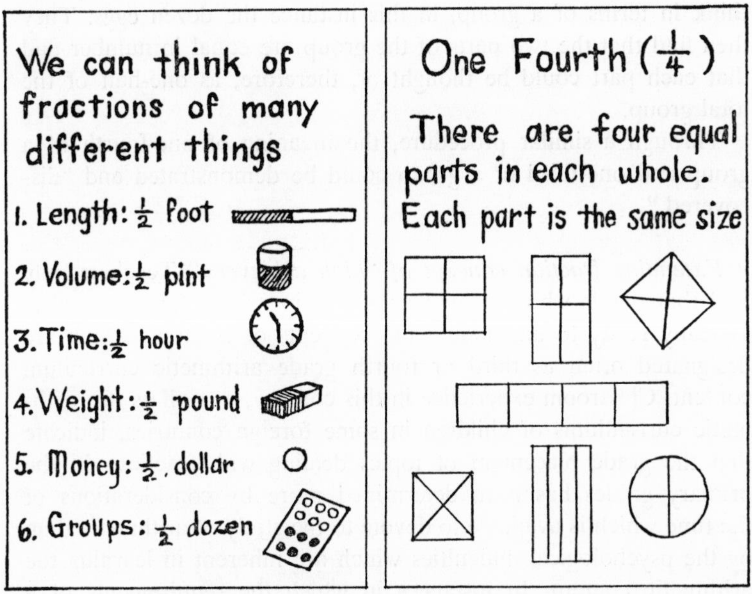

Figure 5.8 Charts used to summarize information.[16]

[16] Enoch Dumas, Charles F. Howard, and Jean E. Dumas, *Arithmetic Charts Handbook* (San Francisco: Fearon Publishers, Inc., 1960), pp. 37, 39.

Extending Concepts of Fractions in the Lower Primary Grades

Introducing a fraction of a group. During the second grade, many children are ready to be introduced to the concept of a fraction of a group. This may be done quite easily by using an egg carton containing a dozen "eggs" made of clay or some other material. When one-half of the eggs are covered, the pupils can perceive, without counting, that as one-half of the carton is covered it must be true in this instance that one-half of the eggs are covered. Then, by counting, they can see that the two halves of the group of twelve eggs are equal-sized groups. In other words, they start by thinking of one-half of a unit, in this instance the egg carton, and then "discover" that at the same time they can think in terms of a group, in this instance the dozen eggs. They then find that the two parts of the group are equal in number and that each part could be thought of, therefore, as one-half of the total group.

Through a similar procedure, the meaning of one-fourth of a group and one-third of a group could be demonstrated and "discovered."

Extending fraction concept of "high achievers." Teachers may find that pupils who are high achievers in arithmetic are psychologically ready to understand the concepts of fractions which are designated often as third or fourth grade arithmetic curriculum content. Classroom experience in this country, as well as the arithmetic curriculums of children in some foreign countries, indicate that the grade placement of topics dealing with fractions in the primary grades has been determined more by considerations of the time which is available to devote to the study of arithmetic than by the psychological difficulties which are inherent in learning the arithmetic content. In instances in which the requirements of a "balanced curriculum" for a particular group of children have been met in all curriculum areas, the teacher need not hesitate to introduce groups of high achievers to the more advanced arithmetic content and to extend the pupils' concepts of fractions by following the procedures suggested in Chapter 9.

Using Arithmetic Films and Filmstrips

General procedures when using arithmetic films. As more motion-picture films dealing with arithmetic subjects become available, a teacher will find it helpful to give increasing consideration to these teaching aids, although, admittedly, such films may be more helpful at the intermediate and upper grade levels. She should examine the catalogues of films which are available for her use and select those which deal with arithmetical concepts which are needed by her class. She should preview the films in order to use them most effectively, because often it is necessary to use preliminary number experiences to prepare the class for the materials included in the films.

A common limitation to the value of arithmetic films is that often several arithmetical concepts are introduced in a relatively short time. These concepts are then extended so rapidly during the short time the film is being shown that they are not fully grasped by any but the more intelligent pupils.

For this reason, it is desirable often not to show a given arithmetic film to a class until the concepts depicted have been introduced and developed in the usual way through using manipulative materials and familiar social settings. The film may be used then to advantage in reviewing several related concepts and illustrating their relationships and applications. The level of a child's arithmetical learning is an important factor in deciding when a given film should be scheduled and what class preparation should precede it. In instances where the arithmetical concepts have been introduced to the class and partially developed, the teacher may find that an arithmetic film may be very helpful in holding the children's attention as these concepts are being reviewed. Novel presentations are possible in a film, especially where animated drawings are used, and thus a new way for the children to see the number processes represented and the uses of number illustrated.

A limitation to the value of an arithmetic film is that during the showing of the film the child is unable to use pencil and paper to get practice in expressing in symbols the arithmetical concepts being illustrated. This disadvantage is partially offset, however, by opportunities to read numerals on the screen while their applications are being illustrated.

In kindergarten and in the first and second grades, types of films which extend a pupil's concepts by illustrating them in social settings new to him and outside of his immediate environment are very helpful. Through a judicious use of color and animated drawings, a film may illustrate many abstract number ideas which are not developed easily through the usual classroom experiences.

In addition to ensuring that a class is prepared for the ideas presented in a film, the teacher should plan to follow the film with a discussion period. During the discussion, she should ascertain what the pupils have learned from the film and help them to clarify those ideas which have not been well understood.

General procedures when using filmstrips. Although the large number of available filmstrips dealing with arithmetical concepts sometimes in itself presents a problem when making a selection, the cost of filmstrips is relatively small, and school authorities should find little difficulty in supplying teachers with this valuable teaching aid.

In some respects, a filmstrip can be used more easily than a motion-picture film for illustrating arithmetical concepts, as the time a teacher allots for the discussion of each frame of a filmstrip can be regulated readily to suit the abilities of the children in the class, making it easier to pace a lesson. Furthermore, a filmstrip usually can be used in a classroom which has not been darkened to the point where the children are unable to use pencils and paper and manipulative materials during the showing, permitting the teacher to supplement the experiences provided by the filmstrip.

Filmstrips often have an advantage over charts, since they are designed by professional artists and are usually made more attractive and interesting through the use of color than are the charts prepared by a classroom teacher. The time required to prepare a series of charts comparable in number to the frames of a single filmstrip would be greater than the time a busy classroom teacher would wish to use for this purpose.

While motion-picture films should be preceded by careful preparation of the class for the showing and should be followed by discussion, filmstrips may be used somewhat differently. Their general use follows more closely the use of charts, and their value is much the same as that of charts.

After determining the learning level at which the class would benefit most by seeing a given filmstrip, the teacher should darken the room only to the extent that is needed, so that there is enough light for the pupils to use manipulative materials or pencils and paper where they are helpful. There should be enough light for the teacher to see the reactions of the pupils without difficulty, so that she can judge the speed at which new frames should be presented. How fast the frames are changed and the number of frames shown during a single lesson depend upon how rapidly the children can comprehend the concepts illustrated and how long the teacher feels the discussion of each frame should continue. There should be no sense of urgency that would indicate that there is a need for a particular filmstrip to be projected completely during any one lesson. The lesson should be paced rather leisurely, so that the pupils have time to observe the details of each frame and to ask questions or discuss differences of opinion when such arise. In instances where the pupils could benefit by using manipulative materials or pencils and paper to increase their understanding, they should be allowed to take whatever time is needed.

Unlike motion-picture films, filmstrips may be used very effectively while an arithmetical concept new to the children is being first introduced, because a frame may be held for an indefinite period while questions are being asked or the pupils are using manipulative materials or pencils and paper. By asking the pupils to explain the content of various frames, the teacher creates opportunities to evaluate the pupils' understanding of the concepts and thus is able to determine whether further explanations or learning experiences are necessary.

Suggested Learning Activities

1. At a level of your choice (kindergarten or first or second grade) list the out-of-school measuring experiences that a child might reasonably encounter.

2. List three activities through which children can learn that all measurements are approximate.
3. List three nonstandard units of measure. To what standard units are they most nearly equivalent?
4. Name measuring instruments which should be available in a first or second grade classroom for purposes of teaching about measurements.
5. List the out-of-school experiences first grade children may reasonably meet through which they learn about fractions.
6. Select a social studies topic for first or second grade and point out the activities involving fractions which may be planned for as the unit is taught.
7. Construct a flannel board and equip it with felt sectors of circles for use in teaching about fractions to first or second graders. Plan a suitable lesson. (A 20″ x 30″ piece of Celotex or similar wall-board covered with cotton flannel secured to the back of the board by thumbtacks serves very well.)
8. Prepare a group of variously weighted objects for use in primary grades in teaching measurement of weight. Good are cylindrical ice cream cartons filled with varying amounts of sand; securely glue and tape the lids to the cartons.
9. Make a large, heavy cardboard "thermometer" for classroom use. Use two pieces of ribbon, one red and one white, to form the "mercury"; thread ribbon through slits at top and bottom of "mercury" column and sew or tie to a piece of elastic. Be sure to arrange markings and numerals in accord with common room thermometers.
10. Preview and record your evaluation of films and filmstrips designed for use at primary grade levels in the teaching of measuring and fractions.
11. Make a collection of pictures appropriate to topics discussed in this chapter. Mount in readiness for use on a classroom bulletin board.

Guided Supplementary Reading

1. Why does Bjonerud suggest that it is possible that some of our common measuring instruments are becoming obsolete as far as common usage is concerned?
2. Buckingham refers to the use of "intermediate devices" as an important step forward in man's development of measuring ability. What does he mean?

3. What reasons do Ceccarini and Dutton give for suggesting that the classroom should be a learning laboratory?
4. According to Clark and Eads, how are a young child's measurement concepts developed?
5. How does DeMay suggest one teach children measures of capacity?
6. What fractions do Grossnickle and Brueckner recommend be taught by the end of grade 2?
7. What procedures did Gunderson use in teaching seven-year-olds (second graders) addition and subtraction of fractions and fractional equivalents?
8. What classroom activities do Hollister and Gunderson recommend for teaching the value of coins?
9. According to Lay, why are certain numbers referred to as "rational numbers"?
10. What point of view do Lee and Lee take regarding the place of application of mathematics to daily life?
11. How does Maria define rational numbers?
12. How do Marks, Purdy, and Kinney define a standard unit of measure?
13. Mueller sketches a brief history of the development of the idea of fractions. What source does he give for the words "numerator" and "denominator"?
14. How does Parker propose that teachers can provide "extra" arithmetic experience for primary boys and girls?
15. Payne and Seber suggest a procedure for teaching children relationships between units of measure. What is it?
16. What conclusions does Schott reach as a result of his research on the use of arithmetic "tools"?
17. How does Wilson suggest measuring should be taught in grades 1 and 2?

Suggested Supplementary References

1. BJONERUD, CORWIN E., "Arithmetic Concepts Possessed by the Pre-School Child," *Arithmetic Teacher,* Vol. 7, pp. 347–350, November, 1960.
2. BUCKINGHAM, BURDETTE R., *Elementary Arithmetic,* Chapter 13. Boston: Ginn and Co., 1953.
3. CECCARINI, FRANCES, AND WILBUR H. DUTTON, *Making Instructional Aids and Independent Seat Work in Arithmetic.* Published by the authors, Box 25342, W. Los Angeles 25, Calif., 1955.

4. CLARK, JOHN R., AND LAURA K. EADS, *Guiding Arithmetic Learning,* Chapter 8. New York: World Book Co., 1954.
5. DEMAY, AMY J., *Guiding Beginners in Arithmetic,* Chapter 10. Evanston, Illinois: Row, Peterson and Co., 1957.
6. GROSSNICKLE, FOSTER E., AND LEO J. BRUECKNER, *Discovering Meanings in Arithmetic,* Chapter 5. Philadelphia: The John C. Winston Co., 1959.
7. GUNDERSON, ETHEL, "Fractions: Seven-Year-Olds Use Them," *Arithmetic Teacher,* Vol. 5, pp. 233–238, November, 1958.
8. HOLLISTER, GEORGE E., AND AGNES G. GUNDERSON, *Teaching Arithmetic in Grades I and II,* Chapter 11. Boston: D. C. Heath and Co., 1954.
9. LAY, L. CLARK, *Arithmetic: An Introduction to Mathematics,* Chapter 8. New York: The Macmillan Co., 1961.
10. LEE, J. MURRAY, AND DORRIS MAY LEE, *The Child and His Curriculum,* Chapter 11. New York: Appleton-Century-Crofts, Inc., 1960.
11. MARIA, MAY RICKEY, *The Structure of Arithmetic and Algebra,* Chapter 7. New York: John Wiley and Sons, Inc., 1958.
12. MARKS, JOHN L., C. RICHARD PURDY, AND LUCIEN B. KINNEY, *Teaching Arithmetic for Understanding,* Chapter 11. New York: McGraw-Hill Book Co., Inc., 1958.
13. MUELLER, FRANCIS J., *Arithmetic, Its Structure and Concepts,* Chapter 5. Englewood Cliffs, N.J.: Prentice-Hall, Inc., 1956.
14. PARKER, B. F., "Primary Arithmetic," *Grade Teacher,* Vol. 72, p. 16, January, 1955.
15. PAYNE, JOSEPH N., AND ROBERT C. SEBER, "Measurement and Approximation," *The Growth of Mathematical Ideas,* Twenty-fourth Yearbook, Washington, D.C.: The National Council of Teachers of Mathematics, 1959.
16. SCHOTT, A. F., "New Tools, Methods for Their Use, and a New Curriculum in Arithmetic," *Arithmetic Teacher,* Vol. 4, pp. 204–209, November, 1957.
17. WILSON, GUY M., *Teaching the New Arithmetic,* Chapter 8. New York: McGraw-Hill Book Co., Inc., 1951.

PART 2

Extending Number Concepts in Grades Three through Eight

CHAPTER 6

Bases for the Arithmetic Program in Grades 3 through 8

A good arithmetic program for children in grades 3 through 8 depends upon four important bases. The first basis concerns the characteristics of children at these grade levels because the efficiency with which children may learn arithmetic is affected by their characteristics. As mentioned previously, each child is different from all others and these differences should be considered; but there are certain stages of development through which all children pass, and there are sufficient similarities among the characteristics of children at any given stage of development to enable us to select material and methods of presenting material which will provide a basis for a sound program.

A second basis for the arithmetic program concerns the social demands upon the school. Children do not have time to learn all mathematics, so those aspects which will be most useful must receive priority. Because the selection of content for an elementary school arithmetic program depends upon the prevailing philosophy of education as to what knowledge has the most worth, the decision will depend upon the needs of the children as seen by the members of the particular group of which they are a part. It will also depend upon the historical setting in which the program is placed. As the needs of society change, the selection of the arithmetic content changes. The arithmetic program which emerges is determined by effective pressure groups which influence the selection of educational curricula in each society.

A third basis for the arithmetic program is determined by the nature of the Hindu-Arabic decimal numeration system which we have inherited. Computational procedures are determined to a large extent by the characteristics of this decimal numeration system, and consequently certain content should be given priority in order to prepare children to use this system effectively. The sequence of topics in the arithmetic program in the intermediate and upper grades will be determined also by the logical nature of the subject matter, since certain concepts and computational procedures should be developed prior to others in order to make learning efficient.

The fourth basis upon which the arithmetic program in grades 3 through 8 should be planned has to do with mathematical concepts regarding the nature of the numbers themselves and with the nature of the operations upon these numbers. Although this aspect of mathematics has been reserved traditionally for students in high schools and colleges where the structure of number systems has been studied, a beginning could and should be made in the elementary school. Such study would provide readiness for a later study of mathematics, and also many pupils would gain an increased interest in arithmetic as they are introduced to material of this type.

Each of the above four bases for the arithmetic program in the third through the eighth grades will now be discussed in more detail.

Maturity Traits of Children in Grade 3 Which Have Implications for the Arithmetic Teacher

Physical characteristics. The child's growth in the third grade continues at about the same rate as it did in the second grade, averaging a gain of approximately six pounds in weight and an increase of two inches in height.[1] When the child has reached

[1] Ernest H. Watson and George H. Lowrey, *Growth and Development of Children* (Chicago: The Yearbook Publishers, revised edition, 1954), p. 44.

the third grade, his muscular coordination has usually improved to the point where he can use his small muscles quite well. His eyes, though not fully developed, can accommodate to varying distances without difficulty. At this grade level the child usually succeeds in adjusting his posture to the type of work required of him without undue strain and is not as easily fatigued by seatwork as in earlier grades.

In the third grade, the arithmetic period may be lengthened and the children may work for longer periods without excessive fatigue. If the activities are varied, the arithmetic period can be from forty to fifty minutes in length. The children may be expected to do written work and to read arithmetic material from either textbook or the chalkboard without undue eyestrain.

Emotional characteristics. The child in the third grade still has a rather short interest span. He is often impatient and may display temper manifestations, but he calms down quickly. He is less introspective and sensitive regarding himself than he was in the second grade.

Children in the third grade usually like school and their teacher, but are less dependent upon him emotionally than in earlier grades. They are inclined to think of their teacher as one of the school group. At this age level the child evaluates his own conduct and that of others more closely than he formerly did. He may be prone to find excuses for his failures, but he differentiates good performance from bad. He likes new types of work and is usually ready and willing to take on new responsibilities.

Social characteristics. Most third grade children are interested in participating in group activities. They like games and are reasonably good at following rules which are clear and definite. By the third grade, the girls and boys may be drawing apart in their group activities and there may be some rivalry between them.

In group activities, third grade children are very willing to set up group standards and attempt to live up to them. They can control their own group activities to some extent, but often are not successful without adult guidance or help from older children.

Teachers can make good use of the children's interest in games by selecting some with arithmetic content. Considerable practice in using the basic facts of addition, subtraction, multiplication, and division can be provided through arranging the material in such an activity in the form of arithmetic games. Games provide children with an immediate purpose for learning the basic facts they need in order to participate successfully.

Intellectual characteristics. Although intellectual differences among third grade children are very apparent, they all show an active intellectual curiosity about their environment. At this grade level, they like to learn the reasons for phenomena. They are able to grasp the implications of material written at their reading level without much difficulty.

The third grade child may be able to read quite well, although here too there are wide differences among the members of a single class. The child is much quicker in his responses than he was in the second grade and he is ready to explore new areas and examine new ideas. Third grade children usually are interested in collecting things and they may be very much interested in money and what it will buy for them.

The arithmetic content at this grade level should be rich in its social implications. New concepts should be introduced in such a way that the rationale and uses of the concepts are made clear. During the arithmetic period the pupils may be expected to work from textbooks or duplicated material without much difficulty. Care should be taken, however, to ensure that the vocabulary needed to express new arithmetical concepts is learned and that particular attention is given to teaching the children how to read arithmetic material.

Maturity Traits of Children in the Intermediate Grades Which Have Implications for the Arithmetic Teacher

The stage of development referred to as "later childhood" includes the ages from the ninth through the eleventh year for boys and the ninth and tenth years for girls. Children of these ages are found in the fourth through the sixth grades. Children appear to have fewer emotional and physical problems at this stage than in either earlier or later stages of development. Their physical health is usually good. The development of muscles requiring finer coordination is adequate. The eyes are mature enough to withstand their normal use in school work without difficulty. The children's emotional health is usually good, as they have had time to adjust to the requirements of children and have not yet had to meet the new and complex problems which arrive with adolescence. The implications of child development for the arithmetic program at this stage are found in the intellectual characteristics of children rather than in their physical and emotional characteristics.

Intellectual characteristics. During later childhood, the neural development of children may be expected to have reached the point where the children are able to do the thinking and logical reasoning needed to understand abstract arithmetic concepts; but as they lack experience, suitable readiness activities should be provided before introducing new material.

The rapid increase in mathematical concepts met by children in the intermediate grades may result in low achievers not grasping all that has been presented, and consequently there may be gaps in their knowledge which impede the understanding of concepts new to them. To avoid this difficulty, the teacher frequently should conduct individual interviews with the slow learners and check their knowledge in order to identify and overcome points of difficulty. The teacher should emphasize the importance of knowing the reasons for the various procedures, so that the pupils will realize that being able to carry out the procedures of arithmetic is not sufficient unless the reasons for the procedures being used also are known to them. Frequent reviews are needed; and before a new step is presented, the readiness for it should be developed by reviewing the steps which have been learned earlier and which pertain to the new concept.

To help the child draw mathematical generalizations from the various instances studied, it is good practice to vary the presentation of a new concept by illustrating it in various ways. For instance, the use of concrete materials may be followed by using diagrams and charts to summarize each new generalization. The use of a number line may help illustrate how numbers could be represented in each particular situation. A variety of instances involving each new concept helps the pupil to abstract from the particular instances the underlying principles.

It should be remembered also that although children may understand the reasons in arithmetic there is still a need for them to get enough practice in processing the numerals to give them facility in computation. This need for practice has been the basis for the facetious comment that the child learns arithmetic through his eyes, ears, and up through his hand and arm.

The progress which children make through practicing an arithmetic process may lead some teachers to feel that the quickest way to teach a child arithmetic is to show him first how to carry through a certain process, and then to show him the rationale for the process later. Any apparent gain in such a procedure is due probably to the child's getting an overview of the process which enables him to identify the various concepts as they enter into the total pattern. At times, high achievers may be able to determine the reasons for the work as they are carrying out a computation, especially if considerable practice is given. However, there is a danger in procedures in which children are required to focus their attention upon the process because they may neglect to pay attention to the reasons involved. Consequently the work in arithmetic may become mechanical in nature and lose much of its interest and meaning.

The interest span of children in the intermediate grades is much longer than that noted in the primary grades. The children are extending their interests to faraway places and to other times in history. They are becoming more interested in the physical world, in science, and in the reasons for things in nature. Boys and girls will enjoy arithmetic for its practical value as well as for its intrinsic interest.

Emotional characteristics. As noted above, the emotional characteristics of children in the intermediate grades do not present particular hazards in learning arithmetic. However, these emotional characteristics must be given careful consideration by the teacher so that the interest of the children in the subject matter is maintained sufficiently to motivate them to expend the mental energy needed to learn a continually increasing range of new concepts. An important characteristic of a good teacher is his ability to develop and maintain the interest of the children in the material they are studying.

At the intermediate grade levels children are usually eager to learn. The gang influence is gaining strength, but the teacher is accepted as the leader in the classroom although his actions probably will be subjected to a rather critical evaluation by the pupils. Children at this stage of development are quite ready to evaluate themselves and their own work. They may be allowed to correct their own work and led through discussion to help to identify their own difficulties.

As the teacher wishes the pupils to develop and maintain a wholesome attitude of inquiry, he should conduct discussions on arithmetic topics in such a way that children are led to discover for themselves the generalizations and short cuts in the procedures. Recognition should be given for good thinking and for good answers, while incorrect answers should be treated in such a way that the pupil is not discouraged from making further attempts to think for himself.

Since children in the intermediate and upper grades respond quickly to a challenge, the puzzle element in arithmetic may be exploited by the teacher to increase interest at these grade levels. These children are interested also in new ideas and in the new vocabulary needed to express these ideas. The teacher must endeavor to maintain the children's interest by pacing the instruction to suit the ability of the class so that the children do not become overwhelmed by the mass of new ideas and become discouraged.

The interest evidenced in a subject by the teacher himself is an important factor in stimulating the interest of the children. Topics dealing with the history of arithmetic, with algorisms used in other countries or at other times, and with puzzles, jokes, riddles, or short cuts connected with arithmetic should be interspersed with topics dealing with learning those skills in arithmetical computations which seem to be rather mechanical or which lack interest in themselves. Enrichment materials are available which contain a variety of topics designed to stimulate interest in arithmetic and mathematics.[2]

Some emotional frustration which may arise during this stage of development is connected with the difficulties some pupils have in reading. At intermediate grade levels, it is not unusual to find a range in reading ability from an adult level to a level showing a degree of retardation amounting to several grade levels.

As the reading level which is required to make effective use of the pupils' textbooks increases rather rapidly, and as much new vocabulary is being introduced to deal with new mathematical concepts, pupils who are retarded in reading will experience considerable difficulty. At these grade levels it becomes even more important for the teacher to emphasize the reading of arithmetic. In such instances, the teacher should spend a few minutes daily with the class in examining the textbook material to be used during the day and in ensuring that the children are able to read it with understanding. New vocabulary should receive special consideration, and the meaning of each term should be reviewed with sufficient frequency to ensure that it is understood.

Children in the intermediate grades enjoy both limited competition and cooperation, although it is more difficult for them to develop attitudes of cooperation than those of competition. The teacher may make use of the enjoyment children derive from competition by using arithmetic games to give the pupils the practice they need to master the basic facts of the fundamental operations and to gain skill in computation. These children also are ready to cooperate with one another in such ways as working in teams of two to practice basic facts to their mutual advantage.

Maturity Traits of Children in the Upper Grades Which Have Implications in Learning Arithmetic

The preadolescent stage of child development is reached by boys during their twelfth and thirteenth years, and by girls during the eleventh and twelfth years. Girls are often more than a year ahead

[2] See references for enrichment material at end of Chapter 14.

of boys in most phases of their development during this period.[3] The important physical and emotional changes tend to induce inconsistent behavior and some emotional insecurity in both boys and girls. Height and weight changes are accelerated and other physical changes are very noticeable.

Emotional problems which arise from feelings of inadequacy and uncertainty as to their status with adults and others in their age group may result in their having difficulty in accepting criticism.

As in the case of children in the previous developmental stage, the physical and emotional characteristics of the children have fewer implications for the arithmetic program than have the intellectual characteristics.

Intellectual characteristics. As the neural development of children in the preadolescent stages of growth is almost complete, the children are ready intellectually to grasp quite difficult and complicated concepts providing that the experiences needed to understand the steps leading up to these concepts have been supplied. Children in this stage of growth make noticeable gains in problem-solving activities and in working with symbols to express the abstract relationships arising from mathematical situations. When they are studying the applications of arithmetic to the adult activities of the business world, their lack of experience in this area presents a difficulty. But since children at this age level will profit considerably from vicarious experiences, such as those secured through reading, listening to oral descriptions, dramatizations, or motion pictures, compensation for real experience may be provided without much difficulty.

Emotional characteristics. Boys in this stage of development maintain their interest in physical science, while the girls become more interested in human relationships. Both boys and girls will maintain their interest in arithmetic if it is well presented. Particular stress should be placed upon having the pupils understand the arithmetic and upon helping them to discover for themselves the

[3] Edward C. Britton and J. Merritt Winans, *Growing from Infancy to Adulthood* (New York: Appleton-Century-Crofts, Inc., 1958), p. 58.

important principles, generalizations, and short cuts. Experiments involving the introduction of contemporary mathematics into the elementary school curriculum have indicated that this type of material has a high interest value for many boys and girls. The value of arithmetic for its practical applications should be stressed as well as the values which come from considering mathematics for its intrinsic interest.

The rate of introducing new material should be regulated carefully to accommodate the capabilities of the pupils in the group, so that each pupil will be motivated by feelings of accomplishment. When work has to be reviewed or a concept which has been formerly learned has to be reintroduced, pupils will gain new insight and new interest if the teacher is able to adopt viewpoints new to the boys and girls and to employ procedures which, though new, are not very different from those with which the pupils are familiar. Activities which are merely repetitions of earlier procedures may deaden interest unless the teacher convinces the pupils that this repetition is a part of the preparation for new learnings or has important applications in social activities outside of the school.

Problem-solving activities in which small groups of pupils work as teams to find solutions and then to describe them for the remainder of the class are stimulating, and may be employed very successfully at these grade levels.

Social Demands upon the Arithmetic Program

The justification for teaching arithmetic in the schools of this country traditionally has been based upon the social usefulness of arithmetic to the average citizen. The public schools were first established in this country during the colonial period for the purpose of teaching children how to read and, in particular, how to read the Bible. Arithmetic was introduced into the elementary school curriculum largely as a result of pressures from the business world, despite considerable early opposition. The first arithmetic textbooks were in the form of reference books containing little more than the various tables used in business and agriculture and descriptions of arithmetical procedures needed by the citizens of that period.

By the early part of the nineteenth century, arithmetic had been accepted as part of the elementary school curriculum throughout this country. The authors of the textbooks written at that time stressed the social value of the content. A textbook by Joseph Ray [4] was entitled *Ray's Practical Arithmetic,* although the contents contained material such as the algorisms for deriving the cube root of a number, a topic which might be considered to be of doubtful value in the everyday life of an average citizen.

The prevailing theory of learning held by educators in the early part of the nineteenth century was influenced by a concept sometimes referred to as the "theory of mental discipline." According to this theory, the mind could be trained to function with efficiency through studying difficult material in one subject-matter area. This efficiency then would be transferred to all other subject-matter areas, as well as providing the individual with general reasoning powers. Accordingly it was thought that the content of an arithmetic program might be secondary in importance to a general value which might be found in solving difficult problems as a means of strengthening the mind. Consequently, the nature of the content of the arithmetic program was widened to include many topics other than those which seemed to possess usefulness in their applications to everyday life.

During the latter part of the nineteenth century, advances in experimental psychology resulted in questioning the doctrine of mental discipline and the theory that there was a general transfer of training from one subject to another. Emphasis was placed once more upon selecting material for the arithmetic program which could be defended upon the grounds that it had high social utility.

During the first part of the twentieth century, considerable research was undertaken to determine the extent to which arithmetic entered into the social life of the average citizen. The conclusions reported in many of these studies indicated that the actual use of

[4] Joseph Ray, *Ray's Practical Arithmetic. Practical Arithmetic by Induction and Analysis* (Cincinnati: Van Antwerp, Bragg and Company, 1857), pp. 286–293.

arithmetic in many occupations was restricted largely to computations involving the fundamental operations with whole numbers. and to a rather limited use of common fractions, decimal fractions, and the application of numbers to measurement. The philosophy of education advanced by the Progressive Education Association strengthened the tendency to restrict the arithmetic content in the elementary school curriculum to those aspects of arithmetic which could be defended upon the basis of social utility. The content of arithmetic then was made up of such topics as those dealing with insurance, installment buying, profit and loss, and the information needed to enable the average citizen to react with some understanding to the mathematical concepts presented through his social environment. Topics dealing with how arithmetic helps one to understand the world in which he lives were introduced to widen the arithmetic program. Arithmetic was considered primarily as a tool subject which would enable a citizen to function more effectively in a democratic society. It was felt that the priority given to a topic should be determined by the extent to which it seemed to function in the life of the average citizen, and that seldom-used processes should be included for appreciation only, rather than as subject matter receiving much emphasis.

During the middle of the twentieth century, largely as a result of the work of Brownell, Wheat, Brueckner and Grossnickle, and others, attention was focused upon the importance of children's learning the mathematical bases of the computational procedures as these are determined by the properties of the decimal numeration system. The value of teaching children to understand the rationale of the algorisms received an emphasis which still is recognized today.

Some curriculum studies, principally on the secondary school level, grew out of new demands for mathematics arising during World War II.[5] After the launching of the Russian satellite, "Sputnik," in 1957 the interest in mathematics increased sharply. Funds provided by the National Science Foundation and other foundations

[5] "The First Report of the Commission on Post-War Plans," *The Mathematics Teacher,* Vol. 37, pp. 226–232, May, 1944; "The Second Report of the Commission on Post-War Plans," *The Mathematics Teacher,* Vol. 38, pp. 195–221, May, 1945; "Guidance Report of the Commission on Post-War Plans," *The Mathematics Teacher,* Vol. 40, pp. 315–339, November, 1947.

were made available to groups composed largely of mathematicians to review the curriculum at the secondary school level with the object of increasing the mathematical competencies of students entering college science programs. These groups have recommended the inclusion of content which would emphasize the structure of mathematics as the central core of the mathematics program, a concept they are now recommending to elementary school arithmetic teachers. They would relegate topics dealing with business and social applications of arithmetic to a secondary position as being only instances of the applications of basic mathematical principles.

Although contemporary mathematics is characterized both by its viewpoint and by the introduction of new concepts, the emphasis is not so much on new concepts as on a new approach to "old ideas." Traditional mathematics is, for the most part, still valid, but the new approach to teaching the ideas is characterized by consistency, unity, and an appeal to basic principles.

The school program traditionally has treated the various branches of mathematics, such as arithmetic, geometry, algebra, and trigonometry as separate subjects, and from a viewpoint which did not give particular emphasis to their relatedness. Each "subject" had its own vocabulary, its own principles which governed the manipulation of its symbols, and its own field of application.

In contemporary mathematics, a conscious effort is directed toward a search for principles, language, and concepts which will emphasize the ways in which arithmetic, geometry, algebra, trigonometry, and other branches of mathematics may be related into one body of content making up the area of mathematics. In contemporary mathematics an emphasis is placed upon studying the structure of number as distinct from studying only the computational procedures and their applications. The study of the structure of number, along with a remarkably flexible means of communication provided by the set concept and its related language and symbolism, has contributed to changes in viewpoint to the extent that a distinction may be made between "traditional" mathematics and "contemporary" mathematics when discussing school mathematics programs.

Although space limitation in a book on procedures for teaching arithmetic preclude an extended discussion of sets, number systems, and other aspects of contemporary mathematics, a review of some of the important concepts which have a bearing upon the procedures for teaching arithmetic in the elementary school will serve as guidelines for a teacher. These concepts will be discussed in more detail in Chapter 15.

The concept of a "set." If we think of a set as referring to any well-defined group of elements, we may use this idea as a basis for describing many other mathematical concepts. The concept of a set has wide application in all branches of mathematics today. Many mathematical concepts can be defined precisely in terms of sets. It may be noted, moreover, that the symbolism used to express set concepts is convenient, flexible, and has been standardized to the point where there is wide agreement on its interpretation among mathematicians. It will be noted in the following paragraphs that it is very convenient to use the concept of a set when describing the early experiences a child has with number.

When a child in the kindergarten or grade 1 learns the cardinal use of his counting numbers, he is identifying each number as being related with a set of groups, each of which contains the same number of elements. For instance, he may think of five as being connected with the set of all groups of five objects, or he may think of seven as being connected with the set of all groups of seven objects.

As the pupil becomes more familiar with the cardinal use of number, he reaches a point in higher grade levels where he may think of the set of counting numbers, one, two, three, and so on, as a set of elements in their own right, apart from their connection with particular objects. This set of numbers may be designated as the "natural numbers." Although in early grade levels his concepts of addition and subtraction are connected closely with groups of objects, at higher grade levels he extends his earlier concepts of addition and subtraction to the place where he can think of these and other fundamental operations as being operations on two elements of the same set which are associated with a unique element in that set. For instance, he finds that the operations of addition and multiplication on natural numbers result in numbers in the set of natural numbers.

The child learns that while he can subtract a small number from a larger number, he is not able to subtract a large number from a smaller one and get a natural number, such as in the instance $3 - 4$, and he learns that negative numbers, such as -1, do not belong to the set of natural numbers. He also learns that sometimes when he divides one number by another, the result is not a natural number, as when he divides 3 by 4 and gets ¾. He is led to understand that a fraction, such as ¾, is a number contained in the set of rational numbers but is not a member of the set of natural numbers.

Concepts regarding sets may be used by pupils at higher grade levels to understand many mathematical ideas related to other branches of mathematics. Elementary concepts of sets, along with the related symbolism, are discussed in more detail in Chapter 15.

The concept of "number systems." In the traditional elementary school program the numbers used by the pupils are restricted largely to the set of "whole" numbers, which is the set consisting of the natural numbers and zero, although the irrational number pi (π) is met in connection with problems dealing with circles, and negative numbers may be introduced in connection with some problems, such as those dealing with changes in temperature. The fact that fractions, negative numbers, and irrational numbers belong to number systems other than the system of whole numbers has not been explained to pupils in the traditional arithmetic programs in the elementary school.

In contemporary mathematics, a careful distinction is made among number systems. Each of the systems of natural numbers, whole numbers, integers, rational numbers, real numbers, and complex numbers is identified, and the rationale is given to show how each system is developed.

Only an informal definition will be used here to identify the various number systems. The references noted at the end of this chapter are among the many books now available which treat the characteristics of various number systems and the properties of the operations on the numbers in those systems. The diagram in Figure 6.1 indicates how the various number systems are related.

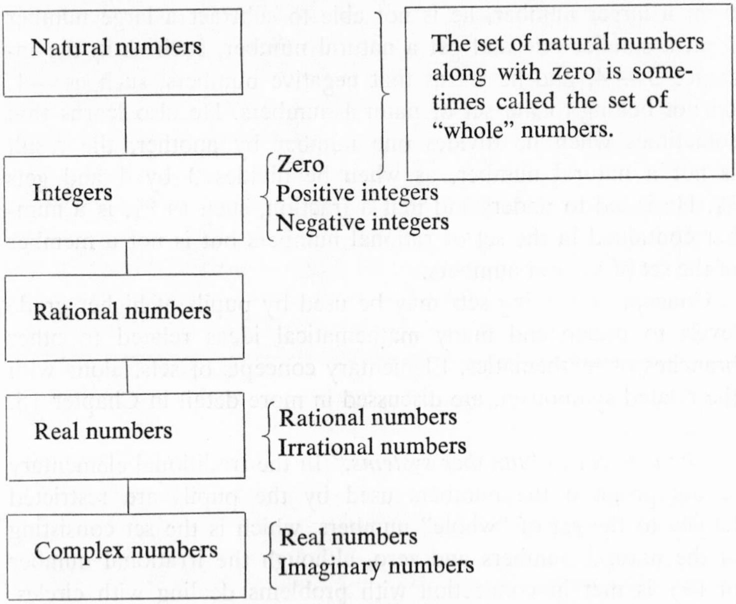

Figure 6.1 A diagram which indicates that the concept of various number systems may be developed by starting from the natural number system.

The natural numbers. The natural numbers refer to the set of numbers we associate with the counting numbers, as the process of counting is a specific use of the set of natural numbers. Usually zero is not considered as a natural number. As mentioned above, the term "whole numbers" is used often to refer to the set composed of the natural numbers along with zero. The system of natural numbers is "closed" with respect to addition and multiplication, which means that these operations upon natural numbers produce a unique number in the same set, that is, another natural number. Examples of natural numbers are 1, 2, 3, 56, 999. Figure 6.2 shows how the natural numbers may be associated with points on a number line.

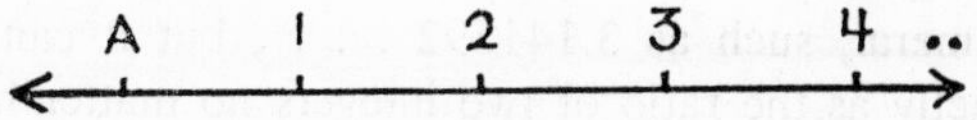

Figure 6.2 A diagram illustrating how natural numbers may be associated with points on a line. The distance between each pair of points is equal to the unit distance between the point associated with 1 and the point "A."

The integers. This system comprises the set of positive numbers, negative numbers, and zero. The operations of subtraction as well as those of addition and multiplication may be performed always to produce a unique (one and only one) integer. For this reason, the system of integers is said to be closed with respect to the operations of addition, subtraction, and multiplication. Examples of integers are $-1, 0, +5, -99, +101$. Integers may be associated with points on a number line, as illustrated in Figure 6.3.

Figure 6.3 A diagram illustrating how integers may be associated with points on a line.

The rational numbers. This system comprises the numbers which may be expressed as the ratio of two integers, excluding the case where zero is the second term, or denominator. The fractions used in the elementary school are rational numbers. A rational number may be thought of as a set of equivalent fractions, as the number $\frac{1}{2}$ may represent the set of equivalent fractions $\frac{1}{2}, \frac{2}{4}, \frac{3}{6}, \frac{4}{8}$, and so on. It may be noted that any of the fractions in this set could be used to represent the set just as well as $\frac{1}{2}$ could. Examples of rational numbers are $\frac{3}{4}, -\frac{15}{6}, \frac{5}{1}$, and their decimal equivalents.[6]

In contrast to rational numbers, the irrational numbers are not generally regarded as constituting a number system in themselves. Irrational numbers may not be expressed as the ratio of two integers. For instance, the number pi (π), which represents the relationship between the circumference of a circle and its diameter, may be expressed to any degree of approximation desired by a

[6] John E. Freund, "Fractions," Chapter 9 of *A Modern Introduction to Mathematics* (Englewood Cliffs, N.J.: Prentice-Hall, Inc., 1956), pp. 125–143.

decimal numeral, such as 3.141592 . . . , but it cannot be expressed exactly as the ratio of two integers no matter how far the division process is extended by using numerals. Examples of irrational numbers are $\sqrt{2}$ and pi (π). An illustration of how rational numbers may be associated with points on a number line is shown in Figure 6.4.

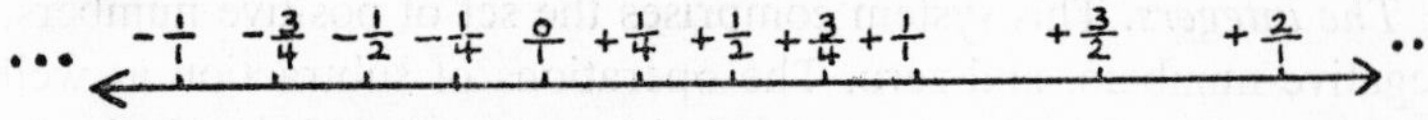

Figure 6.4 A diagram illustrating how rational numbers may be associated with points on a line.

The real numbers. This set may be thought of as the set associated with the set of rational numbers along with the irrational numbers. The operations of addition, subtraction, multiplication, and division, as well as the derivation of roots of non-negative real numbers, may be performed on real numbers, because the system is closed with respect to these operations. Examples of real numbers are 3, $-\frac{5}{6}$, -6, $+7$, $\sqrt{2}$, π, 4.0000 . . . , 2.9.

The complex numbers. The numbers of the systems mentioned above may be represented geometrically by a graph of points on a line. By employing the concept that $\sqrt{-1}$ may be considered to be a number and represented by the numeral "*i*," the complex number system has been developed to the place where it contains certain numbers which may be placed in one-to-one correspondence with the numbers in each of the systems which are mentioned above, and also in one-to-one correspondence with other numbers which are represented by other points in the plane containing the number line. Although complex numbers are not introduced to pupils in the elementary school, they will be met in mathematics at higher levels and they are included here merely to complete our classification of number systems. Examples of complex numbers are $2 + 3i$, $3 - 2i$.

Although children could not be expected to undertake in the elementary school any systematic study of the various number systems, they should be made aware of the fact that number systems exist other than the whole number system which they are using, and that fractions, as well as pi (π) and the negative numbers with which they come into contact, are drawn from these other number systems. In this way the concepts which children develop as they study arithmetic in the elementary school may be made more "compatible" with the concepts they will develop in secondary school. Certain other topics which are emphasized in contemporary mathematics, such as the importance of the principles governing the fundamental operations on numbers, and the topics dealing with the structure of the decimal numeration system, as well as with numeration systems with bases other than ten, pertain closely to the arithmetic of whole numbers as used by the children, and to the study of fractions and decimal fractions. These topics should be developed at appropriate places throughout the elementary school program. They will be discussed further in the chapters which follow.

Today we are being reminded that the "philosophy of education for the good life" must give way to the "philosophy of education for survival," and thus once again we must recognize the fact that the philosophy of education reflected by the society in which we live must determine which knowledge has the most worth and hence which parts of contemporary mathematics shall have emphasis in the elementary school.

Fundamentals of the Decimal Numeration System

Historical retrospect. Mathematics has a long and interesting history. Early historical records show that the mathematical concepts developed in the Orient, Greece, and western Europe have interacted with one another throughout centuries as the various cultures were intermingled by political conquests, trade relationships, and the dissemination of religious philosophies. Many volumes have been written which trace the development of various aspects of the growth of mathematical ideas from the earliest recorded history of Babylon to the present day. The development of systems of numeration in the various cultures and changes in the notation—the system of symbols used to express these number ideas in written form—make up an interesting history in themselves. During some periods, an inadequate system of numeration and its notation have restricted the growth of mathematics until new modes of expression were found which facilitated the further development of mathematical thinking.

The decimal numeration system which we now employ came only slowly into use. The great contributions of Babylonia, Egypt, and Greece were made by mathematicians who were using a numeration system which seems cumbersome and inefficient when compared to the decimal numeration system. The elementary school pupil today, using modern notation, is able to perform computations involving fractions which would have been extremely laborious for the mathematicians of early Babylonia, Egypt, or Greece.

Although various ways of recording number ideas go back beyond the time of recorded history, we are able to surmise the nature of the development of numeration systems in prehistoric times. Some primitive cultures of today employ crude numeration systems which give us a clue to what were probably early stages of development in our own system.

In order to develop a convenient numeration system, some way of naming numbers must be adopted, and in order to express these numbers in written form, some system of using written symbols is needed. The names for the numbers used in primitive cultures often were derived from objects in nature which suggested a certain number. For instance, the number idea of "five" might be suggested by the fingers upon one hand, and the word for "hand" might become the word used to mean the number five, or the word used for "ears" or "eyes" might become the word to signify the number two. In this way, words to indicate each of the first few counting numbers could be adopted, but the difficulty attending the use of a different word for each number beyond the first few numbers would soon result in a system too cumbersome to be used easily. Some method of grouping would then be needed in order to facilitate the expression of larger numbers. The additional problem of expressing these larger numbers in symbols would also tend to encourage the adoption of some systematic grouping procedure.

Before any system of counting developed, man could have kept a record of his cattle or other belongings by using pebbles in a one-to-one relationship with what was being counted or by using tallies in the form of marks upon wood, bone, or other material. In time, as larger numbers were required in daily activities, various ways of grouping these tally marks might be adopted in order to make the recording of numbers more convenient. The practice of grouping by tens, which was used in many cultures, is thought to have grown out of the natural propensity to use the fingers of both hands when indicating small numbers. The use of ten as a base for grouping numbers was widespread, although bases of five, twenty, or sixty were used in some regions. The base of a number system is sometimes referred to as its "compounding point."

Egyptian notation. Symbols which have been simplified to illustrate the system of Egyptian notation are shown in Figure 6.5. Strokes were used to indicate numbers from one through nine. A separate symbol was used to indicate each of the powers of ten. A numeral was constructed by repeating each symbol as often as necessary to indicate a number. For instance, the number 32436 could be expressed as:

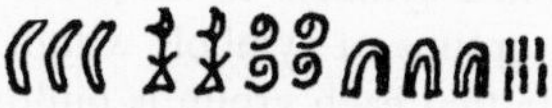

Here we observe the combined use of separate symbols for showing groups of various sizes and the use of the principle of repetition as well as the principle of adding groups to make up the desired number.

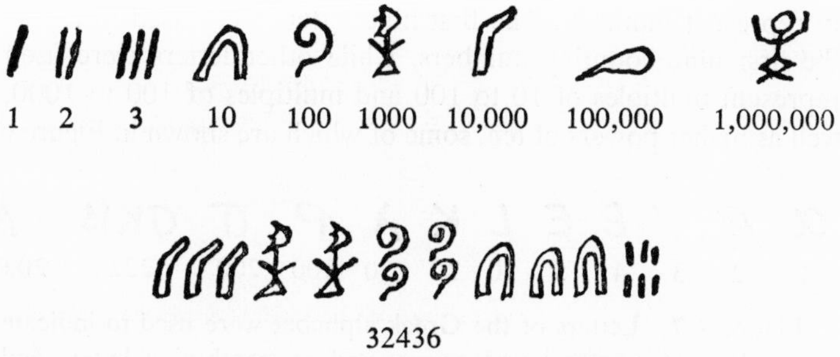

Figure 6.5 Simplified symbols to illustrate an Egyptian notational system. Numerals were constructed by using principles of addition and repetition.

Babylonian notation. The Babylonians used a numeration system with a base of sixty. Separate symbols were used for one and for ten, and these were combined to construct numerals from one to fifty-nine. By leaving a space between groups of symbols within the numeral, multiples of sixty were implied. For example, the numeral for 153 could be written by using the symbol for two in the first group, which would indicate twice sixty, and then leaving a space before writing the symbols in the second group to indicate three tens and three ones. At times a special symbol was used to indicate that two groups of symbols were separated. In some instances the context in which the numeral was placed would be used to determine the meaning of the numeral. Figure 6.6 indicates how the principles of addition and repetition were employed in Babylonian notation.

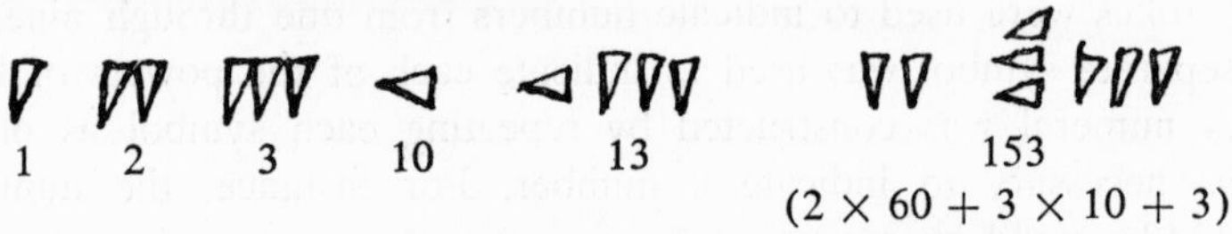

Figure 6.6 Simplified symbols to illustrate a Babylonian notation system. When groups of symbols within a numeral are separated, they indicate that each group is multiplied by a power of sixty. Both an additive principle and the principle of position are used in constructing numerals, as well as the principle of repetition.

Greek notation. The Greeks used the letters of their alphabet to represent numbers. The first nine letters were used to represent the first nine counting numbers, while other letters were used to represent multiples of 10 to 100 and multiples of 100 to 1000, as well as higher powers of ten, some of which are shown in Figure 6.7.

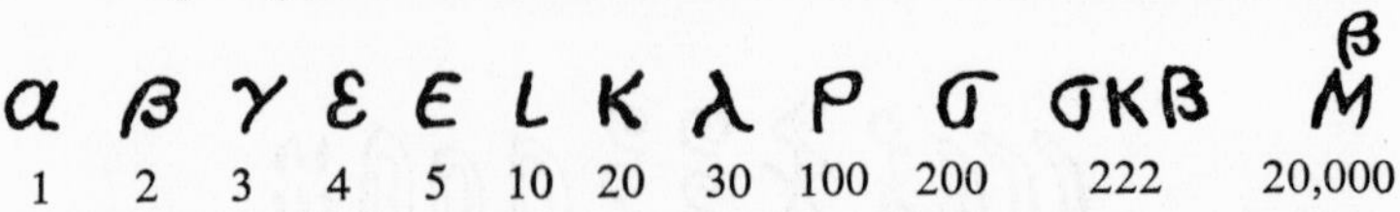

Figure 6.7 Letters of the Greek alphabet were used to indicate numbers. A numeral was constructed by combining letters and using an additive principle. A multiplicative principle was used for large numbers.

By combining letters, a given number could be represented. In conjunction with this additive principle, a multiplicative principle was used for large numbers:

$$\sigma\iota\beta = 200 + 10 + 2 = 212 \quad \text{and} \quad \overset{\beta}{M} = 2 \times 10{,}000 \text{ or } 20{,}000$$

Roman notation. The Romans made use of the symbols shown in Figure 6.8. A limited use was made of positional notation to

I	II	III	V	IX	X	XI	C	D	M	MDXXII	$\overline{X}$
1	2	3	5	9	10	11	100	500	1000	1522	10,000

Figure 6.8 Roman notation employed principles of repetition, addition, subtraction, and multiplication. A limited use of position was employed to indicate subtraction.

indicate the value of a numeral, as seen in IX and XI, where a "one" to the left of the symbol for ten indicates "nine," while a "one" to the right of the symbol for ten indicates "eleven." A multiplicative principle was used for large numbers where a stroke over a symbol would indicate that the number had been multiplied by one thousand:

$$\overline{D} = 1{,}000 \times 500 = 500{,}000$$

Chinese notation. The Chinese included a multiplicative principle in their notation. In Figure 6.9 it will be noted that instead of repeating the symbol for ten a number of times to indicate fifty, they combined symbols for five and for ten to show that ten was multiplied by five.

一	二	三	四	五	十	百	千	三千二百三十五	五十
1	2	3	4	5	10	100	1000	3235	50

Figure 6.9 Chinese notation included both an additive and a multiplicative principle to construct numerals.

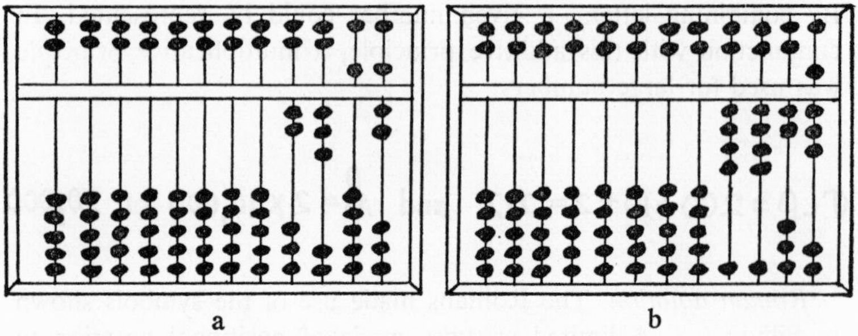

Figure 6.10 The Chinese abacus used rods to indicate powers of ten. The beads at the bottom each represented one while those above the bar represented five. Beads were moved to the bar to indicate a number. In "a" the number 2357 is shown. In "b" 2071 has been added to show a sum of 4428. The beads on rods at the left are used to keep track of the multiplier in multiplication and the divisor in division.

Mayan notation. The most advanced system of notation used by the Indians in the Western Hemisphere was that developed by the Mayans of Central America and southern Mexico.[7] The numerals for one through nineteen were constructed by arranging dots and lines in the manner shown in Figure 6.11. Place value was indicated in a vertical arrangement of the symbols which assigned the lowest position, or place, for units, the second lowest position for multiples of twenty, and the third lowest position for multiples of 360. The fourth lowest position indicated multiples of 7200. This is shown in Figure 6.11. It will be noted that, with the exception of the third position, the base of the system was twenty.[8] The exception is attributed to the fact that the Mayans recorded their year as 18 months of 20 days each, plus an extra five days. The Mayans employed a symbol to indicate an empty place.

[7] Herbert J. Spinden, *Ancient Civilizations of Mexico and Central America* (New York: American Museum of Natural History, 1917), pp. 118–122.

[8] The third position indicated multiples of 360 for the many calculations the Mayans made involving the calendar. For commercial purposes, multiples of 400 were employed.

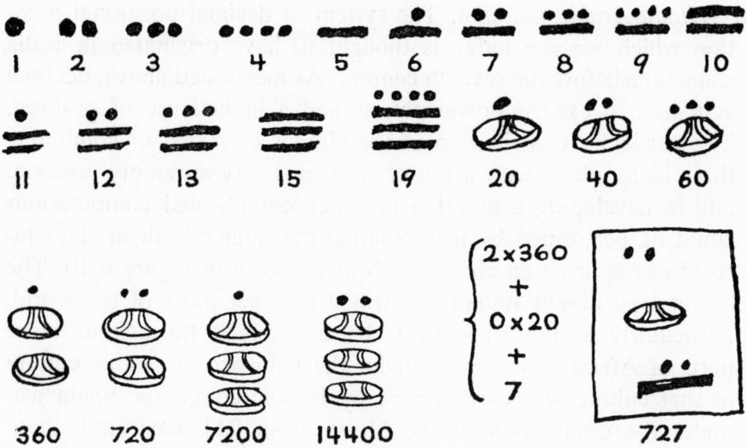

Figure 6.11 The Mayans arranged dots and lines to indicate numbers from one through nineteen. For larger numbers, the symbols were arranged by groups in a vertical order. A base of twenty was used with the exception of the third position. The symbol [symbol] was used to indicate an empty position.

Aztec notation. The Aztec notational system, like that of the Mayans, had a base of twenty. The symbols used to construct their numerals are shown in Figure 6.12. The Aztecs did not use a symbol to indicate an empty place.

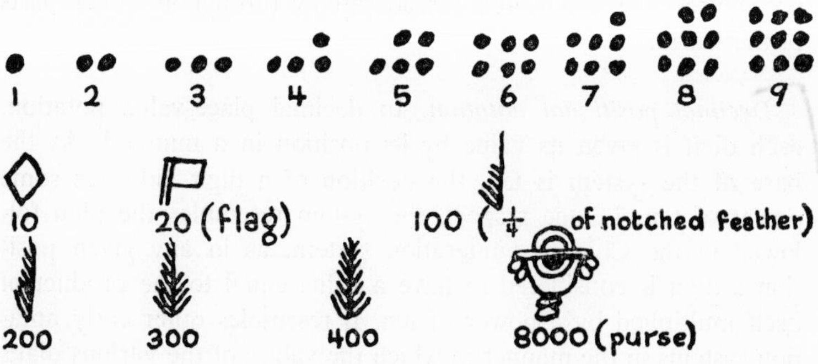

Figure 6.12 The Aztecs used a base of twenty.

Hindu-Arabic notation. The system of decimal positional notation which we use today is thought to have originated in India some time before the seventh century. As mentioned above, decimal systems had existed previously, as had a limited use of position. The particular contribution of the Hindus consisted of combining these ideas, along with a use of zero to signify an empty position, and in developing a notation in which complicated computations could be performed by manipulating the numerals themselves instead of requiring an abacus such as is shown in Figure 6.10. The decimal positional system penetrated to other parts of the world, particularly to the Near East. Its use spread throughout those parts of Africa which came under the influence of Arabic culture as that culture was carried west by Islamic conquests. Spain was under the domination of the Moors from 711 A.D. until about 1200 A.D. During this time, the writings of Arabic mathematicians played an important role in introducing the Hindu decimal place-value notation into western Europe, along with the mathematical concepts which had been assimilated from Greece, Babylonia, Egypt, and the Orient.

Though the Arabs developed rapid ways of computing without the mechanical assistance of the abacus or counting board, general acceptance of the Hindu-Arabic notation in Europe was slow. The proponents of the two principal methods of computation were known as the *algorists* and the *abacists.* After about five hundred years of contention, the former won (about 1600 A.D.) and the procedures they advocated spread rapidly throughout other parts of the world.

Decimal positional notation. In decimal place-value notation, each digit is given its value by its position in a numeral. As the base of the system is ten, the position of a digit indicates some power of ten. In one respect, the system resembles the plan followed in the Chinese numeration system, as in any given position a digit is considered to have a value equal to the product of itself multiplied by a power of ten. It resembles other early notation systems in the manner in which the values of the various digits are added to give the total value of the numeral. In Figure 6.13 it is shown how a numeral such as 2405 derives its value from a

$$2405 = 2(10^3) + 4(10^2) + 0(10^1) + 5(10^0)$$

$$= 2 \times 1000 + 4 \times 100 + 0 \times 10 + 5 \times 1$$

$$= 2000 + 400 + 0 + 5$$

Figure 6.13 The value of a numeral is derived from a combination of principles and other attributes involving multiplication, addition, place value, a base of ten, the idea of zero, and symbols for each natural number from one through nine and for zero. Note that 10^0 is equivalent to one.

combination of assumptions including the principles of multiplication and addition, place value, a base of ten, the idea of zero, and symbols for each of the counting numbers, one through nine, and for zero.

As noted above, the particular advantage inherent in this system of notation is that by following certain rules we are able to add, subtract, multiply, divide, find roots, and perform complicated computations by using the numerals themselves and without the use of an abacus. Such computations are called *algorisms.* In earlier systems of notation, an abacus could be used easily to carry out the simpler forms of computation, but the more complicated computations could be performed only by those who had acquired considerable skill in the use of the mechanical device.

Principles for the numbers of arithmetic. One purpose of arithmetic instruction during the time the children are in the elementary school is to enable them to acquire the competencies needed to deal with mathematical situations which arise throughout their daily lives, as well as throughout their childhood and adult life. We also wish children to acquire a knowledge of arithmetic and an interest in it because arithmetic is an important part of our social heritage which we believe should be known to each educated person. Another important reason for teaching children arithmetic, however, is to provide them with both the concepts and the skills upon which any further study of mathematics may be based. For this reason, it is desirable that during the time children are studying the use of the numbers of arithmetic they should become familiar with certain principles and concepts which will have an application not only throughout their study of arithmetic, but which will have an even wider application when they later study various other aspects of mathematics.

When children are studying the place value and other properties of the decimal numeration system in the lower grades, they are gaining readiness for understanding, at a later date, numeration systems with bases other than ten. The latter, in turn, will provide still further insight into the decimal numeration system. A thorough understanding of the properties of the decimal numeration system will help pupils understand how the algorisms they use are determined by these properties. As children study the way the operations are performed upon numbers in the whole number system, they are being prepared to understand, at still higher levels, the way operations are performed on integers and rational numbers.

As noted above, the symbols for numbers are called "numerals" and the way we write or read them is determined by the fact that in our decimal system of numeration we are using a base, or compounding point, of ten, and the value of each digit in the numeral depends upon its position. The algorisms we use when we add, subtract, multiply, or divide provide us with ways of processing these numerals, and consequently the computational procedures used by the pupils are determined partially by the fact that they are using a numeration system with a base of ten. There are other considerations, however, which determine the computational procedures, apart from the system of numeration. These are the "laws" or principles which have been defined for the operations on the numbers themselves. As will be noted later, these principles go deeper than an understanding of how we may use our decimal numeration system, because they apply to the operations upon the numbers themselves, irrespective of the base of the numeration system we happen to be using.

These principles should be introduced to children and developed at various places throughout the elementary school program, but they are being identified as a group at this point so that the teacher will be made aware of their importance and give them the emphasis which is needed as they are met at various stages of the children's mathematical education. These principles will be identified again from time to time in various places throughout the following chapters in connection with descriptions of the teaching procedures recommended for introducing arithmetic concepts to children at each grade level.

Binary operations. A binary operation on a pair of numbers in a set may be thought of as being a process which allows us to derive a unique (one and only one) number in the same set. For instance, the binary operation of addition on the ordered pair of numbers (3, 4) results in the number 7, and the binary operation of multiplication on the same ordered pair (3, 4) results in the number 12.[9] Expressing this in algebraic symbols, the binary operation of addition on the ordered pair (a, b) results in the number $a + b$, while the binary operation of multiplication on the ordered pair (a, b) results in the number $a \times b$, or $a \cdot b$, or ab.

After the operations of addition and multiplication have been defined for a number system, the operation of subtraction can be defined as the inverse of addition, while the operation of division can be defined as the inverse of multiplication.

The commutative principle for addition. This principle may be expressed algebraically as $a + b = b + a$, where a and b may be replaced by numbers. An instance of the application of this principle is recognized when the child learns that $3 + 4 = 4 + 3$, or when he learns that the order in which two numbers are added does not affect their sum.

The commutative principle for multiplication. This principle may be expressed as $a \times b = b \times a$, where a and b may be replaced by numbers. In learning multiplication facts, the child should understand that the order in which two numbers are multiplied will not affect their product, as when he learns that $3 \times 4 = 4 \times 3$.

[9] Note that the term "unique" does not mean necessarily a number different from either of those in the ordered pair. For example, the binary operation of addition on the ordered pair (3, 0) results in the number 3.

The associative principle for addition. The child should learn that when three or more numbers are added, the way they are grouped will not affect their sum. An instance of this principle is seen when we note that $(3 + 4) + 5 = 3 + (4 + 5)$. The principle is expressed algebraically as $(a + b) + c = a + (b + c)$, where the operations on the numbers within the parentheses are to be completed before the other operations.

The associative principle for multiplication. When three or more numbers are multiplied, as $a \times b \times c$, they may be grouped in various ways without affecting their product. This law may be expressed as $(a \times b) \times c = a \times (b \times c)$, and an instance is noted when we recognize that $(3 \times 4) \times 5 = 3 \times (4 \times 5)$.

The distributive principle of multiplication over addition. This principle may be expressed in words as the product of the multiplier and the sum of two or more addends is equal to the sum of the products of the multiplier and the separate addends. Algebraically this principle is expressed as $a(b + c) = (ab) + (ac)$. An instance of this principle, using natural numbers, is $2(3 + 4) = (2 \times 3) + (2 \times 4)$.

The principle for adding zero. Zero is called the *identity element* for the operation of addition because a number is not changed when zero is added to it. This is expressed algebraically as $a + 0 = 0 + a = a$. From this principle it also follows that subtracting zero from a number will not change the number, as $a - 0 = a$.

The principle of multiplying by one. The number one is an identity element for the operation of multiplication because a number is not changed when it is multiplied by one. This is expressed algebraically as $a \times 1 = 1 \times a = a$. From this principle it follows that dividing a number by one will not change the number, as $a \div 1 = a$.

The principle of multiplying by zero. When a number is multiplied by zero the product is zero. This is expressed algebraically as $a \times 0 = 0 \times a = 0$. It does not follow, however, that a number may be divided by zero. Division by zero is undefined in the numbers of arithmetic, and therefore may not be employed. The reason for this exception is given in Chapter 8.

Introducing the principles of arithmetic to children. The principles mentioned above are very important because they determine the ways numbers may be used in arithmetic. An understanding of these principles, along with an understanding of the decimal numeration system, will provide children with insight into why the computational procedures they use may be relied upon, and why these procedures produce the results they do. Because the child is being exposed to a large number of arithmetic concepts, he may not by himself recognize the importance of these principles when he meets them. For this reason the teacher should ensure that these principles receive the emphasis needed to guarantee that they will be understood by the child. Throughout the various grade levels, as instances of the applications of these principles are encountered, the teacher should reinforce the child's understanding of them until they are recognized as fundamental to all operations with the numbers of arithmetic.

An Overview of the Arithmetic Program in Grades 3 through 8

Many series of pupils' textbooks in arithmetic are now available which indicate in detail the sequences of topics suitable for children in the intermediate and upper grades of the elementary school. In selecting and organizing the content of the arithmetic program, the writers of these textbooks have made extensive use of research. Psychological factors have been considered when arranging the material, and careful consideration has been given to providing pictures, diagrams, and various visual aids in clarifying the arithmetical concepts. Provision has been made for practice material, review material, testing procedures, and for the level of reading ability expected at each grade level. Specific suggestions for presenting concepts and for making provision for individual differences among the pupils have been provided in carefully planned teacher's manuals. A teacher would be well advised to make use of one of the modern series of arithmetic textbooks now available as the foundation upon which to build the arithmetic program for his particular class of pupils. While adjustments should be made to provide for the unique needs of his class, there are many advantages in using the materials now available as a starting point from which to plan a program.

On examining a modern arithmetic textbook, it will be found that each series of topics follows the sequence suggested by the logical nature of the subject matter itself. Although the placement of these topics has been modified during recent years by the findings of research, their grade location often depends upon the traditional placement suggested by that which teachers have learned by experience to be the approximate level at which average achievers succeed in mastering the various concepts. Since the traditional arithmetic program in the elementary school has been developed as only a part of the total curriculum, and has been dependent upon the time available for studying arithmetic, topics placed at any grade level may not be psychologically beyond the ability of pupils at lower grade levels. For instance, often it will be found that some grade 2 pupils have no difficulty in mastering material which is usually placed at the third grade level, providing that time is available for them to spend on these topics. Sometimes administrative difficulties arise when pupils are permitted to advance as quickly as they are able through the various levels of an arithmetic program, and for this reason teachers are sometimes expected to broaden the program at each level with enrichment activities while limiting the rate of advancement. Teachers should understand, however, that this procedure is dictated generally by the administrative factors governing the total curriculum of the child rather than by the psychological difficulty of the arithmetic topics at the next highest grade level.

General Organization of Arithmetic Topics

Research has shown that children get a better understanding of the fundamental processes of addition, subtraction, multiplication, and division when these operations are studied concurrently.

For this reason, the meanings of multiplication and division are introduced soon after those of addition and subtraction, and then the basic facts for each process and the algorisms used in computation are developed more or less concurrently.

During the third and fourth grades, particular attention is given to these fundamental processes, although some steps are delayed until the fifth and sixth grades so as not to make the program too heavy in the lower grades.

Concepts of common fractions which were introduced in the first and second grades receive some attention in the third and fourth grades, with particular emphasis being given to them in the fifth and sixth grades. Decimal fractions are introduced after some competency has been developed in using common fractions, and then are given particular emphasis in the sixth grade.

Concepts of per cent and its applications have been reserved traditionally for the seventh and eighth grade pupils. However, as a result of the recent emphasis on the introduction of elementary set concepts and other aspects of contemporary mathematics in the seventh grade, many of the topics of per cent may now need to be taught in the sixth grade.

Throughout all grade levels of the elementary school the meaning of arithmetic, as well as its applications to social situations, should be stressed. An increasing degree of skill in computation is expected of the children in successive grade levels. The maintenance of the children's interest in arithmetic becomes increasingly important. Providing for individual differences within each class becomes a necessity in a good program. Those phases of the arithmetic program which must be understood and directed by a good teacher form the subjects for detailed discussion in the chapters which follow.

Suggested Learning Activities

1. At a grade level of your choice, 3 through 8, examine the cumulative records and note events in the school lives of each of ten pupils which might be expected to affect learning of arithmetic. Look for age at entering school, kindergarten and nursery school experience, illness, family breakup, change of schools, and the like.
2. Examine the arithmetic and reading achievement records for ten

pupils at a grade level (3 through 8) of your choice. In how many cases do you find a variation of more than one year between the arithmetic age and the reading age? What might cause the variations?

3. List ten instances in which one-to-one correspondence is used in modern life.
4. Write 135 using the notation system of each of the following: Egyptian, Babylonian, Greek, Roman, Chinese, Mayan, Aztec.
5. Make up a numeration system employing the basic principles of the Hindu-Arabic numeration system of place value, additive property, use of zero, and base. Invent symbols and use some other base than ten.
6. Make a chart suitable for middle grades showing the name and an example of each of the following principles: commutative, associative, distributive.
7. Is *one* an identity element for addition? For multiplication? For subtraction? For division? Give examples.
8. Discuss pro and con the statement, "The topic of per cent should be taught in the sixth grade."

Guided Supplementary Reading

1. What example does Banks use to illustrate the associative law for addition?
2. What four kinds of change in elementary school arithmetic programs does Brownell predict?
3. Buckingham names six arithmetic operations taught in the sixteenth century. What were they?
4. What point of view do Burton, Kimball, and Wing take regarding the transfer of logical thinking skills from mathematical learning to life situations?
5. How does the Soviet arithmetic program for elementary schools compare with ours?
6. What conclusions do Dawson and Ruddell draw from their study of the "meaning-theory" approach to teaching arithmetic?
7. What are some of the conclusions De Francis reached in his comparison of a Russian first grade arithmetic text with American texts?
8. According to Freund, what is the main feature of the Hindu-Arabic notation?
9. Haan suggests that the term "arithmetic" can no longer be used to describe the elementary school mathematics program. Why?

10. Which of the three common goals of arithmetic teaching traditionally has been stressed least?
11. If you were to read to children about the history of the number system, stressing Chinese numeration, what sources listed by Kreitz and Flournoy might you use?
12. How does Maria define the "commutative property of conjunctions"?
13. The principle of compensation in addition can be helpful to pupils in what way, according to Marks, Purdy, and Kinney?
14. According to Sister McFarland, what should be the chief content of elementary mathematics?
15. According to Mueller, the English use the word "billion" to designate a different number from 1,000,000,000. To what number does their use of the term refer?
16. What implication does Osborn draw from his review of our lack of good histories of arithmetic?
17. What experiment in probability does Page suggest for the middle grades?
18. According to conclusions drawn by Pikal, what are the major areas of arithmetic applied by children in out-of-school situations?
19. How does Schaaf explain the distributive property exhibited by counting numbers?
20. According to Schaaf, when did the word "arithmetic" begin to be used to cover both the computational and the application aspects of the subject?
21. What four changes does Spitzer predict for arithmetic as a result of the current interest in science and mathematics?
22. According to Spitzer, how many years elapse between a given date 3 B.C. and the same date 3 A.D.?
23. What conclusion does Stokes reach after reviewing the data from a study of 80,000 children's reactions?
24. According to Stright's interesting study, by what grade level had attitudes toward arithmetic become definite?
25. Sueltz points out that the "scratch method" of division has been discarded. What reason does he give? Is it easier or more difficult than the method we use?
26. Using the "handfuls" and "pairs" table given by Swain, add as the Romans would, MCMXLIV + CCXXXVII.
27. What four basic considerations does Weaver recommend be applied to mathematics improvement programs?

Suggested Supplementary References

1. BANKS, J. HOUSTON, *Elements of Mathematics,* Chapter 4. Boston: Allyn and Bacon, Inc., 1961.
2. BROWNELL, WILLIAM A., "Arithmetic in 1970," *National Elementary Principal,* Vol. 39, pp. 42–45, October, 1959.
3. BUCKINGHAM, B. R., "Perspective in the Field of Arithmetic," *Arithmetic Teacher,* Vol. 2, pp. 1–5, February, 1955.
4. BURTON, WILLIAM H., R. B. KIMBALL, and R. L. WING, *Education for Effective Thinking,* Chapter 19. New York: Appleton-Century-Crofts, Inc., 1960.
5. CHETVERUKHIN, NIKOLAI F., "Mathematics Education in the Soviet 7-Year School," *Arithmetic Teacher,* Vol. 6, pp. 1–5, February, 1959.
6. DAWSON, D. T., AND A. K. RUDDELL, "Case for the Meaning Theory in Teaching Arithmetic," *Elementary School Journal,* Vol. 55, pp. 393–399, March, 1955.
7. DE FRANCIS, J., "Beginnings of Mathematics Education in Russia," Vol. 6, pp. 6–11, February, 1959.
8. FREUND, JOHN E., *A Modern Introduction to Mathematics,* Chapter 6. Englewood Cliffs, N.J.: Prentice-Hall, Inc., 1956.
9. HAAN, AUBREY, *Elementary School Curriculum: Theory and Research,* Chapter 8. Boston: Allyn and Bacon, Inc., 1961.
10. HANNON, H., "Role of Meaning in Teaching the Fundamental Processes," *School Science and Mathematics,* Vol. 58, pp. 83–89, February, 1958.
11. KREITZ, H. M., AND F. FLOURNOY, "Bibliography of Historical Materials for Use in Arithmetic in the Intermediate Grades," *Arithmetic Teacher,* Vol. 7, pp. 287–292, October, 1960.
12. MARIA, MAY H. *The Structure of Arithmetic and Algebra,* Chapter 1. New York: John Wiley and Sons, Inc., 1958.
13. MARKS, JOHN L., C. RICHARD PURDY, AND LUCIEN B. KINNEY, *Teaching Arithmetic for Understanding,* Chapter 6. New York: McGraw-Hill Book Co., Inc., 1958.
14. MCFARLAND, M. F., "Mathematics: Our Common Heritage," *Journal of General Education,* Vol. 11, pp. 170–181, July, 1958.
15. MUELLER, F. J., *Arithmetic, Its Structure and Concepts,* Chapter 1. Englewood Cliffs, N.J.: Prentice-Hall, Inc., 1956.
16. OSBORN, JESSE, "Perspective in Arithmetic," *Arithmetic Teacher,* Vol. 5, pp. 275–278, November, 1958.
17. PAGE, DAVID A., "Probability," *The Growth of Mathematical Ideas,*

Chapter 6, Twenty-fourth Yearbook. Washington, D.C.: National Council of Teachers of Mathematics, 1959.

18. PIKAL, FRANCES, "Review of Research Related to the Teaching of Arithmetic in the Upper Elementary Grades," *School Science and Mathematics,* Vol. 57, p. 41, January, 1957.
19. SCHAAF, WILLIAM L., *Basic Concepts of Elementary Mathematics,* Chapter 4. New York: John Wiley and Sons, 1960.
20. SCHAAF, WILLIAM L., "Mathematics as a Cultural Heritage," *Arithmetic Teacher,* Vol. 8, pp. 5–9, January, 1961.
21. SPITZER, HERBERT F., "How Will the New Emphasis on Science Affect Arithmetic Teaching?" *Instructor,* Vol. 68, p. 6, April, 1959.
22. SPITZER, HERBERT F., "Some Questionable Arithmetical Practices," *Arithmetic Teacher,* Vol. 4, pp. 175–178, October, 1957.
23. STOKES, C. N., "80,000 Children's Reactions to Meanings in Arithmetic," Vol. 5, pp. 281–286, *Arithmetic Teacher,* December, 1958.
24. STRIGHT, VIRGINIA M., "Study of the Attitudes toward Arithmetic of Students and Teachers in the Third, Fourth, and Sixth Grades," *Arithmetic Teacher,* Vol. 7, pp. 280–286, October, 1960.
25. SUELTZ, B. A., "Arithmetic in Historical Perspective," *National Elementary Principal,* Vol. 39, pp. 12–16, October, 1959.
26. SWAIN, ROBERT L., *Understanding Arithmetic,* Chapter 1. New York: Rinehart and Co., Inc., 1957.
27. WEAVER, FRED J., "Basic Considerations in the Improvement of Elementary School Mathematics Programs," *Arithmetic Teacher,* Vol. 7, pp. 269–273, October, 1960.

CHAPTER 7

Extending Concepts of Addition and Subtraction

Readiness for learning the addition and subtraction algorisms. In Chapter 4 a procedure for developing readiness for learning addition and subtraction was described in which the pupils analyzed small groups of objects in order to observe that these groups could be thought of as being made up of smaller groups. The children learned that in somewhat the same way we may think of a number as being made up of other numbers.

The pupils then learned to associate the combining action on two groups of objects with the addition of numbers, and the separating of a single group into two groups, or the comparison of two groups, with subtraction and to think of that process as one of finding the difference between two numbers. They learned how to express the addition and subtraction of numbers by means of numerals, and how to use the symbols for "plus," "minus," and "equal."

During the first and second grades, the children began to learn the meaning and the use of the basic facts of addition and subtraction by studying them as related facts, in "families," as this enabled them to understand the relationships between the addition and subtraction facts, and at the same time it introduced them to the idea that the operation of subtraction was the inverse of addition.

With the exception of the zero facts, all the basic facts which could be illustrated with groups of ten or fewer objects were learned, making a total of forty-five basic facts for each of the processes of addition and subtraction.

An understanding of the above-mentioned concepts provides the children with readiness for understanding the meaning and use of the algorisms which are employed in addition and subtraction computations. The sequence in which each of the various steps in learning the computational procedures may be taken is shown on pages 174–176. The first four of these steps in the sequence may be introduced to children during the first and second grades in situations where the pupils are ready for them and where time is available.

The learning of the remaining fifty-five basic facts in each of the processes of addition and subtraction should be completed by average achievers by the end of the third grade. These basic facts could be introduced as "families," following the same procedure for each family as that suggested in Chapter 4, as soon as the pupils have mastered the basic facts for each preceding family. The steps in learning the algorisms need not be delayed until all the basic facts have been learned, providing that the basic facts needed in each instance are selected from those with which the pupils are already familiar. In this way, the task of memorizing the basic facts may be spread over a longer interval of time, and may be learned concurrently with the computational procedures which are being introduced during the third grade.

Emphasizing the Principles, or "Laws," of Addition and Subtraction

As was noted in the previous chapter, certain principles concerning addition and subtraction are basic to number systems. These principles should be emphasized by the teacher in various instances as they are being used so that they will be noted and understood by the pupils. The principle of commutation implies that the value of an expression is not changed by adding two numbers in the reverse order, and it should be emphasized frequently while the pupils are learning the basic facts. The principle of association as applied to the operation of addition asserts that the value of the sum of three or more addends is not changed by the way these addends are grouped. This principle has a wide application throughout elementary school arithmetic. It is used, for instance, in situations where the pupil checks the addition of three or more addends by adding the column of addends in the reverse order. In this instance he uses a combination of the associative and the commutative laws.

The principle involved in adding zero to a number or in adding a number to zero, and also in subtracting zero from a number, needs particular attention when pupils are learning basic facts. The children should understand that zero is a number which has particular importance in our number system, and that it should be used carefully. The various basic facts involving zero should be considered frequently as a group and the generalizations regarding its use reviewed. Although children should have little difficulty in understanding the use of zero in addition and subtraction when the principles have been carefully developed and reviewed frequently, they make many mistakes involving the incorrect use of zero in situations where the teacher has not given adequate recognition to the principles governing its use.

The principle of "likeness." Another principle to which the attention of the children should be directed is referred to as "the principle of likeness," and it implies that when we add numbers, the units to which the numbers refer must be alike. For example, a group of three sheep and four sheep would make up a group of seven sheep. In other instances, when the pupils add numbers in expressions when more than one type of unit is involved, the various units are considered separately, such as in the addition of what sometimes have been called "denominate numbers." In an instance where 2 feet 7 inches is being added to 3 feet 8 inches, the numbers referring to inches are added separately from those referring to feet. An application of the principle of likeness is evident also in computations when we add the digits in the ones' place of numerals and then add the digits in the tens' place separately. We find it necessary to regroup the ones to tens in computational procedures in order to not violate this principle. This is illustrated in Figure 7.1.

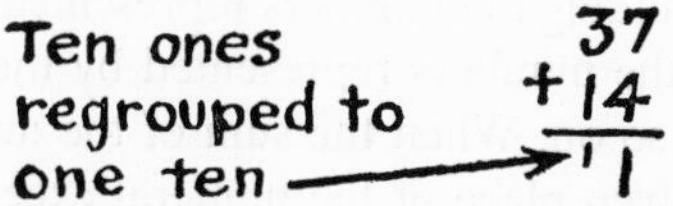

Figure 7.1 The principle of "likeness" is applied when ten ones are regrouped to one ten before being added to tens.

The principle of compensation. This principle implies that we do not change the sum of two addends if we increase one of them and reduce the other by the same number. For instance, in adding 98 and 27, we could increase 98 by two and decrease 27 by two without changing the sum. This principle may be applied sometimes by children when they are adding numbers "mentally" without paper and pencil. In the example shown above, it may be easier to add 98 and 27 by increasing 98 to 100, and then adding 25, than to use the standard algorism for adding two-place numbers.

In subtraction situations, the principle of compensation implies that we do not change the difference between two numbers by adding the same number to both the minuend and the subtrahend. This principle is employed in the computational procedure used in the "equal additions" algorism for subtraction which will be described later in this chapter.

Generalizing expressions of the principles. Although the formalized expression through algebraic symbols of the principles of addition and subtraction may be delayed until higher grade levels, children in the elementary school should explore these principles as they apply in various instances. When they intuitively grasp these concepts, they should be told the names of the principles, or laws, and given a clear understanding of their importance in mathematical thinking.

Need for learning computational procedures. When the numbers to be added are very small, the sum may be found without difficulty by counting. When larger numbers are being considered, counting would be very tedious, and so we wish children to learn to use a computational procedure, or algorism, to find the answer. For addition, this algorism consists basically of adding the numbers represented by the digits shown in the ones' place of the numerals, and then adding the numbers represented by the digits in the tens' place, then the numbers represented by the digits in the hundreds' place, and so on. When the sum of the numbers represented by digits in any given place of the numeral exceeds nine, a "carrying" or regrouping procedure is needed, a description of which will be given later.

The algorism for subtraction consists basically of finding the difference between the numbers represented by the digits in any given place in the numerals of the minuend and subtrahend; but when the digit in the minuend is smaller than that in the subtrahend, a regrouping procedure is necessary. This procedure, which is sometimes called "borrowing" or "exchanging," will be described later.

It should be noted in the sequence of steps given below that the computational procedures for addition and subtraction are developed concurrently.

Sequence for Introducing the Addition and Subtraction of Numbers Involving Two-Place and Three-Place Numerals

A logical sequence which might be followed in introducing new steps in learning algorisms for addition and subtraction is as follows:

1. Addition involving two-place numerals without regrouping.

$$\begin{array}{r} 33 \\ +24 \\ \hline \end{array}$$

2. Subtraction involving two-place numerals without regrouping.

$$\begin{array}{r} 36 \\ -14 \\ \hline \end{array}$$

3. Addition involving three-place numerals without regrouping.

$$\begin{array}{r} 324 \\ +112 \\ \hline \end{array}$$

4. Subtraction involving three-place numerals without regrouping.

$$\begin{array}{r} 324 \\ -112 \\ \hline \end{array}$$

5. Addition involving two-place numerals with regrouping.

$$\begin{array}{r} 24 \\ +17 \\ \hline \end{array}$$

6. Subtraction involving two-place numerals with regrouping.

$$\begin{array}{r} 24 \\ -17 \\ \hline \end{array}$$

7. Addition involving three-place numerals with regrouping to the tens' place.

$$\begin{array}{r} 324 \\ +117 \\ \hline \end{array}$$

8. Subtraction involving three-place numerals with regrouping from the tens' place.

$$\begin{array}{r} 364 \\ -126 \\ \hline \end{array}$$

9. Addition involving three-place numerals with regrouping from the tens' to the hundreds' place.

$$\begin{array}{r} 342 \\ +174 \\ \hline \end{array}$$

10. Subtraction involving three-place numerals with regrouping from the hundreds' to the tens' place.

$$\begin{array}{r} 342 \\ -161 \\ \hline \end{array}$$

11. Addition involving three-place numerals with regrouping to the tens' place and to the hundreds' place.

$$\begin{array}{r} 346 \\ +158 \\ \hline \end{array}$$

12. Subtraction involving three-place numerals with regrouping from the hundreds' place and from the tens' place.

$$\begin{array}{r} 325 \\ -168 \\ \hline \end{array}$$

13. Addition and subtraction involving numbers requiring more than three places in their numerals.

An examination of any modern arithmetic textbook for pupils in the third and fourth grades will show that some logical sequence, such as that given above, is being used. It is suggested that a teacher should follow the sequence given in the textbook which is being used by his class when introducing new steps in addition or subtraction.

Adding numbers involving two-place numerals and regrouping. The procedure for adding numbers in such instances may be introduced easily by having the pupils use bundles of sticks to illustrate the addition of two numbers, such as 23 and 45, where regrouping, or "carrying," is not required. As shown in Figure 7.2a, "23" is represented by two bundles of ten sticks and three single sticks, while "45" is represented by four bundles of ten sticks and five single sticks. Figure 7.2b shows that when all the sticks are placed together in one large group, there are six bundles of ten and eight single sticks, or 68 sticks altogether.

The pupils are led to understand that addition has the same meaning when large numbers are used as it has when small numbers are used, but that by adding the numbers represented by the

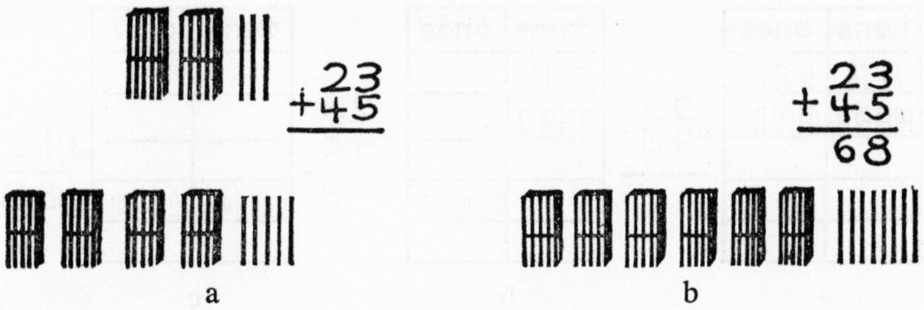

Figure 7.2 Bundles of sticks used to illustrate addition involving two-place numerals without regrouping.

single sticks, and then the numbers represented by the bundles of ten, the sum of the numbers might be expressed as "tens" and "ones" and written as "68."

The meaning of the addition algorism may be illustrated also by using a place-value box. Figure 7.3 shows how 23 tickets and

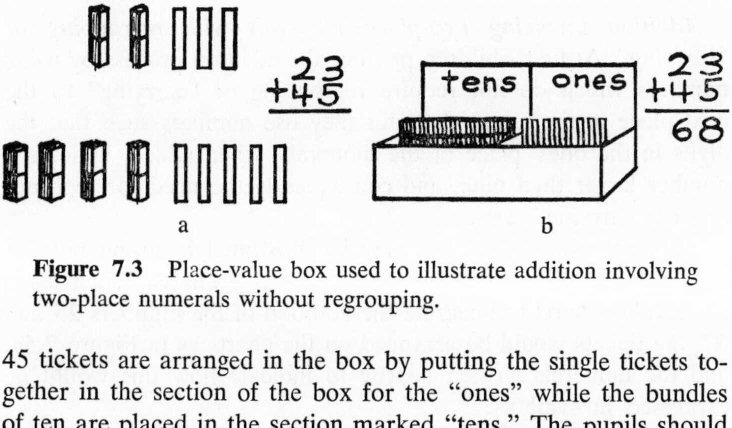

Figure 7.3 Place-value box used to illustrate addition involving two-place numerals without regrouping.

45 tickets are arranged in the box by putting the single tickets together in the section of the box for the "ones" while the bundles of ten are placed in the section marked "tens." The pupils should see that this process may be expressed in writing by using numerals.

A place-value pocket-chart illustrating the addition of 23 and 45 is shown in Figure 7.4. First, the chart shows 23 tickets and 45 tickets arranged before the addition process is begun, with the numerals to express the problem written on a nearby chalkboard. Then the tickets in the ones' place are collected and placed in the

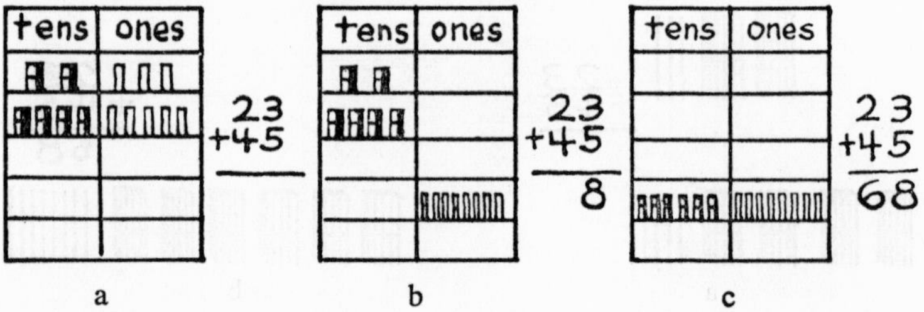

Figure 7.4 Combined use of pocket-chart and chalkboard to illustrate addition involving two-place numerals without regrouping.

answer pocket, and this is expressed in writing by showing "8" in the ones' place of the answer. Next, the bundles of ten tickets are moved to the answer pocket, and this is expressed in writing by showing "6" in the tens' place of the answer.

Addition involving two-place numerals with regrouping or "carrying." At first, children practice the addition process by using numbers which do not require regrouping or "carrying" to the next place in the numeral. Later they use numbers such that the digits in the ones' place of the numerals, when added, indicate a number larger than nine, and consequently the need for regrouping, or "carrying," arises.

Addition with regrouping may be illustrated by using bundles of sticks, the place-value box, or place-value charts. When using place-value charts to illustrate the addition of the numbers 25 and 37, the tickets would be arranged on the charts as in Figure 7.5a, and the numerals written nearby to indicate how this would be expressed in symbols.

The tickets in the ones' place would then be removed and placed together, and the pupils asked to note that this would make a group of thirteen tickets. Ten of these tickets would then be made into a bundle and moved to the tens' place of the answer, while the three remaining tickets would be put into the ones' place of the answer pocket, as in Figure 7.5b. This step would be indicated by writing "2" in the ones' place of the algorism.

All the bundles of ten would then be put into the tens' place

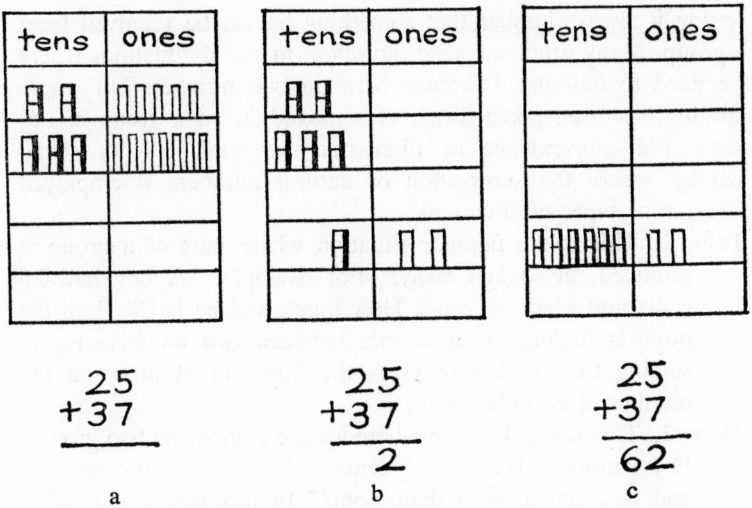

Figure 7.5 Combined use of place-value charts and chalkboard to illustrate addition involving two-place numerals with regrouping.

of the answer pocket, and this step would be indicated by writing "6" in the tens' place of the algorism, as shown in Figure 7.5c.

When pupils are learning addition involving three-place numerals at a later time, the same general procedure may be used with place-value charts arranged to show the hundreds' place as well as the place for "tens" and "ones."

When the pupils are introduced to the addition of numbers requiring four or more digits in the numerals, it would be impractical to use a pocket-chart because of the number of tickets which would be needed. In such instances, an abacus could be used to illustrate the process.

Using Subtraction in Social Settings

The meaning of subtraction is introduced to children in grade 1 when they learn how to find how many counters are left in a group after some given number of counters has been "taken away," or removed. As has been noted above, there is a danger here of the children's thinking that when subtraction is used in a social setting it always implies that something has to be removed from a group. Many problems arise, however, in social situations where we need to find the difference between two numbers but where nothing has been taken away, or removed, from a group of objects. For convenience of discussion we shall classify social settings where the subtraction of natural numbers is employed under four types of situations.

TYPE 1. This is the familiar situation where part of a group is removed, or "taken away." For example, "A boy had 25 cents and spent 10 cents. How much had he left?" Here the pupil is finding the difference between two numbers representing the number of cents the boy had at first and the number of cents he spent.

TYPE 2. This is the situation where we are comparing two groups. For example, "Bill had 25 cents and Tom had 10 cents. Bill had how much more than Tom?" In this instance, nothing has actually been removed from either group, as we are merely comparing the two groups. The amount each boy had remains as before. Here we are finding the difference between the two numbers which represent what each boy had.

TYPE 3. This is where we are finding how many more are needed to make a certain number. For example, "A boy had 10 cents. How much more would he need to buy a book costing 25 cents?" In this instance, we are again finding the difference between two numbers, one of which represents what the boy had, and the other the price of the book.

TYPE 4. The situation where a given number is thought of as being made up of two smaller numbers and one of these is known but the other has to be determined. For example, "There are 25 pupils in a class. Ten of them are boys. How many girls are there?" This is an example of a situation where we are required to find the difference between two numbers, one of which, along with an unknown number, makes up the other number.

It will be noted that although all four types of subtraction situations require the finding of a difference between two numbers, only one situation, Type 1, requires something to be "taken away." As pupils are usually introduced to the meaning of subtraction through a "take-away" situation, such as is indicated in Type 1, there is a possibility that they might think that subtraction is always a "take-away" situation unless the teacher helps them to understand the meaning of the other types of subtraction situations. The teacher should emphasize the fact to the pupils that in subtraction they are really finding the difference between two numbers. Then, when the pupils meet problems of the four types described above, they will recognize that the problems are describing subtraction situations because in each case it is necessary to find the difference between two numbers.

Illustrating Type 1 subtraction situations. The following problem could be used as an example of a Type 1 subtraction situation. "John had seven cents and gave Bill three cents. How much did he have left?" In this instance, seven discs could be placed on a flannel board to represent what John had at first, as in Figure 7.6a. Three discs could then be moved to another place on the

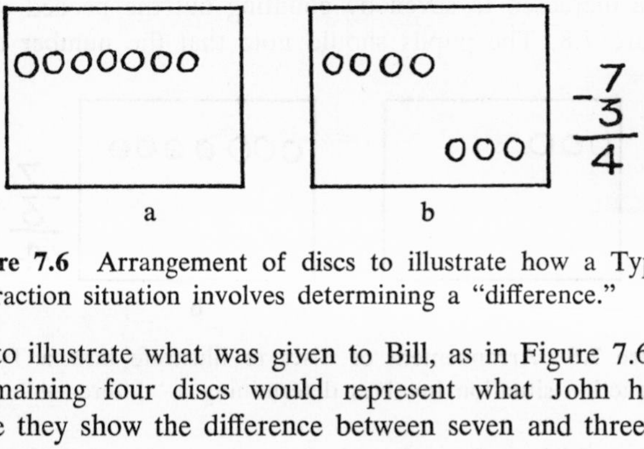

Figure 7.6 Arrangement of discs to illustrate how a Type 1 subtraction situation involves determining a "difference."

board to illustrate what was given to Bill, as in Figure 7.6b, and the remaining four discs would represent what John had left because they show the difference between seven and three.

Illustrating Type 2 subtraction situations. The following problem is an example of the second type of subtraction situation. "John had seven cents and Bill had three cents. John had how much more than Bill?" In this situation seven discs could be put on the flannel board to represent the number of cents John had, and three more discs could be put below these to show what Bill had, as in Figure 7.7. By one-to-one matching, the pupils could

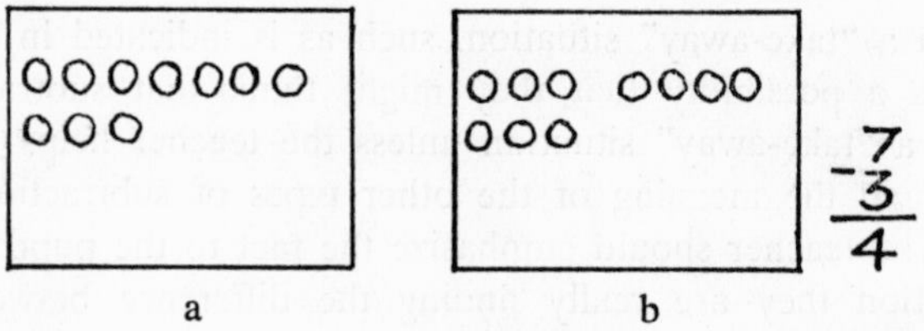

Figure 7.7 Arrangement of discs to illustrate how a Type 2 subtraction situation involves determining a "difference."

then see that the difference indicates how many more cents John had than Bill.

Illustrating Type 3 subtraction situations. This type of situation could be illustrated by the following problem. "John had three cents. How much more would he need to buy a pencil costing seven cents?" To illustrate this situation, three discs could be put on the flannel board to show what John had. This number could then be increased to seven by counting out the needed discs, as in Figure 7.8. The pupils should note that the number of cents

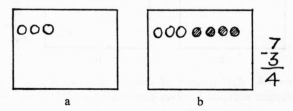

Figure 7.8 Arrangement of discs to illustrate how a Type 3 subtraction situation involves determining a "difference."

needed could have been found without counting if they had subtracted three from seven in order to find the difference between these two numbers.

Illustrating Type 4 subtraction situations. The problem to indicate this situation could be stated as follows: "Seven children were on a committee. Three of them were boys. How many girls were there?" In this instance, seven discs of which only three are the same color could be placed on the flannel board, as in Figure 7.9. The children should then be led to see that the difference

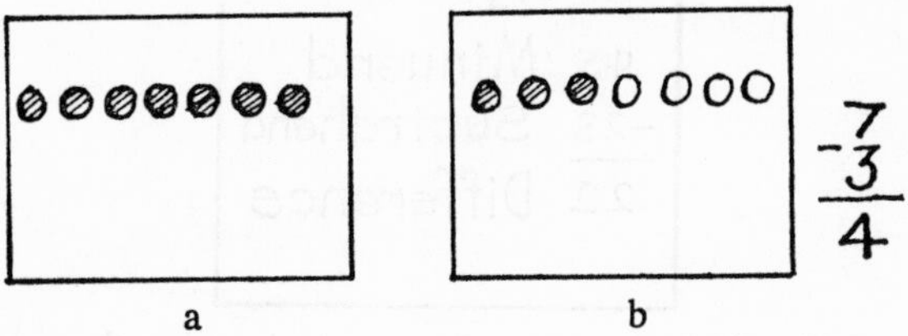

Figure 7.9 Arrangement of discs to illustrate how a Type 4 subtraction situation involves determining a "difference."

between the number of children on the committee and the number of boys would indicate the answer.

Although children at this grade level may not be expected to identify the type to which a subtraction situation in a certain problem belongs, they should understand that whenever we wish to find the difference between two numbers in a problem, we may use the subtraction process instead of counting in order to determine the answer. It should be explained that although it is easy to determine the difference by counting when the numbers are small, it is much easier to use the subtraction process, once it has been learned, when the numbers involved are very large.

Learning Computational Procedures for Subtraction

The nature of the subtraction algorism. Where no regrouping, or "borrowing," is needed in subtraction, the basic procedure consists of finding the difference between the number represented by the digit in each place of the numeral in the "minuend" and the number represented by the digit in the corresponding place of the numeral in the "subtrahend," as shown in Figure 7.10. This may be illustrated easily by using a place-value chart to solve a problem such as: "John had 45 cents and Bill had 23 cents. How much more did John have than Bill?" The pupils should first discuss the problem to be made aware of the fact that they will need to find the difference between 45 and 23.

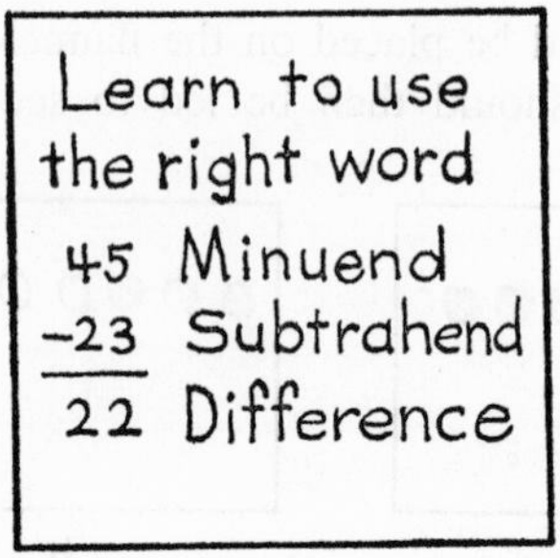

Figure 7.10 Wall chart to aid pupils in learning the names of the parts of a subtraction algorism.[1]

Tickets could be arranged on the place-value chart, as shown in Figure 7.11a, to represent the number of cents John had by placing four bundles of ten in the tens' place and five tickets in the ones' place. The number of cents Bill had would be represented by two bundles of ten and three single tickets placed in the appropriate pocket.

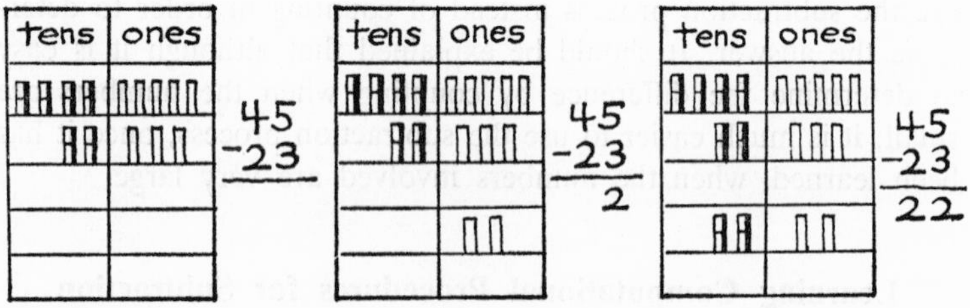

Figure 7.11 Combined use of place-value chart and chalkboard to illustrate the subtraction algorism where no regrouping is required.

The pupils should then be encouraged to see that because the difference between the numbers represented by the digits in the ones' place of the minuend and subtrahend is two, this difference may be shown by putting two tickets in the ones' place of the answer pocket, as in Figure 7.11b. They would then note that the difference between the numbers represented by the digits in the

[1] Enoch Dumas, Charles F. Howard, and Jean E. Dumas, *Arithmetic Charts Handbook* (San Francisco: Fearon Publishers, Inc., 1960), p. 32.

tens' place of the minuend and subtrahend can be shown by two bundles of ten tickets, so two bundles of ten tickets would be put into the tens' place of the answer pocket, as in Figure 7.11c.

After the pupils have understood how the problem could be solved through the use of tickets, their attention should be directed to how the same problem could be solved by using numerals, and the resemblance between the procedure when using tickets and the procedure when using numerals could be noted.

In the example given above, a problem involving a Type 2 subtraction situation was used, as it is one of the simplest types of subtraction situations to illustrate with a place-value chart. In using a place-value chart to represent a subtraction problem of the first type, a difficulty sometimes arises when the pupil fails to distinguish the difference between an instance in which the tickets are being used to represent objects and one in which tickets are being used to represent numbers. This distinction is exemplified by using a place-value chart in connection with solving the following problem involving the first type of subtraction situation: "Tom had 45 cents. He spent 23 cents. How much had he left?"

If we wish to arrange the place-value chart to show what actually takes place during the solving of this problem, that is, to illustrate the meaning of this problem, 45 tickets could be placed in a pocket of the place-value chart to represent 45 cents. 23 of these tickets would then be removed to represent what was spent. The 22 remaining tickets would show what was left. This is illustrated in Figure 7.12. In this example, the tickets are being used

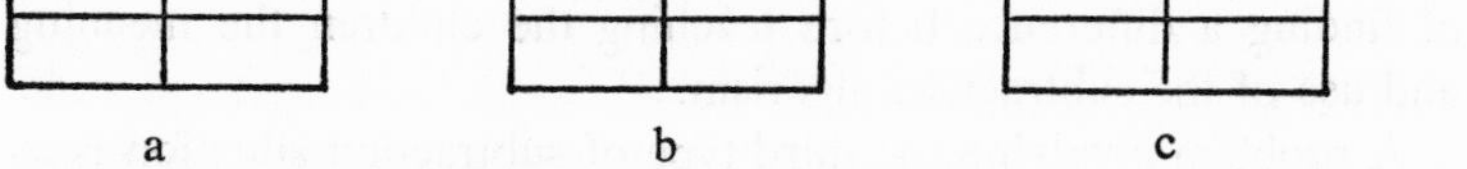

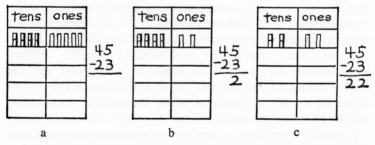

Figure 7.12 Combined use of place-value chart and chalkboard to illustrate a Type I subtraction situation where the tickets are used to represent objects.

to represent pennies, and would be used as would any other manipulative material by actually removing some to find out how many remained.

When the primary purpose of using the place-value chart is to illustrate how subtraction computations are carried out with numerals, then another arrangement, such as that shown in Figure 7.13, is suggested. In this instance, 45 tickets in the upper pocket

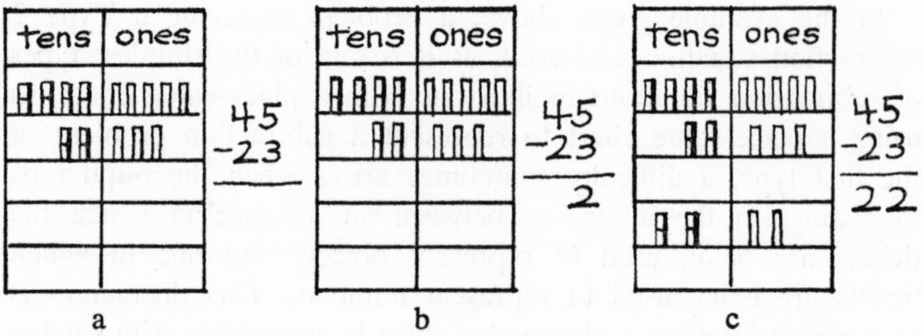

Figure 7.13 Combined use of place-value chart and chalkboard to illustrate the use of the subtraction algorism to determine the "difference" between two numbers.

of the chart would represent the *number* of cents Tom had at first. The 23 tickets in the second pocket would represent the *number* of cents he spent. The 22 tickets in the answer pocket would represent the difference between 45 and 23, or the *number* of cents he had left.

At the stage where the place-value chart is being used to explain the meaning of the computational procedure, the arrangement in Figure 7.13 is closer in form to the arrangement of the numerals in the subtraction algorism than that shown in Figure 7.12, and would probably be more helpful in enabling children to understand the algorism. It should be understood that the teacher should develop the meaning of subtraction as the process of finding a difference before teaching the children the meaning and use of the subtraction algorism.

A problem involving the third type of subtraction situation is as follows. "If John had 23 cents, how much more would he need to buy an article costing 45 cents?" In this instance, 45 tickets would be arranged in the upper pocket of the chart, as in Figure 7.13, to show the number representing the cost of the article. The 23 tickets in the next pocket would represent the number of cents he had. The tickets in the answer pocket would indicate the difference between the number of cents he had and the cost of the article.

An example of a problem of the fourth type of subtraction situation is as follows. "There are 45 pupils in a class. 23 of them are boys. How many girls are there?" The tickets on the place-value chart would again be arranged as in Figure 7.13. Those in the upper pocket would indicate the number of children in the class. Those in the next pocket would represent the number of boys. The 22 tickets in the answer pocket would show the difference between the other two numbers, which represents the number of girls.

It should be noted by the pupils that when tickets or other manipulative objects are used to indicate the application of subtraction to different social situations, there are four different arrangements needed to show the four subtraction situations, but when tickets are used on a place-value chart to illustrate the computational procedure used in subtraction, only one arrangement is needed for all four subtraction situations. Just as we use one form of computational procedure for all four situations, so we use one form of ticket arrangement on the pocket-chart because the tickets are then being used to represent the numbers themselves rather than to represent the objects in the social situation.

Compound subtraction algorisms. Two principal computational procedures for subtraction have been taught in the schools of this country and of Europe. One procedure is referred to as the "decomposition" procedure, while the other is referred to as the "equal additions" procedure. The decomposition algorism is shown in Figure 7.14. Here one of the tens has been thought of as having been regrouped with three ones to make thirteen. Seven is then subtracted from thirteen, and two is subtracted from three in the tens' place. This is sometimes referred to as "borrowing" ten, although the term "regrouping" would probably better describe the procedure.

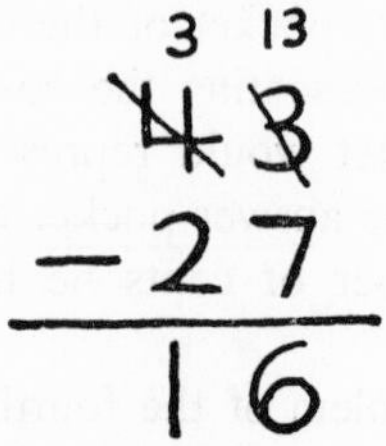

Figure 7.14 Illustration of the algorism for subtraction where a decomposition procedure is used with "crutches."

The "equal additions" algorism is shown in Figure 7.15. Here, ten ones have been added to the minuend to make thirteen ones, while one ten has been added to the subtrahend to make three tens. As there have been "equal additions" of ten to both the minuend and the subtrahend, the difference remains unchanged.

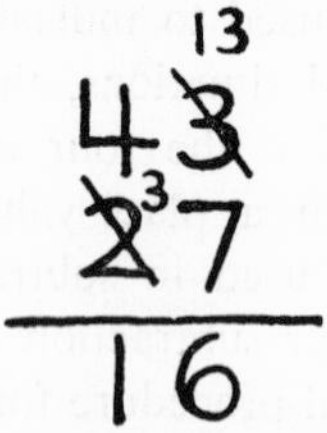

Figure 7.15 Illustration of the algorism for subtraction where an equal additions procedure is used with "crutches."

As the decomposition algorism can be made meaningful to children in the third grade without much difficulty, it is gaining favor with teachers in this country, and is the procedure suggested here as the one to use.

Providing readiness for understanding regrouping. To provide readiness for children to understand regrouping, some simple verbal problems involving the required subtraction situation could be used to help the pupils visualize the purpose of regrouping. A problem of the following type would be suitable. "Tom took four dimes and three pennies from the jar in which he has saved many dimes and pennies. He wanted to give his brother twenty-five cents. How could he do this?" The pupils should be given time to "discover" that by changing one dime to pennies Tom would have a simple way to solve the problem. The pupils' attention should be directed to the fact that when Tom changed one of his dimes to pennies, it did not in any way affect the total value of the money which he had, but it made it convenient for him to complete the transaction.

Learning the decomposition algorism for compound subtraction. After the pupils have been prepared for the subtraction algorism by recognizing that a dime changed into ten pennies does not affect the total value of the amount, bundles of tickets in a place-value chart may be used to illustrate an instance where decomposition involving the changing of a ten into ones takes place. A verbal problem describing a social situation involving a Type 2 subtraction situation would provide a gradual approach to understanding the subtraction algorism where decomposition is used. A suitable problem would be: "Mary had 43 cents and Alice had 25 cents. How much more did Mary have than Alice?"

Tickets would be arranged on the place-value chart as shown in Figure 7.16a. The number of cents that Mary had would be

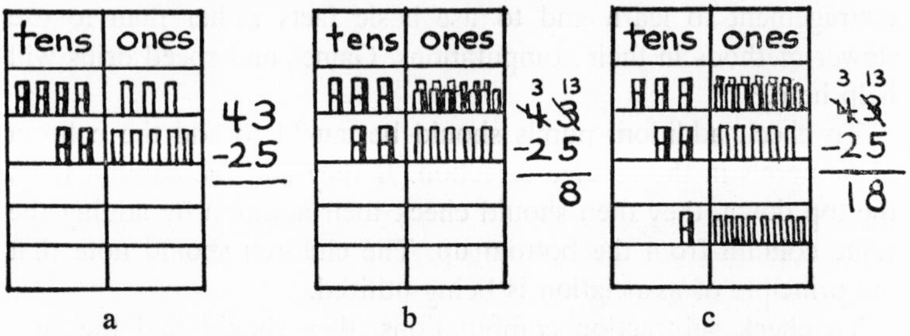

Figure 7.16 Combined use of pocket chart and chalkboard to illustrate the subtraction algorism where the decomposition procedure is used.

represented by four bundles of ten tickets and three single tickets. The number of cents that Alice had would be represented by two bundles of ten tickets and five single tickets. As the number of tickets in the ones' place of the upper pocket is less than the number of tickets in the ones' place of the lower pocket, one bundle of ten is regrouped, or changed to ones, and moved to the ones' place, as in Figure 7.16b. Eight tickets would then be placed in the answer pocket of the ones' place to show the difference between the numbers five and thirteen. One bundle of ten would be placed in the answer pocket of the tens' place to show the difference between three tens and two tens, as in Figure 7.16c.

At each step of the procedure described above, numerals should be used on the chalkboard to indicate how they may be employed to express what was done on the place-value charts with tickets.

Checking Computations

The teacher should encourage the pupils to form the habit of checking all of their computations. The importance of correctness in arithmetic computation should be stressed frequently, and the pupils should learn that speed in arithmetical computations is secondary to accuracy. If pupils are taking more time than seems reasonable, it may be because they are using counting or other inefficient procedures rather than using their knowledge of the basic facts. Under these circumstances, pupils should be given more encouragement to learn and to use basic facts rather than to use slower methods in their computations. Games and speed drills will help here.[2]

To check addition, pupils should be taught to add the column of numerals in the reverse direction. If they add the column from the top down, they then should check their addition by adding the same column from the bottom up. The children should note that the principle of association is being utilized.

To check subtraction computations, they should find the sum of the subtrahend and the difference, and then compare it with the minuend, as indicated in Figure 7.17. The pupils should be helped to understand that the procedure employs the idea that subtraction is the inverse of addition.

[2] Enoch Dumas, *Arithmetic Games* (San Francisco: Fearon Publishers, Inc., 1960), pp. 28–34.

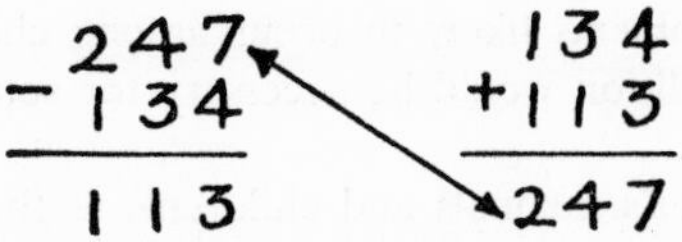

Figure 7.17 An illustration of a procedure for checking subtraction computation.

Using Social Settings to Develop Problem-Solving Techniques

Although the use of addition and subtraction to solve problems in social settings has not been discussed in this chapter, it should be remembered that one important reason for teaching children arithmetic is to enable them to use number effectively in their daily activities. As each step in learning the computational procedures is being mastered, the pupils should be given abundant practice in solving verbal problems to facilitate the "carry-over" of arithmetic skills to the solving of problems in out-of-school situations. Research indicates that instruction and practice in solving verbal problems helps pupils to develop skill in this type of activity.[3] Procedures for developing problem-solving ability are discussed in Chapter 13.

Suggested Learning Activities

1. Using the principle of compensation how would you mentally add: 49 and 98? 198 and 79? 225 and 175? 16 and 49? How would you mentally subtract: 198 minus 48? 295 minus 35?
2. Learning the basic facts of addition and subtraction can be very tedious for some children. Describe three ways in which a teacher can make such work more palatable.
3. List other examples of addition and subtraction algorisms characteristic of each of the steps in the teaching sequence given on pages 174–176.
4. For each of the four types of subtraction, describe an illustrative situation which might arise in the life of a fourth grade pupil.
5. Show by using a place-value chart how you would illustrate: 12 + 26, 17 + 25, 27 − 14, 32 − 18.

[3] Herbert F. Spitzer and Frances Flournoy, "Developing Facility in Solving Verbal Problems," *Arithmetic Teacher,* 3:177–182, November, 1956.

6. Write three problems likely to occur among children in which regrouping in addition would be necessary for solution. Do the same for subtraction.
7. Examine teacher's manuals and children's textbooks at third grade level and compare how the teaching of regrouping in subtraction is presented in each.
8. Which of the principles mentioned in this chapter (commutative, associative, compensative) apply to addition? to subtraction? Give an example of each.

Guided Supplementary Reading

1. Banks defines subtraction in terms of addition. Why?
2. Check the sum of the following addends by casting out elevens as described by Buckingham: 2461, 3972, 8031. Show your procedure.
3. What, according to Clark and Eads, is a prerequisite to learning to estimate sums and remainders?
4. Clendenon suggests a plan for efficiently teaching basic facts. What are the chief features of his plan?
5. DeBethune describes some interesting variations to the common procedures for completing algorisms. What are some of the values he attributes to them?
6. How does Eads characterize the most efficient drill procedures?
7. What is Flournoy's opinion regarding the adequacy in textbooks of practice exercises with higher-decade addition?
8. In Gibb's study of children's responses to subtraction situations, what circumstances seemed to facilitate successful solutions?
9. In discussing subtraction, Gibb, Jones, and Junge suggest that teachers should not say to pupils that one cannot take 9 from 4. How should the teacher comment on the problem?
10. Grossnickle and Brueckner give three conclusions they have reached concerning checking in addition and subtraction. What are they?
11. What social situation and related materials does Harding, Huck, and Norman use to illustrate teaching changing, or "borrowing," in subtraction?
12. For which method of subtraction does Johnson show preference?
13. Approximate the sum of 861, 325, and 196 using the estimating procedure suggested by Marks, Purdy, and Kinney.
14. What is the place of drill in arithmetic?

15. Add 382 and 139 using the "scratch" method described by Mueller. Show all five steps as he does, even though in practice the numbers would be written only one time.
16. What did Olander and Brown recommend regarding the teaching of mental arithmetic processes?
17. How does Sister Marie Francile suggest "carrying" and "borrowing" can be "concretized"?
18. Spitzer suggests the use of "study cards" in learning addition. What advantage is there in cutting off a corner of each card?
19. Swain identifies four methods of subtraction. What are they?

Suggested Supplementary References

1. BANKS, J. HOUSTON, *Learning and Teaching Arithmetic,* Chapter 6. Boston: Allyn and Bacon, Inc., 1959.
2. BUCKINGHAM, BURDETTE R., *Elementary Arithmetic,* Chapter 5. Boston: Ginn and Co., 1953.
3. CLARK, JOHN R., AND LAURA K. EADS, *Guiding Arithmetic Learning,* Chapter 4. New York: World Book Co., 1954.
4. CLENDENON, EARL, "Efficiency in Teaching Basic Facts," *Arithmetic Teacher,* Vol. 6, pp. 144–147, April, 1959.
5. DEBETHUNE, ANDRÉ J., "A Method of Front-End Arithmetic," *Arithmetic Teacher,* Vol. 6, pp. 23–29, February, 1959.
6. EADS, LAURA K., "Teaching Mathematics in Grade Three," *Grade Teacher,* Vol. 76, p. 52, January, 1959.
7. FLOURNOY, FRANCES, "Controversy Regarding the Teaching of Higher-Decade Addition," *Arithmetic Teacher,* Vol. 3, pp. 170–173, October, 1956.
8. GIBB, E. GLENADINE, "Children's Thinking in the Process of Subtraction," *Journal of Experimental Education,* Vol. 25, pp. 71–80, September, 1956.
9. GIBB, E. GLENADINE, PHILLIP S. JONES, AND CHARLOTTE W. JUNGE, "Number and Operation," *The Growth of Mathematical Ideas,* Twenty-fourth Yearbook. Washington, D.C.: National Council of Teachers of Mathematics, 1959.
10. GROSSNICKLE, FOSTER E., AND LEO J. BRUECKNER, *Discovering Meanings in Arithmetic,* Chapter 7. Philadelphia: The John C. Winston Co., 1959.
11. HARDING, LOWRY W., CHARLOTTE H. HUCK, AND MARTHA NORMAN, *Arithmetic for Child Development,* Part 2, Section 4. Dubuque, Iowa: William C. Brown Co., 1959.

12. JOHNSON, J. T., "Whither Research in Compound Subtraction?" *Arithmetic Teacher,* Vol. 5, pp. 39–42, February, 1958.
13. MARKS, JOHN L., C. RICHARD PURDY, AND LUCIEN B. KINNEY, *Teaching Arithmetic for Understanding,* Chapter 6. New York: McGraw-Hill Book Co., 1958.
14. MOTHER JEAN EUDES, "Drill in Arithmetic," *Catholic School Journal,* Vol. 57, pp. 130–131, April, 1957.
15. MUELLER, FRANCIS J., *Arithmetic, Its Structure and Concepts,* Chapter 2. Englewood Cliffs, N.J.: Prentice-Hall, Inc., 1956.
16. OLANDER, HERBERT T., AND BETTY IRENE BROWN, "Research in Mental Arithmetic Involving Subtraction," *Journal of Educational Research,* Vol. 53, pp. 97–102, November, 1959.
17. SISTER MARIE FRANCILE, "Visualizing Carrying and Borrowing," *Catholic School Journal,* Vol. 56, p. 24, January, 1956.
18. SPITZER, HERBERT F., *The Teaching of Arithmetic,* Chapter 3. Boston: Houghton Mifflin Co., 1961.
19. SWAIN, ROBERT L., *Understanding Arithmetic,* Chapter 4. New York: Rinehart and Co., 1957.

CHAPTER 8

Developing Concepts of Multiplication and Division

As in other instances when a new concept is introduced, a child's understanding of multiplication and division is developed through helping him to use his earlier learnings to grasp the new meanings. The child is introduced to the meaning of the operations of multiplication and division on whole numbers by using illustrative examples in situations where he may see the new ideas represented with concrete materials. At this time, he learns how numerals are employed in multiplication and division algorisms involving whole numbers. Later, when he learns to use numerals to represent fractions, he learns how multiplication and division apply to non-negative rational numbers. At still higher grade levels, his concepts are extended to enable him to understand multiplication and division as these operations apply to numbers in other number systems. Thus the relatively limited concepts of these operations which children first form at an immature level are extended gradually as the children proceed through the elementary and secondary schools.

A problem for the teacher is to ensure that, while the children's concepts are being developed, those things which they learn in their early years remain compatible with the mathematical concepts which the teacher wishes them to develop later.

Before discussing the procedures for guiding children to an understanding of multiplication and division, we shall identify some of the basic concepts concerning these operations in order to remind the teacher of certain important concepts and principles toward which the children are being led during the years they are studying mathematics in the elementary and secondary schools.

Enlarging the Meaning of Multiplication

At first, the child may be led to think of multiplication as another way of finding the sum of a number of equal groups of objects. He may think of 3×4 as being a way of finding how many objects are in three groups of four objects each. This concept will serve him as a model in many situations when he thinks of multiplication as applied to whole numbers.

At higher grade levels, he learns that multiplication may be considered as a way of finding a number which bears the same relationship to the multiplicand that the multiplier bears to one. This is a ratio idea which may be employed in a situation where he is considering a problem such as "Bill has 5 cents and Jim has three times as much. How much has Jim?" Here the number 15 has the same ratio to 5 that 3 has to 1. This concept, which is applicable to whole numbers, may also be applied to non-negative rational numbers in a situation in which the problem is that of finding the product of $\frac{3}{4} \times 4$. Here he is finding a number which has the same relationship to 4 that $\frac{3}{4}$ has to 1.

At a more mature level, he is led to think of multiplication as a certain binary operation which may be performed on a pair of numbers in a set and which results in a unique number in the same set. This concept, as well as the one above, may be applied to whole numbers and to rational numbers; but it is equally applicable to irrational numbers and complex numbers, once the procedure for finding the unique number which is the product has been defined.

It should be noted that while we may not expect an eight-year-old child to grasp the full meaning of the operations of multiplication and division when he is first introduced to them, we do expect that later he will develop concepts of multiplication and division which extend the meaning of these operations beyond those of his earlier concepts. A definition of multiplication such as "Multiplication is merely a quick way of adding" is certainly not compatible with the concepts of multiplication which we wish him to develop later, even though such a statement might seem to apply to situations in which he is multiplying whole numbers.

Some Basic Concepts Concerning Multiplication

Products and factors. The binary operation of multiplication on two numbers results in a unique number called the *product.* Each of the numbers on which the operation is performed is called a *factor* of the product. For example, if a, b, and c are replaced by numbers, and if $a \times b = c$, then a and b are called factors of the product c.

In the system of natural numbers, any number greater than one which has no factors other than itself and one, is said to be a *prime number.* Thus the first five prime numbers are 2, 3, 5, 7, and 11. If a number has factors other than itself and one, it is said to be a *composite number.* Thus, the natural numbers may be classified as prime numbers, composite numbers, and the number one, which is considered to be neither a prime nor a composite number.

The principle of commutation. Children should learn that the order in which factors are multiplied does not affect the product. This may be expressed algebraically as $a \times b = b \times a$, when a and b are replaced by numbers, e.g., $2 \times 3 = 3 \times 2$.

The principle of association. This principle implies that when three or more numbers are multiplied, they may be grouped in different ways without affecting their product. For example, $(a \times b) \times c = a \times (b \times c)$, when a, b, and c are replaced by numbers, as $(2 \times 3) \times 4 = 2 \times (3 \times 4)$.

The distribution of multiplication over addition. This principle may be expressed algebraically as $a(b+c) = ab + ac$, where a, b, and c are replaced by numbers. Expressed in words, this principle implies that when the sum of two numbers is multiplied by a given number, the product is the same number as that obtained by multiplying each of the numbers by the given number and then adding the two products thus obtained, e.g., $2(3+4) = (2 \times 3) + (2 \times 4)$.

The identity element for multiplication. The children should understand that the operation of multiplication on the number one and any given number results in a product which is equal to the given number. For example, $a \times 1 = 1 \times a = a$, where a is replaced by a number, as $4 \times 1 = 1 \times 4 = 4$.

Using zero in multiplication. The operation of multiplication on the number zero and any given number results in the number zero as the product. For example, $a \times 0 = 0 \times a = 0$, where a is replaced by a number, as $3 \times 0 = 0 \times 3 = 0$.

Enlarging the Meaning of Division

Following a pattern somewhat similar to that used to introduce multiplication, a teacher may introduce division to children by having them consider how certain groups of objects may be thought of as being made up of a number of smaller equal groups. They may then be led to think of division in such instances as a process either of finding the number of equal groups when the size of each group is given, or of finding the size of each group when the number of groups is given.[1] For instance, the division of 12 by 3 could be compared to the process of repeatedly removing 3 objects at a time from a group of twelve objects, in order to find how many groups of three would make up a group of twelve. This is illustrated in Figure 8.1a. The division of 12 by 3 could be compared also to the process of breaking a group of twelve objects into three equal groups in order to find how many objects would be in each of these smaller groups. This is

[1] See pp. 203–205 for amplification.

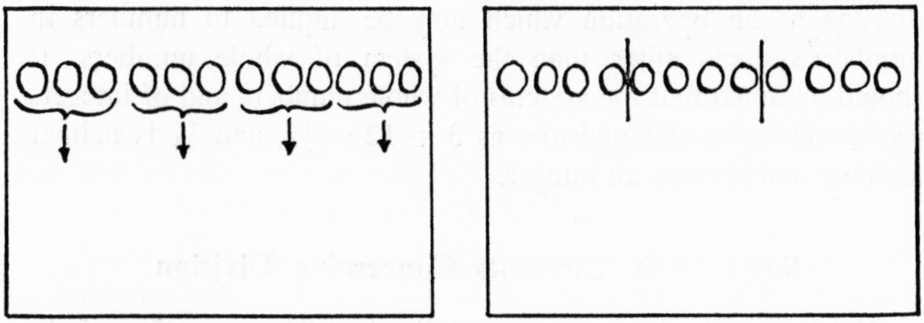

a b

Figure 8.1 Discs arranged on a flannel board to illustrate two division situations involving $12 \div 3$.

illustrated in Figure 8.1b. These concepts of division will help children understand how division may be applied in many situations where whole numbers are being used.

At a more mature level, a child could be led to think of division as the process of finding a number which bears the same relationship to the dividend that the number one bears to the divisor, as illustrated in Figure 8.2. This concept will help the pupil to under-

a	b
$3\overline{)12}$ with quotient 4	$3 \div \frac{3}{4} = 4$
$4:12::1:3$ or $\frac{4}{12} = \frac{1}{3}$	$4:3::1:\frac{3}{4}$ or $\frac{4}{3} = 1/\frac{3}{4}$
(Read "4 is to 12 as 1 is to 3")	(Read "4 is to 3 as 1 is to $\frac{3}{4}$")

Figure 8.2 An application of the concept that division is finding a number which has the same relationship to the dividend that the number one has to the divisor.

stand division as applied to non-negative rational numbers in instances where he is using fractions as numerals in division situations.

At a still more mature level, division may be considered as a process of finding the number by which a second number must be multiplied in order to derive a given product, or as being a certain operation on an ordered pair of numbers which produces a unique number. This concept enables the child to think of division as an operation which may be applied to numbers in number systems other than the system of whole numbers. It should be noted that the systems of whole numbers and of integers are not closed under division, as $3 \div 12 = \frac{1}{4}$, and $\frac{1}{4}$ is neither a whole number nor an integer.

Some Basic Concepts Concerning Division

Division as the inverse of multiplication. The operation of division may be considered to be the inverse of multiplication in the sense that it "undoes" what has been done by multiplication. If we know the product which has resulted from the operation of multiplication on two factors, and if we know one of these factors, we can find the other by division. In other words, division answers the question "By what must the known factor be multiplied in order to secure the known product in a situation?" For example, $12 \div 3$, $^{12}\!/_{3}$, or $3\overline{)12}$ may be thought of as ways of asking the question "By what must 3 be multiplied in order to give 12 as the product?"

Zero not used as a divisor. From the manner in which division has been defined, it will be noted that $a/b = c$ if and only if $b \times c = a$. If in the expression $a/b = c$ the letter b were replaced by zero, and if a were replaced by a number which is not zero, as $4/0 = ?$ there is no number which could replace c and make $b \times c = a$, i.e., $0 \times ? = 4$.

If in the expression $a/b = c$, both a and b were replaced by zero, then any number could replace c and make $b \times c = a$, e.g., $0 \times 4 = 0$, and so we say that $0 \div 0$ is indeterminate.

For the reasons given above, division by zero is undefined, and zero cannot be used as a divisor.

Some properties of division. Division is not commutative except in the special instance where some number other than zero is divided by itself. For instance, $3 \div 4$ is not the same as $4 \div 3$. This may be expressed as $a/b \neq b/a$, unless $a = b$. For the symbol $\neq$ read "is not equal to."

Division is not associative generally. Where a, b, and c are replaced by numbers, $(a \div b) \div c$ is not the same as $a \div (b \div c)$; e.g., $(12 \div 4) \div 3 \neq 12 \div (4 \div 3)$.

Division is distributive with respect to addition and subtraction, with the exception that the divisor cannot be zero. This is expressed algebraically as $\frac{a+b}{c} = \frac{a}{c} + \frac{b}{c}$ and $\frac{a-b}{c} = \frac{a}{c} - \frac{b}{c}$, where $c \neq 0$; e.g., $\frac{6+4}{2} = \frac{6}{2} + \frac{4}{2}$ and $\frac{6-4}{2} = \frac{6}{2} - \frac{4}{2}$.

Any number other than zero when divided by itself is equal to one. $a/a = 1$, when $a \neq 0$; e.g., $4/4 = 1$.

When any number is divided by one, its quotient is the given number. $a/1 = a$ or $4/1 = 4$, since $1 \times a = a$.

The Order of Computations When Different Operations Are Combined

When an expression involves more than one type of operation, the following convention has been adopted regarding the order in which the computations should be performed.

The operation of deriving the root of a number or the power of a number should precede other operations, as $3 \times 4^2 = 48$ and $3 \times \sqrt{16} = 12$.

Multiplication and division should be performed before addition and subtraction. For example, $3 + 4 \times 5 = 23$, $12 - 2 \times 3 = 6$, $4 + 8 \div 2 = 8$, and $12 - 6 \div 3 = 10$.

Where parentheses, braces, or brackets are employed, the operations indicated within these symbols should be performed before other computations. For example, $(3 + 4) \times 2 = 14$.

Introducing Basic Principles to Children in the Primary and Intermediate Grades

As has been implied above, the teacher should use an inductive approach when introducing mathematical concepts to children. By employing situations involving the use of concrete materials, diagrams, and social situations to illustrate the mathematical principles, the teacher is assisting the children to grasp the abstract concepts. After experiencing many examples of how a principle applies to a concrete situation, a child is encouraged to "discover" for himself the mathematical principles involved. He should then be encouraged to apply this principle in other situations until he is familiar with it and until it seems "reasonable" to him. At first he applies the principle to the physical world where concrete materials are being used. When he begins to think of numbers as abstract elements rather than as something which must be connected closely with concrete objects, he will learn that the principles are a consequence of how numbers and the operations upon them have been defined, and that they do not depend upon models taken from the physical world. At that time, the teacher will find that an approach to mathematics which is essentially deductive will be more rewarding.

As most of the children in the primary and intermediate grades are in the stage of development where the teacher needs to use an inductive approach, the teaching procedures suggested in the following pages are inductive in nature. The teacher should be alert, however, to note children who are capable of profiting from a more abstract presentation, and be prepared to encourage children who are capable of dealing with number on a more advanced level than that which is within the ability of the majority of children.

Readiness for Multiplication

During grade 2, children have learned to count by tens, by twos, and by fives. To help the children think of multiplication as a process of finding a number which is made up of two or more equal numbers, the teacher should ask them, for instance, to count ten objects by twos and then to note that this may be shown in the form of addition as $2 + 2 + 2 + 2 + 2 = 10$. They may be told then that five twos may be written also as $5 \times 2 = 10$, or as $\begin{array}{r} 2 \\ \times 5 \\ \hline 10 \end{array}$ and that the process is indicated here by the symbol "$\times$" and is called "multiplication."

The pupils should be led to understand that when they are finding the number of objects in a group which is made up of five groups of two, there are three different procedures which they may follow in order to find the answer. They can count the objects to find the answer. By using repeated additions of two they can find the answer also by addition. If they remember that five twos are ten, they could think, "five twos are ten," which would be finding the answer by using a multiplication fact. It should be made clear to the pupils that to find the answer by multiplication they must learn certain basic facts in multiplication, just as they need to learn certain basic facts in addition in order to use that process.

Developing Readiness for Division

There are two types of division situations which the pupils meet frequently in problem solving. The first type is sometimes called a "measurement" situation and is illustrated by the following problem: "How many pieces of candy costing three cents each could John buy for twelve cents?" In this problem, the task is that of finding how many groups of three are in twelve, and this could be illustrated on a flannel board by the arrangement shown in Figure 8.3.

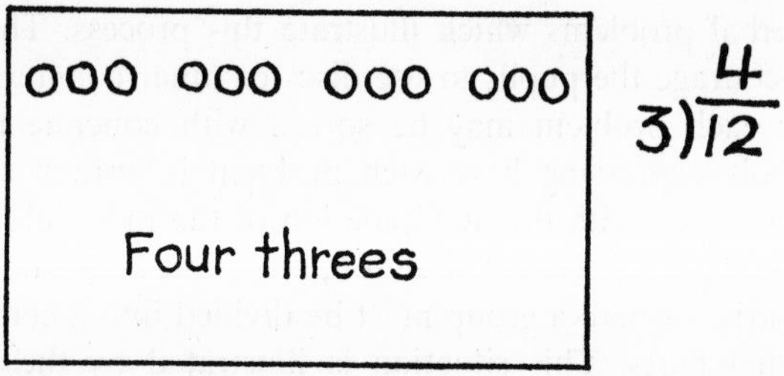

Figure 8.3 Discs arranged on a flannel board to illustrate a measurement situation.

When objects such as discs are used to illustrate the procedure, the discs may be counted off in groups of three to find how many of these groups are contained in the original group. The pupils should note that the number of groups of three in a group of twelve could also be obtained by repeated subtractions, as shown in Figure 8.4.

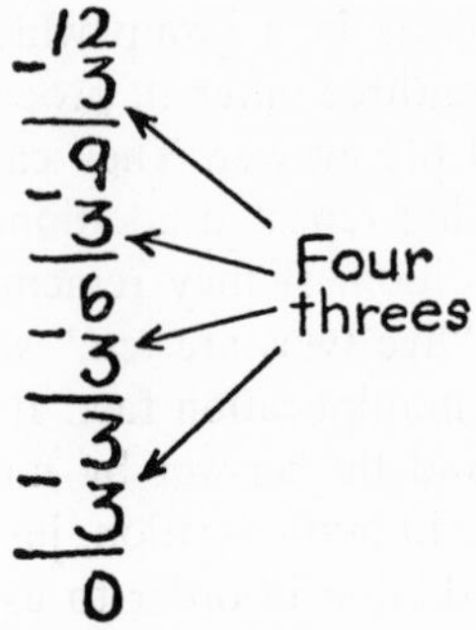

Figure 8.4 Using numerals to show a relationship between repeated subtractions and division.

The pupils should then discover that if they can remember the basic fact that there are four threes in twelve, they do not need to count nor to subtract to find the answer, but they simply think, "In twelve there are four threes," and they may write this as $12 \div 3 = 4$ or as $3\overline{)12}$ with 4 written above the 12.

After the pupils have grasped this meaning of division in measurement situations, they should be given abundant practice in solving verbal problems which illustrate this process. The teacher should encourage the pupils to use discs or other counters to illustrate how each problem may be solved with concrete materials. The symbols expressing how each problem is written should be used concurrently with the manipulation of the material.

A second type of division situation, sometimes called a *partition* situation, arises where a group must be divided into a certain number of equal parts. This situation is illustrated by the following problem. "A mother divided twelve cookies among her three children. How many cookies did each child receive?" Figure 8.5 shows how the solution of this problem could be illustrated on a flannel board.

In this instance, the group of discs representing the twelve cookies could be divided into three smaller groups by placing the discs, one at a time, in the three groups in turn until all were dispersed. A similar procedure for dividing a group into equal parts is followed often by children when they are making up teams

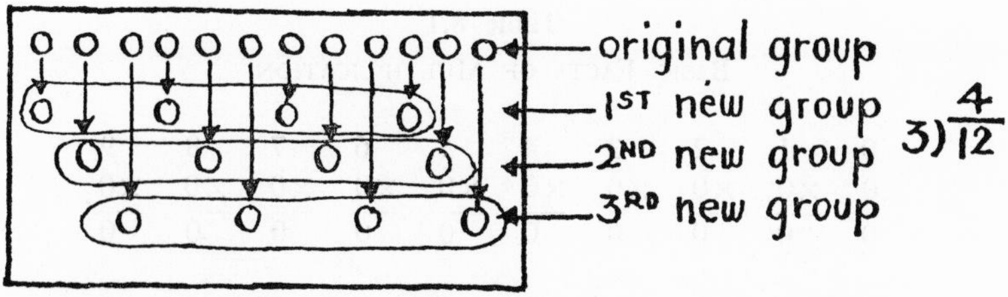

Figure 8.5 Discs arranged on a flannel board to illustrate a partition situation.

for their games. The children are selected for each team in turn until all are placed.

After the pupils understand the purpose and the meaning of division used in a partition situation, they should be given considerable practice in solving verbal problems where this type of division situation is used. Pupils should be encouraged to use discs and other counters to help them to visualize the solution of each problem, and then they should be required to illustrate with manipulative material or diagrams how they obtained the solution. In each instance, they should be required to show how the solution of the problem could be expressed also with arithmetic symbols.

The pupils should note that although they could solve the division problems by counting procedures, as was done with the manipulative material, it is much easier to solve the problems by using the basic facts of division, once these basic facts have been learned. They should note that the algorism is the same for both types of division situations, but that in the measurement situations they are finding the number of groups, while in the partition situations they are finding how many objects are in each of a given number of groups.

The Basic Facts of Multiplication and Division

Some of the one hundred basic facts of multiplication are shown in Table 8.1.

With the exception of division by zero, there is a basic fact in division for each basic fact in multiplication. These 90 division facts are shown in Table 8.2.

Table 8.1
BASIC FACTS OF MULTIPLICATION

0	1	2	3	4	5	6	7	8	9
×0	×0	×0	×0	×0	×0	×0	×0	×0	×0
0	0	0	0	0	0	0	0	0	0
0	1	2	3	4	5	6	7	8	9
×1	×1	×1	×1	×1	×1	×1	×1	×1	×1
0	1	2	3	4	5	6	7	8	9
0	1	2	3	4	5	6	7	8	9
×2	×2	×2	×2	×2	×2	×2	×2	×2	×2
0	2	4	6	8	10	12	14	16	18

0	1	2	3	4	5	6	7	8	9
×9	×9	×9	×9	×9	×9	×9	×9	×9	×9
0	9	18	27	36	45	54	63	72	81

Table 8.2
BASIC FACTS OF DIVISION

0	1	2	3	4	5	6	7	8	9
1)0	1)1	1)2	1)3	1)4	1)5	1)6	1)7	1)8	1)9
0	1	2	3	4	5	6	7	8	9
2)0	2)2	2)4	2)6	2)8	2)10	2)12	2)14	2)16	2)18

0	1	2	3	4	5	6	7	8	9
9)0	9)9	9)18	9)27	9)36	9)45	9)54	9)63	9)72	9)81

Discovering basic facts. To help pupils "discover" the basic facts for themselves, and in order to help them to get a clear idea of a purpose of multiplication, it is suggested that the pupils use discs or other suitable counters to help them prepare tables illustrating basic facts. For instance, an arrangement such as is shown in Figure 8.6 could be used in finding the value of three fours, and

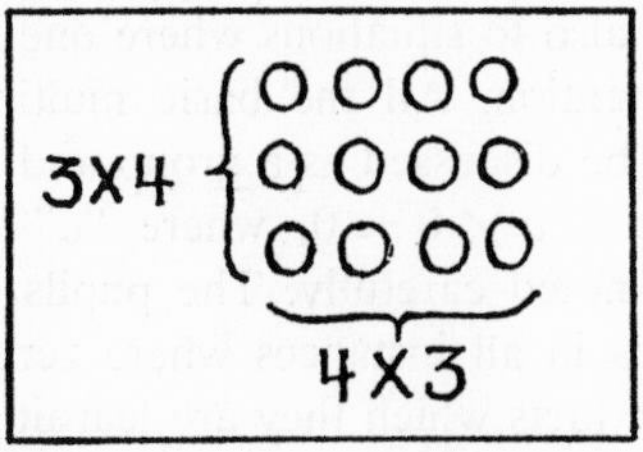

Figure 8.6 An arrangement of discs to illustrate basic multiplication and division facts.

then this fact could be written as $3 \times 4 = 12$. At the same time, the pupils should note that three fours would have the same value as four threes, and that this fact could be written as $4 \times 3 = 12$.

The division facts $\overset{4}{3\overline{)12}}$ and $\overset{3}{4\overline{)12}}$ are illustrated at the same time with the same arrangement of discs.

A composite table such as Table 8.3 should be developed and

Table 8.3

MULTIPLICATION AND DIVISION FACTS

n	0	1	2	3	4	5	6	7	8	9
1	0	1	2	3	4	5	6	7	8	9
2	0	2	4	6	8	10	12	14	16	18
3	0	3	6	9	12	15	18	21	24	27
4	0	4	8	12	16	20	24	28	32	36
					– – – – – – – –					
9	0	9	18	27	36	45	54	63	72	81

built up as the pupils derive the needed information from suitable arrangements of counters. Pupils should be encouraged to notice the relationships found between various basic facts which are indicated in the table and to understand why these relationships exist.

Noting properties of multiplication. During the period when children are discovering the basic facts, particular attention should be given to the principle of commutation as it is applied to the operation of multiplication. Each of the basic multiplication facts provides an example for showing how this principle is applied.

The operation of multiplication as it applies to a situation where zero is a factor and also to situations where one is a factor should be given special attention. All the basic multiplication facts involving zero should be discussed as a group and the application of the principle $0 \times a = a \times 0 = 0$, where "$a$" is replaced by a number, should be noted carefully. The pupils should learn that this principle applies in all instances where zero is a factor, and not only to the basic facts which they are learning at this time.

The operation of multiplication as it applies to a situation in which one of the factors is the number one should be discussed in connection with the group of basic facts involving one. The pupils should be taught that the principle $1 \times a = a \times 1 = a$, where "$a$" is replaced by a number, applies to all numbers, e.g., $1 \times 5 = 5$, $1 \times 0 = 0$.

Memorizing basic facts. The eventual memorization of the basic facts is essential to pupils who are expected to use the algorisms easily and accurately, and considerable importance should be attached to learning them. In order to break down into smaller tasks the chore of learning the facts, pupils should first build a table where two is the multiplier, as in Figure 8.7a, and practice these

2 X 0 = 0	3 X 0 = 0
2 X 1 = 2	3 X 1 = 3
2 X 2 = 4	3 X 2 = 6
2 X 3 = 6	3 X 3 = 9
2 X 4 = 8	3 X 4 = 12
2 X 5 = 10	3 X 5 = 15
2 X 6 = 12	3 X 6 = 18
2 X 7 = 14	3 X 7 = 21
2 X 8 = 16	3 X 8 = 24
2 X 9 = 18	3 X 9 = 27
a	b

Figure 8.7 Examples of tables prepared by pupils to clarify the relationships among basic multiplication facts.

facts. A table where three is the multiplier could then be learned (Figure 8.7b), and this would be followed by building tables where the multiplier is, in turn, each of the whole numbers through nine. Eventually the facts should be learned well enough to permit their being recalled immediately and in any order. For this reason their recall should be practiced by using the facts in an irregular order, rather than in the order in which they appear in a table.

As in the case of learning the addition and subtraction facts, the task of learning the multiplication and division facts may be made more interesting to pupils by giving them practice in the form of games, or by using flash cards, spinners, or other devices, such as are shown in Figure 8.8.

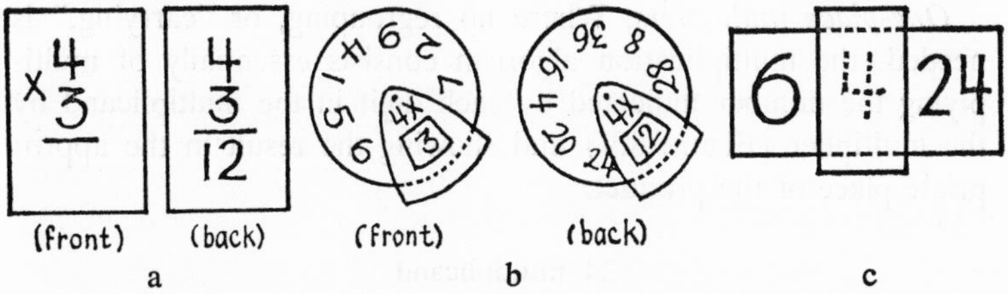

Figure 8.8 Some devices to motivate pupils to practice the basic facts of multiplication and division. The slide on device "c" makes this device useful for practicing either multiplication or division facts for this card. Other cards to show other facts would be included.

It is suggested that each arithmetic period should be begun with a very brief review of the basic facts which are being studied by the class, and that this procedure should be continued as long as it is needed. A valuable purpose of these daily reviews is to impress upon the pupils the importance of learning the facts; a very brief review, lasting only four or five minutes, may be sufficient, providing that the pupils are encouraged to work individually during their independent work period on the facts which they still need to learn.

Teaching the algorisms for multiplication and division need not be delayed until the time when all the facts have been mastered by the children. While learning to use the algorism, pupils may be allowed to use a table showing the needed facts. They should be encouraged, however, to memorize the basic facts as soon as possible, so that the need for using the table would be reduced gradually and eventually would cease to exist. The teacher will find, however, that unless a pupil is allowed to use a table of the facts which have not been learned, there is a danger of his using counting or adding procedures in computations which could be completed more efficiently by using multiplication or division facts. In such instances, the pupil is not getting practice in using the multiplication and division facts where they are most needed, and consequently he may be developing inefficient procedures in computation.

Learning the Multiplication Algorism

One-place multipliers. Where no regrouping, or "carrying," is needed, the multiplication algorism consists essentially of multiplying the number indicated by each digit in the multiplicand by the multiplier (Figure 8.9) and showing the result in the appropriate place of the product.

$$\begin{array}{rl} 24 & \text{multiplicand} \\ \times 2 & \text{multiplier} \\ \hline 48 & \text{product} \end{array}$$

Figure 8.9 Multiplication where no regrouping is needed.

When the need for regrouping from ones to tens, or from tens to hundreds, arises during multiplication, the process may be illustrated with a place-value chart. In Figure 8.10a the tickets have

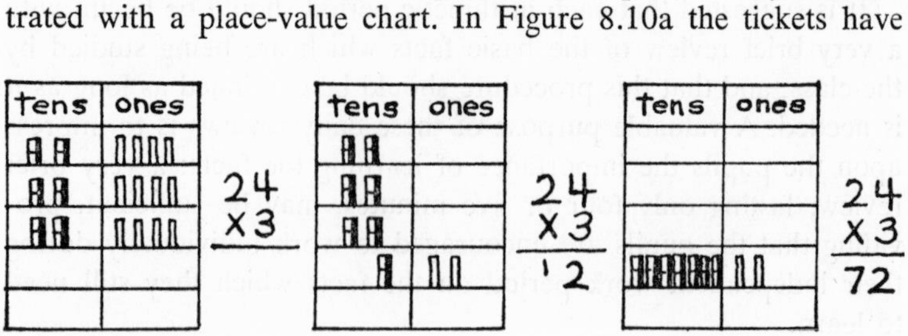

a b c

Figure 8.10 Place-value chart arrangement to illustrate regrouping.

been arranged on the chart to show 3 × 24. The pupils should be asked to note that to find the number of ones it would be possible to count the tickets or to add the tickets, but since they are learning how to multiply, they should use the multiplication fact that three fours are twelve. They thus find the total number of ones without either counting or adding. Ten of the twelve tickets would then be grouped and moved to the tens' place of the answer pocket, and the two single tickets would be left in the ones' place of the answer, as shown in Figure 8.10b. In the algorism, "2" would be put into the ones' place of the product while a small "1" could be shown to represent ten being carried to the tens' place.

Before taking the next step, the pupils should be reminded again that we could count the bundles of ten or add them to get the answer, but that as they are learning multiplication, they should find the answer by using the basic facts of that process. The three groups of two bundles would give 3 × 2, or six bundles of ten. The bundle of ten tickets which had been carried would now be included with the other six bundles and put into the tens' place of the answer pocket, as in Figure 8.10c. In the algorism "7" should be written in the tens' place of the product to indicate that there are seven tens.

The pupils should be asked to explain why the multiplication to find the number of tens must be completed before the ten which has been carried can be added. They should note that in order to use the multiplication fact $3 \times 2 = 6$, the three groups of two bundles were processed first, and then the other bundle was added to make the total.

By using a hundreds' place on the place-value chart, a similar procedure could be followed to illustrate the multiplication of a three-place number by a one-place number, as illustrated in Figure 8.11.

When the pupils are first learning the multiplication algorism and are using small numbers, they may be inclined to use counting or addition procedures rather than multiplication because they are more familiar with these processes. Irrespective of this inclination, they should be encouraged to use the multiplication facts when they are using the multiplication algorism so that they will get practice in using the algorism correctly and efficiently. It should be

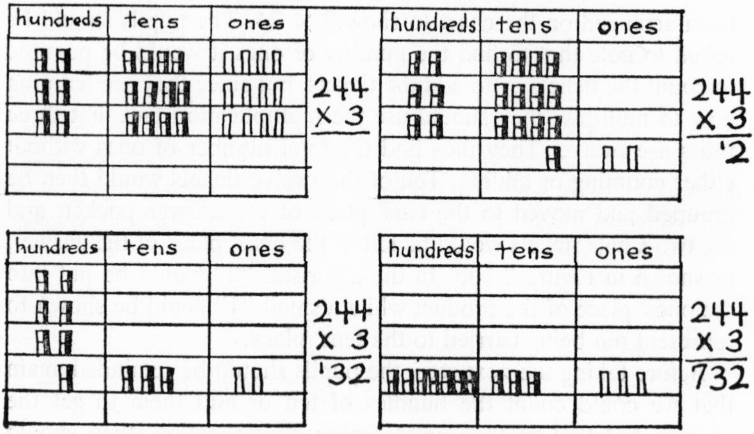

Figure 8.11 Place-value chart arrangement to show regrouping where three-place numerals are involved.

explained to the pupils that while they are using small numbers, such as two or three, for a multiplier it may be easier for them to count or to add instead of using multiplication facts, but that when a large number needs to be used as a multiplier, it is much faster to use the multiplication facts once they have been learned.

Multipliers with more than one digit. The multiplication algorism using a multiplier of more than one digit is based upon the principle that each digit in the multiplier may be used to derive a partial product, and that these partial products may then be added to determine the product. This is an application of the principle of the distribution of multiplication over addition, and is illustrated in Figure 8.12. Here the multiplier, 13, may be thought of as ten and three. As shown in Figure 8.12b, 3 × 23 gives a partial product of 69, and 10 × 23 gives a partial product of 230. When these partial products are added, their sum is seen to be the product of 13 × 23, as shown in Figure 8.12c. Thus the pupils are led to understand the distributive property of multiplication as it is applied in algorisms where the multiplier has more than one digit.

In the algorism shown in Figure 8.13, when the digit in the tens' place is being used as the multiplier, the second partial product

Capacity concepts

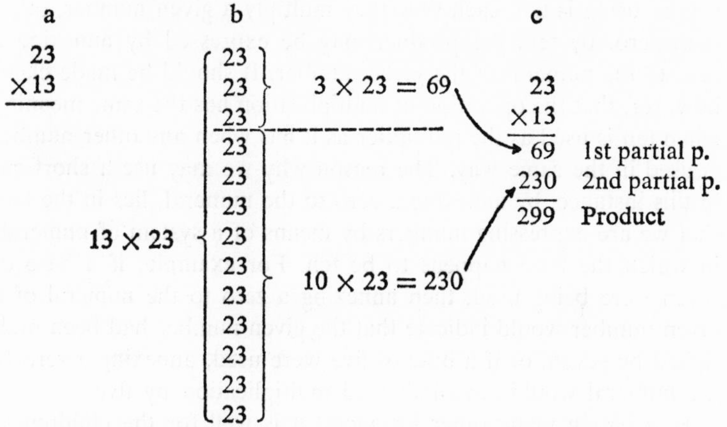

Figure 8.12 Illustrating how the principle of the distribution of multiplication over addition applies in a multiplication algorism.

will indicate the number of tens, so zero could be shown in the ones' place. When the digit in the hundreds' place is being used as the multiplier, the third partial product would indicate the number of hundreds, so zeros could be shown in the tens' place and in the ones' place. Although using zeros in this way is a matter of personal preference and it is more efficient not to use them, their inclusion in early stages of learning the algorism is suggested, as pupils may find the procedure more meaningful when this more complete form is used.

```
   234
  ×232
   468   1st partial product
  7020   2nd partial product
 46800   3rd partial product
 54288   Product
```

Figure 8.13 Using zeros in the partial products to clarify the meaning of the algorism.

Multiplication by ten or a power of ten. The pupils should be led to discover that because the base of the number system which we are using is ten, each time they multiply a given number, other than zero, by ten, the product may be expressed by annexing a zero to the numeral of the given number. It should be made clear, however, that the operation of multiplication has the same meaning when ten is used as the multiplier as it has when any other number is used in the same way. The reason why we may use a short cut in this instance, by annexing a zero to the numeral, lies in the fact that we are expressing numbers by means of a system of numerals in which the base happens to be ten. For example, if a base of seven were being used, then annexing a zero to the numeral of a given number would indicate that the given number had been multiplied by seven, or if a base of five were used, annexing a zero to the numeral would have indicated multiplication by five.

Here, as in many other instances, it is well for the children to note that our computational procedures are determined partially by the properties of the numbers themselves and the operations on them, and they are determined partially by the nature of the numeration system we happen to be using.

Zero in the multiplier. In Figure 8.14a, a zero is shown in the multiplier as "holding" the tens' place, and consequently a zero in

```
  223        223       223
 ×301       ×301      ×320
 ----       ----      ----
  223        223      4460
 6690        000      669
 -----      669       -----
 67123      -----     71360
            67123

   a          b         c
```

Figure 8.14 The form of the algorism in which the partial products composed of zeros are omitted is shown in (a) and (c).

the second partial product will hold the corresponding place. This short cut makes it unnecessary to use the algorism shown in Figure 8.14b, in which the second partial product is made up of zeros. The procedure shown in Figure 8.14c where the multiplier ends in zero is a similar short cut. If the teacher leads the children to discover short cuts in the algorisms for themselves, the children will find them more meaningful.

Learning the Division Algorism

One-digit divisor with no regrouping needed. A pocket-chart may be used to help pupils to understand the nature of the division algorism. A verbal problem, such as the following, helps pupils visualize the division process in a social setting. "Sixty-nine children were taken to a picnic in three school buses. How many children would go in each bus if the buses were loaded equally?"

Sixty-nine tickets would first be arranged on the place-value chart, as shown in Figure 8.15a, and the class would be told that

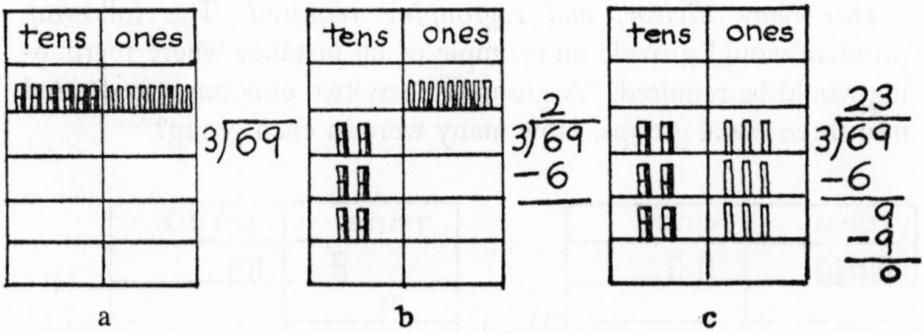

Figure 8.15 Arrangement on a place-value chart to illustrate division.

these tickets would represent the sixty-nine children while the three lower pockets of the chart would represent the three buses.

The six bundles, each of ten tickets, would then be removed from the chart and distributed, one bundle at a time, into each of the three pockets in turn. Then it would be noted that two bundles of ten would be in each pocket representing a school bus, so "2" would be put in the tens' place of the algorism, as shown in Figure 8.15b. It would be noted from the chart that three groups, each of two bundles, had been distributed; and consequently this would be indicated in the algorism by subtracting "6" from the "6" in the tens' place (Figure 8.15b).

The nine tickets from the ones' place should then be distributed, one at a time, into the three pockets representing the three buses (Figure 8.15c). It would be seen then that there were three tickets in each place of each of the answer pockets, and consequently "3" would be put into the ones' place of the algorism, as in Figure 8.15c. As the chart shows three groups of three tickets in the ones' place, "9" would be subtracted from "9" in the algorism. The pupils' attention would be directed to how the "9" which shows the number of ones in the algorism was moved to a lower position on the paper in order to make it more convenient to complete the subtraction. The divisor in the algorism, in this case "3," shows the number of groups, or buses in this instance; while the quotient, which is "23," shows the number in each group, or the number of children in each bus in this instance.

One-figure divisor, and regrouping required. The following problem would provide an example of an instance where regrouping would be required. "A group of forty-two children was divided into three equal groups. How many were in each group?"

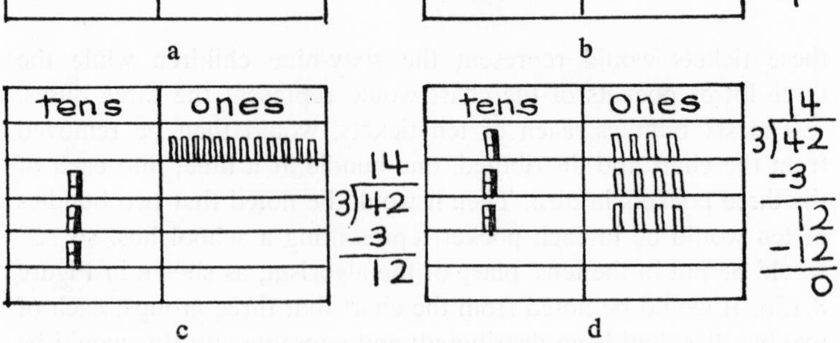

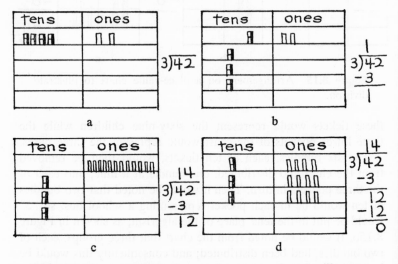

Figure 8.16 Arrangement on a place-value chart to illustrate division where regrouping is involved.

Forty-two tickets could be arranged on the pocket-chart, as shown in Figure 8.16a. The three lower pockets would represent the three groups. The four bundles of ten tickets would be taken from the chart and distributed, one bundle into each of the three answer pockets. The remaining bundle would be held while the first step in the algorism was being recorded, as in Figure 8.16b.

The bundle of ten would then be changed to ones and added to the two tickets in the ones' place of the chart to make twelve tickets in that place. The next step of the algorism would be recorded, as in Figure 8.16c.

The twelve tickets would then be distributed, one at a time, into the three answer pockets, and the algorism completed, as in Figure 8.16d.

Expressing remainders in division. If the problem given above had involved forty-three rather than forty-two children, a remainder of one would have resulted. The place-value chart then could be used in much the same way as it was used in Figure 8.16 to show the division of forty-two into three parts, but in this instance the single ticket representing the remainder would have to be returned to its original pocket to show that it did not enter into the division. The quotient of the algorism would then be shown as 14 r 1, as in Figure 8.17a, and in this instance would mean that

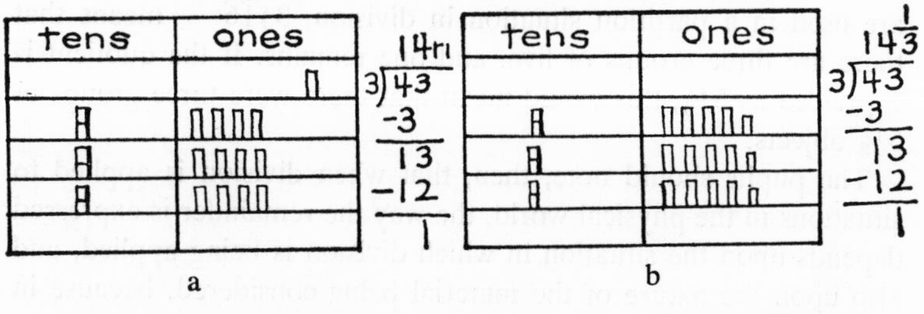

Figure 8.17 Arrangement on a place-value chart to illustrate two ways of treating a remainder.

there were fourteen children in each of the three groups, while one child had not yet been placed in any group.

If the problem dealt with objects which were individually divisible, such as when forty-three chocolate bars are divided among three boys, the remaining ticket, which represented a chocolate bar in this instance, would be cut into three equal parts and one part would be added to each answer pocket in the chart, as shown in Figure 8.17b. In this instance, the quotient of the algorism would be written as 14⅓, and would indicate that there were three equal groups of 14⅓ each.

The children should note that the remainder would be expressed as a fraction when the objects being considered in the problem were divisible and where this could be done sensibly. In computations where the numerals are not representing the number of any particular objects, the remainder should be expressed as a fraction, as this would indicate that the division has been completed.

The difficulty pupils have in understanding how to deal with remainders in division deserves special attention. When using concrete material such as discs pupils perceive that while some groups of objects may be divided exactly into a number of smaller equal groups, other groups cannot be so divided. For example, when making use of counters, the pupil will note that in a measurement situation in division, $3\overline{)16}^{\;5\text{ r }1}$ means that there are five groups of three, and one counter remains. If the answer is expressed as 5⅓, this would mean that there were 5⅓ groups. When the counters are used in a partition situation in division, $3\overline{)16}^{\;5\text{ r }1}$ means that there are three groups of five, and one remains. If the quotient is expressed as 5⅓, this would mean that there were three groups of 5⅓ objects.

The pupils should note, then, that when division is applied to situations in the physical world, the way the remainder is expressed depends upon the situation in which division is being applied, and also upon the nature of the material being considered, because in some instances it would not make sense to express the remainder as a fraction.

Estimating the digits in the quotient when using the standard algorism for division. The customary division algorism for 639 ÷ 3 is shown in Figure 8.18. As 639 may be expressed as 600 +

```
        a                      b

       213           200
     3)639         3)600
       6                   10
       -
        3                3)30
        3
        -                          3
         9                       3)9
         9
         -
```

Figure 8.18 The standard algorism for division employs the principle that division is distributive with respect to addition.

30 + 9, the problem 639 ÷ 3 may be expressed as ⅓(600 + 30 + 9). Applying the principle of distributing multiplication over addition, ⅓(600 + 30 + 9) may also be expressed as ⅓(600) + ⅓(30) + ⅓(9). In the algorism shown in Figure 8.18a, the "2" in the quotient indicates the number of hundreds when 600 is divided by 3. The "1" in the quotient indicates the number of tens when 30 is divided by 3, and the "3" in the quotient indicates the number of ones when 9 is divided by 3.

Figure 8.19 shows the standard algorism for 739 ÷ 3. Here,

```
      a                    b

     246⅓        200
   3)739       3)600
     6
     -                 40
     13              3)120
     12
     --                          6
      19                       3)18
      18
      --
       1                               3)1
```

Figure 8.19 The principle of association for addition is being employed in the division algorism as well as the principle that division is distributive with respect to addition.

739 may be thought of as (700 + 30 + 9), and the problem could have been expressed as ⅓(700 + 30 + 9). In the algorism, how-

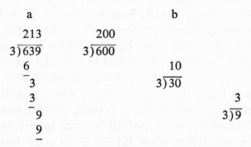

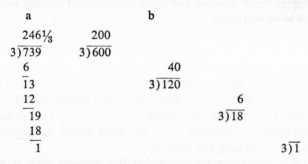

ever, it will be noted that $739 \div 3$ is being treated as $\frac{1}{3}(600) + \frac{1}{3}(120) + \frac{1}{3}(18) + \frac{1}{3}(1)$, because when 7 is divided by 3, the "2" in the quotient represents two hundred. The remainder after the first subtraction is one hundred, which is thought of as 10 tens, and then 3 more tens are added to make 13 tens. The "4" in the quotient represents 4 tens, and the remainder after the second subtraction is 1 ten, to which 9 ones are added to make 19 ones. The "6" in the quotient indicates 6 ones, and the one remaining after the third subtraction is divided by three to give $\frac{1}{3}$.

It will be noted that when $\frac{1}{3}(700 + 30 + 9)$ was expressed as $\frac{1}{3}(600 + 120 + 18 + 1)$ in the example given above, the associative property of addition was employed.

When a two-digit divisor is used, the difficulty of estimating the quotient digits is increased. In Figure 8.20a the number repre-

a

$$\begin{array}{r} 3 \\ 25\overline{)776} \\ \underline{75} \end{array}$$

b

$$\begin{array}{r} 3 \\ 25\overline{)744} \\ \underline{75} \end{array}$$

Figure 8.20 Showing instances where the "apparent" method of estimating the quotient digit resulted in the estimated quotient's being the "true" quotient and where the estimated quotient would need to be corrected.

sented by the first digit of the dividend is divided by the number represented by the first digit of the divisor in order to determine the first digit in the quotient. If this quotient digit is found to be too large, as in the instance shown in Figure 8.20b, a smaller quotient digit is tried until the suitable one is found. This procedure for estimating the quotient digits has been called the "apparent" method of estimating the quotient.

Another procedure for estimating the quotient digit is to increase the first digit of the divisor by one in instances where the second digit of the divisor is "5" or larger. In Figure 8.21a, the first digit is "2"; but as the second digit in the divisor is "5," the first digit is increased by one, and three is used instead of two when estimating the digit in the quotient. This procedure has been

$$\begin{array}{r} 2 \\ 25\overline{)744} \\ \underline{50} \end{array} \qquad\qquad \begin{array}{r} 2 \\ 25\overline{)776} \\ \underline{50} \end{array}$$

a b

Figure 8.21 Showing an instance where the rounding-off method of estimating the quotient digit resulted in the estimated quotient's being the "true" quotient and an instance where the estimated quotient would need to be corrected.

called the "increase-by-one" method of estimating the quotient, and is referred to also as the "rounding-off" method.

It is suggested that pupils first be taught to use the apparent method of estimating the quotient digits, as this follows directly from the procedure they use with a one-digit divisor. As the pupils become more proficient, they should be led to "discover" that the rounding-off method will add to the number of their correct estimates of the quotient digits.

"Long" and "short" division. Long division refers to the form of the algorism where each step in the computation is shown, such as $\begin{array}{r} 8 \\ 3\overline{)25} \\ \underline{24} \\ 1 \end{array}$, while short division refers to the form where the steps involving multiplication and subtraction are not shown, such as $\begin{array}{l} \;\;8 \text{ r } 1 \\ 3\overline{)25} \end{array}$. It is suggested that the children should be taught to use the long division form before learning the short division form, as the short form requires a more sustained mental effort when the numerals to be processed present difficulties. The short form may be developed as a shortcut for use with one-digit divisors.

Expanded forms of the division algorism. A form of division algorism is shown in Figure 8.22a, which some children might find simpler to use than the standard form, as it permits them to be less accurate in their first estimate of the quotient digit at each step of the process. As the children increase their ability to estimate

```
        a                  b                 c
                                            33
   26 | 883 |       26 | 883 |        26 | 883
      | 260 | 10        | 780 | 30        | 780
      | 623 |           | 103 |           | 103
      | 260 | 10        |  78 |  3        |  78
      | 363 |           |  25 | 33        |  25
      | 260 | 10
      | 103 |
      |  52 |  2
      |  51 |
      |  26 |  1
      |  25 | 33
```

Figure 8.22 Showing how an expanded division algorism may be shortened as pupils increase their proficiency in estimating the quotient digits.

the quotient digits correctly, the form may be shortened to that shown in Figure 8.22c.

Another expanded form of division algorism is shown in Figure 8.23. This form presents the same difficulty in estimating the quotient as that found in the customary form, but the purpose for each step in the process is made somewhat clearer.

```
     4
    90
   200        294 r 1
3)883
   600
   283
   270
    13
    12
     1
```

Figure 8.23 An expanded form of division algorism designed to clarify the purpose for each step in the process.

Expanded forms of the division algorism, though less compact than the customary form, have the advantage of showing in more detail how the numerals which indicate the quotient are determined. One further advantage of these expanded forms is that the pupil is working with partial quotients that are "complete" numbers rather than "parts" of the numeral for the quotient. It is suggested that if children are taught to use expanded forms of the division algorism, they should be led to "discover" and to use the more compact customary form as they gain proficiency.

Determining Divisibility of Whole Numbers

Some of the rules for determining the divisibility of a number by certain small numbers may be rationalized by employing the concept of a *number excess* of a given number.

Divisibility by ten. The *tens excess* of a given number is the remainder obtained when a number is divided by ten. For example, the tens excess of 95 is 5, of 43 is 3, of 241 is 1.

As the digits in a number indicate powers of ten, a natural number may be shown to be divisible by ten when the digit in the ones' place is zero. For example, the number 1240 may be expanded and written as

$$(1 \times 10^3) + (2 \times 10^2) + (4 \times 10^1) + (0 \times 10^0)$$

As each digit to the left of the ones' place indicates a power of ten which is greater than zero and is divisible, therefore, by ten, only the digit in the ones' place would indicate any excess of tens. In this instance, where the digit in the ones' place is zero, there is no excess of tens, and the number 1240 must be divisible by ten.

Divisibility by five. As a number which is divisible by ten is also divisible by five, a number whose digit in the ones' place is zero must be divisible by five as well as by ten. In instances where the digit in the ones' place is 5, the number must be divisible also by 5, as in this instance there would be no remainder when dividing by 5, or in other words, the *excess of fives* would be zero. For example, $295 = (2 \times 100) + (9 \times 10) + 5$, so the fives excess is zero.

Divisibility by two. As a number which is divisible by ten is also divisible by two, a number whose digit in the ones' place is zero must be divisible by two as well as by ten.

In instances where the digit in the ones place is 2, 4, 6, or 8 the given number must be divisible by two because there would be no *twos excess* in such a number. For example, $296 = (2 \times 100) + (9 \times 10) + 6$, so the twos excess is zero.

Divisibility by nine. The *nines excess* of a number is the remainder after the number is divided by nine. For example, the nines excess of 11 is 2, of 27 is 0, of 64 is 1, and of 2 is 2.

The sum of the digits of a given whole number expressed in the decimal system of numeration may be used to determine the excess of nines in that number, and consequently determine whether or not it is divisible by nine. For example, 243 may be expressed in expanded form as

$$\begin{aligned} &(2 \times 100) + (4 \times 10) + 3 \\ \text{or } &2(99 + 1) + 4(9 + 1) + 3 \\ \text{or } &(2 \times 99) + 2 + (4 \times 9) + 4 + 3 \\ \text{or } &(2 \times 99) + (4 \times 9) + 2 + 4 + 3 \end{aligned}$$

As both 99 and 9 are divisible by nine, and as $2 + 4 + 3$ is also divisible by 9, the nines excess is zero; consequently the number 243 is divisible by nine. A number is divisible by nine if the sum of the digits is divisible by nine.

Divisibility by three. The *threes excess* of a given number is indicated also by the sum of its digits of the given number. For example, 246 may be expressed in expanded form as follows:

$$\begin{aligned} 246 &= (2 \times 100) + (4 \times 10) + 6 \\ &= 2(99 + 1) + 4(9 + 1) + 6 \\ &= (2 \times 99) + 2 + (4 \times 9) + 4 + 6 \\ &= (2 \times 99) + (4 \times 9) + 2 + 4 + 6 \end{aligned}$$

As both 99 and 9 are divisible by 3, and as the sum of $2 + 4 + 6$ is divisible by 3, the threes excess of 246 is zero, and the number 246 is divisible by 3 because the sum of its digits is divisible by 3.

Casting Out Nines

The phrase "casting out nines" has been used traditionally to refer to a procedure for checking algorisms, particularly multiplication algorisms, to detect possible errors. As noted above, the nines excess of a number may be determined from the sum of its digits. For example,

$$
\begin{array}{rlrl}
246 & (\text{nines excess} = 3) & 3 & \\
\times 23 & (\text{nines excess} = 5) & \times 5 & \\
\hline
738 & & 15 & (\text{nines excess} = 6) \uparrow \\
492 & & & \\
\hline
5658 & (\text{nines excess} = 6) \leftarrow & \text{check} &
\end{array}
$$

It should be noted that this check will not detect an error caused by the digits in the product being out of their proper order. For instance, if in the example given above the product had been written incorrectly as 5685, the check would not have indicated this error.

Suggested Learning Activities

1. A) Name the next three prime numbers after eleven. B) All prime numbers beginning with three are odd numbers. Why?
2. Name the first five composite numbers. Give two factors of each (do not include the number one).
3. In addition, zero is referred to as an identity element. Is zero an identity element for multiplication? Defend your answer.
4. Describe two social situations likely to occur among children in which partition division is needed. Do the same for measurement division.
5. Tell which operation is to be done first in each of the following:

   A) $\frac{\sqrt{49}}{7}$; B) $8 \times 6 - 3$; C) $7 + 8^2$; D) $6 \div \frac{18}{3}$.
6. Make a device for motivating practice of multiplication or division facts. See Figure 8.8, page 209, or use an idea of your own.
7. Using a place-value chart, demonstrate how you would teach 3×123. Do the same for $84 \div 4$.

8. Explain how the principles of association and distribution are employed in the standard algorism for $372 \div 3$.
9. Using both of the methods described on pages 36–37, estimate the quotient for: $1701 \div 27$; $1453 \div 24$; $17362 \div 255$.
10. Using each of the expanded forms of the division algorism shown on pages 38–39, divide 4487 by 35.

Guided Supplementary Reading

1. Following the suggestions of Banks, show how the distributive property can be applied to checking the multiplication of 653×17.
2. Using the "lattice" method described by Buckingham, multiply 387 by 85.
3. What curious way to multiply numbers between 5 and 10 is used by French peasants as reported by Dantzig?
4. What implications for teaching are suggested by Dawson and Ruddell as a result of their experiment with introductory teaching of division?
5. What kinds of activities does Deans recommend should precede the developmental work in multiplication and division?
6. What definition of middle-grade arithmetic does Dickey give?
7. What numbers as well as nine can be used in checking by the "casting out" procedure?
8. What kind of experiences does Eads recommend in teaching division to fourth graders?
9. What conclusion did Flournoy reach with regard to the two common methods of estimating the quotient figure?
10. Grossnickle and Brueckner state that the grade placement of a topic is satisfactory if it can be taught to most of the class in such a way that learning will take place under "optimum mental hygienic conditions in the classroom." What do they mean by this statement?
11. What does Gunderson conclude from her study of the thought patterns grade 2 children used in solving multiplication and division problems?
12. How does Hannon relate the distributive law to our common multiplication algorism?
13. What recommendations does Hartung make regarding what to teach children about how to find a trial quotient?
14. What device does Hassell use to shorten the long-division process?
15. How did Jackson use a simple algebra equation to provide review of multiplication facts for slow learners?

16. Following the reasoning of Marks, Purdy, and Kinney, show how the law of distribution is applied in dividing 32,895 by 85.
17. Using the Sieve of Eratosthenes described by Mueller, find the prime numbers between 30 and 40.
18. What values does Sauble attach to the ability to estimate answers?
19. Sawyer points out that the final digits of what table read backwards are the same as the final digits of the multiplication table of three?
20. What generalizations do Spencer and Brydegaard draw about divisions in which the divisor is constant? In which the dividend is constant?
21. What kind of scale does Stern suggest for teaching certain multiplication facts?
22. Substituting blocks for the "star" diagram given by Swain, show the associative relation $(3 \times 4) \times 2 = 3 \times (4 \times 2)$.
23. What simple diagnostic procedure does Thorpe suggest be used when pupils are having difficulty with division?
24. What principal advantage does Yearout claim for having elementary school teachers know some fundamental mathematical principles?

Suggested Supplementary References

1. BANKS, J. HOUSTON, *Learning and Teaching Arithmetic,* Chapter 5. Boston: Allyn and Bacon, Inc., 1959.
2. BUCKINGHAM, BURDETTE R., *Elementary Arithmetic,* Chapter 7. Boston: Ginn and Co., 1953.
3. DANTZIG, TOBIAS, *Number, the Language of Science,* Chapter 1. New York: The Macmillan Co., 1954.
4. DAWSON, D. T., AND A. K. RUDDELL, "Experimental Approach to the Division Idea," *Arithmetic Teacher,* Vol. 2, pp. 6–9, February, 1955.
5. DEANS, E., "Teaching Multiplication and Division Facts," *Childhood Education,* Vol. 32, pp. 326–333, March, 1956.
6. DICKEY, JOHN W., "Comments on Middlegrade Arithmetic," *Arithmetic Teacher,* Vol. 5, pp. 37–38, February, 1958.
7. DRISCOLL, LUCY E., "Casting Out Nines and Other Numbers," *Arithmetic Teacher,* Vol. 5, pp. 82–83, March, 1958.
8. EADS, LAURA K., "Teaching Mathematics in Grade Four," *Grade Teacher,* Vol. 76, p. 22, February, 1959.
9. FLOURNOY, FRANCES, "Children's Success with Two Methods of Estimating the Quotient Figure," *Arithmetic Teacher,* Vol. 6, pp. 100–104, March, 1959.

10. GROSSNICKLE, FOSTER E., AND LEO J. BRUECKNER, *Discovering Meanings in Arithmetic,* Chapter 8. Philadelphia: The John C. Winston Co., 1959.

11. GUNDERSON, A. G., "Thought Patterns of Young Children in Learning Multiplication and Division," *Elementary School Journal,* Vol. 55, pp. 453–461, April, 1955.

12. HANNON, HERBERT, "A New Look at the Basic Principles of Multiplication with Whole Numbers," *Arithmetic Teacher,* Vol. 7, pp. 357–361, November 1960.

13. HARTUNG, M. L., "Estimating the Quotient in Division; a Critical Analysis of Research," *Arithmetic Teacher,* Vol. 4, pp. 100–111, April, 1957.

14. HASSELL, RUBY S., "A Short Method of Long Division," *Arithmetic Teacher,* Vol. 5, pp. 100–101, March, 1958.

15. JACKSON, H. C., "Techniques for Drill in Arithmetic Fundamentals," *Mathematics Teacher,* Vol. 49, pp. 47–48, January, 1956.

16. MARKS, JOHN L., C. RICHARD PURDY, AND LUCIEN B. KINNEY, *Teaching Arithmetic for Understanding,* Chapter 7. New York: McGraw-Hill Book Co., Inc., 1958.

17. MUELLER, FRANCIS J., *Arithmetic, Its Structure and Concepts,* Chapter 3. Englewood Cliffs, N.J.: Prentice-Hall, Inc., 1956.

18. SAUBLE, IRENE, "Development of Ability to Estimate and to Compute Mentally," *Arithmetic Teacher,* Vol. 2, pp. 33–39, April, 1955.

19. SAWYER, W. W., *Prelude to Mathematics,* Chapter 2. Baltimore: Penguin Books, 1955.

20. SPENCER, PETER L., AND MARGUERITE BRYDEGAARD, *Building Mathematical Concepts in the Elementary School,* Chapter 5. New York: Henry Holt and Co., 1952.

21. STERN, CATHERINE, "New Experiments with Multiplication," *Arithmetic Teacher,* Vol. 7, pp. 381–388, December, 1960.

22. SWAIN, ROBERT L., *Understanding Arithmetic,* Chapter 3. New York: Rinehart and Co., Inc., 1957.

23. THORPE, CLEATA B., *Teaching Elementary Arithmetic,* Chapter 14. New York: Harper & Brothers, 1962.

24. YEAROUT, PAUL, "Divisibility and Prime Numbers," *Arithmetic Teacher,* Vol. 5, pp. 79–81, March, 1958.

CHAPTER 9

Extending Concepts of Fractions

In Chapter 6 it was noted that numbers may be classified into systems and that the elements of one of these systems were called *rational* numbers. Before discussing the procedure for extending concepts of fractions held by children, we shall review some of the concepts regarding the nature of rational numbers which provide a useful mathematical background for a teacher. Although some differences exist among authorities regarding the manner in which fractions are defined,[1] the viewpoint presented here is one which reflects an approach widely noted in contemporary mathematics.[2]

[1] Francis J. Mueller, "On the Fraction as a Numeral," *Arithmetic Teacher,* 8:234–238, May, 1961.

[2] Lee E. Boyer, Charles Brumfiel, and William Higgins, "Definitions in Arithmetic," *Instruction in Arithmetic,* 25th Yearbook of the National Council of Teachers of Mathematics (Washington: National Council of Teachers of Mathematics, 1960), 268–269; Robert S. Fouch and Eugene D. Nichols, "Language and Symbolism in Mathematics," *The Growth of Mathematical Ideas,* 24th Yearbook of the National Council of Teachers of Mathematics (Washington: National Council of Teachers of Mathematics, 1959), p. 334; Irving Adler, *The New Mathematics* (New York: John Day Company, 1958), pp. 75–78.

A Rational Number as a Number Which Is Associated with a Set of Equivalent Fractions

A common fraction may be considered to be an ordered pair of integers, the numerals for which are expressed in the form "a/b" where $b \neq 0$, e.g., $3/4$, $5/6$, $-2/3$, $0/5$. By definition, the fractions a/b and c/d are said to be *equivalent* if, and only if, $ad = bc$; e.g., 3/4 is considered to be equivalent to 6/8 because $3 \times 8 = 4 \times 6$.

Each set of equivalent fractions is associated with a rational number, and this rational number may be represented by any one of the fractions from the particular set to which it belongs. For instance, the rational number associated with the set of fractions $1/2$, $2/4$, $3/6$, . . . could be represented by $1/2$, or $2/4$, or $3/6$, and so on.

The number line in Figure 9.1 provides an illustration of how

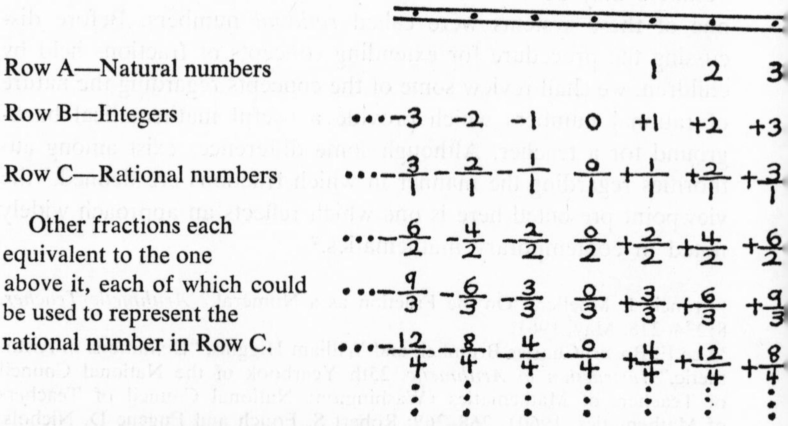

Figure 9.1 Illustrating how certain natural numbers, integers, and rational numbers may be represented by the same point on the number line.

some of these numbers could be represented graphically. The numerals of fractions shown in Row C are some of those which may be associated with points on the number line. These points could be associated also with the integers in Row B and with the natural numbers in Row A.

In Figure 9.2, the point *A* is associated with the set of fractions

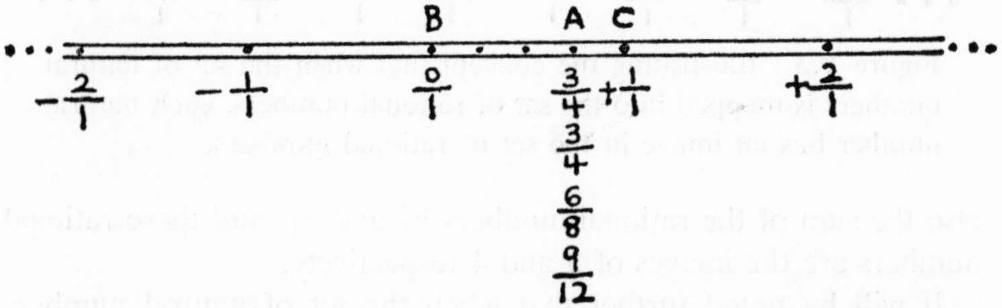

Figure 9.2 Illustrating how a point on a number line may be associated with a rational number which represents a set of equivalent fractions.

$\frac{3}{4}$, $\frac{6}{8}$, $\frac{9}{12}$, . . . and this set may be represented by the rational number $\frac{3}{4}$ or by any other fraction from the same set. To locate the point representing $\frac{3}{4}$ on the line, we might think of the unit distance, *BC*, being divided into four equal parts and the point being located to the right of the origin at a distance equal to the length of three of these parts.

The concept of *isomorphism* is useful at this stage of the discussion to describe an important relationship between the system of rational numbers and either the system of natural numbers or the system of integers.

As noted in Chapter 6, when set *A* is mapped into set *B*, an element of set *B* is said to be the *image* of the element in set *A* with which it is matched. For instance, when the set of natural numbers is mapped into the set of rational numbers, as illustrated in Figure 9.3, the rational number $\frac{1}{1}$ is the image of the natural number 1, the rational number $\frac{2}{1}$ is the image of the natural number 2, the rational number $\frac{3}{1}$ is the image of the natural number 3, and so on. It will be noted that the *image* of the sum of any two natural numbers is the sum of the *images* of these same numbers. For instance, the sum of 3 and 4 is the natural number 7, and the *image* of this sum in the set of rational numbers is $\frac{7}{1}$. But $\frac{7}{1}$ is

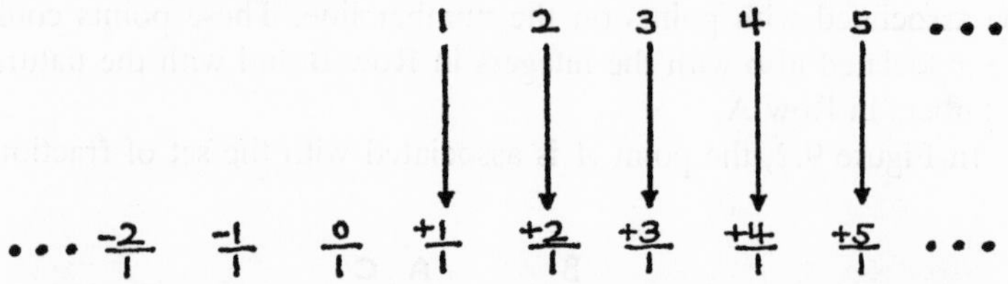

Figure 9.3 Illustrating the concept that when the set of natural numbers is mapped into the set of rational numbers, each natural number has an image in the set of rational numbers.

also the sum of the rational numbers $3/1$ and $4/1$, and these rational numbers are the images of 3 and 4 respectively.

It will be noted further that when the set of natural numbers is mapped into the set of rational numbers the product of the *images* of the natural numbers is the same as the *image* of their product; e.g., $12/1$ is the image of the product of the natural numbers 3 and 4, and $12/1$ is also the product of $3/1$ and $4/1$, which are the images of the natural numbers 3 and 4.

A system of numbers may be said to be isomorphic to part of another system of numbers when the sum of the images of two numbers is the image of their sum, and the product of their images is the image of their product. Thus it will be seen that the set of natural numbers is isomorphic to the set of positive integers, and also to the set of positive rational numbers represented by fractions in which the second component in each ordered pair is the number 1, e.g., $1/1, 2/1, 3/1, \ldots$, as illustrated in Figure 9.3.

It will be noted also that by following a similar procedure we could illustrate how the set of integers is isomorphic to the subset of rational numbers, both positive and negative, which may be represented by fractions in which the second component of each ordered pair is the number one, e.g., $\ldots -3/1, -2/1, -1/1, 0/1, +1/1, +2/1, +3/1 \ldots$

Two number systems which are isomorphic to each other are really models of the same mathematical system and, since they possess the same structure as such a system, must conform to the same principles. Consequently we may "pass" from one system to the other in the sense that a computation in one system will result in a number which is the image of the number obtained by a similar computation with numbers in the other system, e.g., $3 \times 4 + 2 = 14$, and $\frac{3}{1} \times \frac{4}{1} + \frac{2}{1} = \frac{14}{1}$.

Addition and Multiplication of Rational Numbers

The addition and multiplication of rational numbers are *defined* in such a way that results of these operations conform to the results obtained by the same operations on the numbers in the systems of natural numbers and integers with which they are isomorphic.

The operation of addition on rational numbers is defined by the expression $a/b + c/d = \frac{ad + cb}{bd}$, e.g., $\frac{3}{4} + \frac{5}{6} = \frac{18 + 20}{24}$, and multiplication is defined by the expression $a/b \times c/d = \frac{ac}{bd}$, e.g., $\frac{3}{4} \times \frac{5}{6} = \frac{15}{24}$.

As an example of how these definitions determine that the rational numbers will "behave" like the natural numbers, note that the product of $\frac{3}{1} \times \frac{4}{1}$ would thus be the *image* of the product of 3×4, e.g., $\frac{12}{1}$, and the sum of $\frac{3}{1} + \frac{4}{1}$ would be the image of the sum of 3 and 4, e.g., $\frac{7}{1}$.

It is important for the teacher to note that the meanings of the operations of addition and multiplication on rational numbers are matters of definition, and that while he may use concrete materials to illustrate the meanings of these operations, such instances are illustrations only and must not be considered as proofs of what is meant by these operations. The meaning of these operations lies within the definition itself and is not dependent upon examples taken from the physical world.

It is recognized that the teacher should use an inductive approach to enable pupils to extend gradually their concepts of fractions. Through the use of concrete materials in many situations which illustrate how fractions are employed, the pupils form generalizations from their experiences. The teaching procedures suggested in the following pages are based upon such an approach. It is important, however, for the teacher to have a clear idea of the mathematical principles implicit in the experiences pupils have with fractions so that the language he uses will be sufficiently precise to enable the pupils to develop concepts of fractions compatible with those which he wishes them to develop as they become more mature.

Introducing Fractions to Children

As noted in Chapter 5, the meaning of fractions is introduced to children in the first and second grades by using the fractions one-half, one-fourth, and one-third in various measurement situations. The pupils observe how these fractions are used in connection with measuring time when we speak of a half hour or a quarter hour, or in connection with weighing objects when we speak of a half pound or quarter pound of material while making purchases in a market. They may examine cartons and containers containing a half pint of cream or a half gallon of ice cream. They may measure lengths of objects to one-half an inch, and use simple fractions in various other ways during their daily experiences.

The use of sectors of circles of various sizes to develop the meaning of fractions is particularly helpful as it enables pupils to perceive how the size of a fraction of an object depends upon the size of the object; that is, they observe that the size of the fractional part depends upon the unit to which the fraction refers. It is less difficult to keep in mind the unit to which any particular fraction refers when manipulative materials are used because then the child can perceive the relationship between sectors of the circle and the complete circle which is the unit. It would be much more difficult for him if he were required to visualize these relationships while using written or verbal symbols for the fractions but without seeing the objects to which the fractions refer.

Table 9.1 shows a sequence through which the concepts of

Table 9.1

A SEQUENCE FOR DEVELOPING AND EXTENDING FRACTION CONCEPTS

Grade placement	Important Steps in Learning to Use Fractions
Kindergarten	Recognition of the words "one-half," "one-fourth," and "one-third" in familiar contexts.

Grade placement	Important Steps in Learning to Use Fractions
I, II	Using $\frac{1}{2}$, $\frac{1}{3}$, and $\frac{1}{4}$ in connection with measures of time, weight, and capacity and in familiar contexts. Finding one-half of small groups by manipulating objects.
III	Using manipulative materials such as sectors of circles to recognize $\frac{1}{2}$, $\frac{1}{3}$, $\frac{1}{4}$, $\frac{1}{6}$, and $\frac{1}{8}$ of whole objects. Learning the meaning of $\frac{1}{2}$, $\frac{1}{3}$, and $\frac{1}{4}$ of small groups and how to find a fraction of a group by division.
IV	Using smaller unit fractions such as $\frac{1}{10}$ and $\frac{1}{12}$. Using fractions other than unit fractions, and comparing the sizes of sectors of circles. Learning the meaning of fractions with mixed numerals. Understanding and using fractions of an inch. Addition and subtraction of like fractions.
V	Learning how to find fractions equivalent to other fractions. Using a common denominator. Addition and subtraction of unlike fractions. Using "improper" fractions and fractions with mixed numerals. Learning the relationship of common fractions to decimal fractions. Learning the meaning of ratio.
VI	Learning how to multiply and divide numbers involving fractions. Learning to use fractions as ratios. Learning to solve three common types of fraction problems. Learning to find fraction and decimal fraction equivalents.
VII, VIII	Using fractions in connection with problems involving per cent situations and with ratio concepts.

fractions may be extended logically. The grade levels indicated are those at which the concepts are introduced in many of the series of textbooks used today, and should be considered to be approximations only, as some children are psychologically capable of understanding the fraction concepts more easily than others.

Extending Concepts of Unit Fractions

Unit fractions are those having a numerator "1" in the numeral, such as $\frac{1}{2}$, $\frac{1}{5}$, and $\frac{1}{8}$. Once the child understands that one of two equal parts of a whole is called "one-half," that one of three equal parts is called "one-third," and that one of four equal parts is called "one-fourth," he may be shown sectors of circles and diagrams illustrating other unit fractions such as $\frac{1}{6}$ or $\frac{1}{8}$. Through questions, the pupils may be led to recognize and write the numerals for these fractions. The teacher should use a variety of material to illustrate various instances of how these fractions are used, and encourage the child to find applications of fractions in his environment. Charts such as those shown in Figure 9.4 may be used to illustrate concepts of fractions and to help the child visualize them.

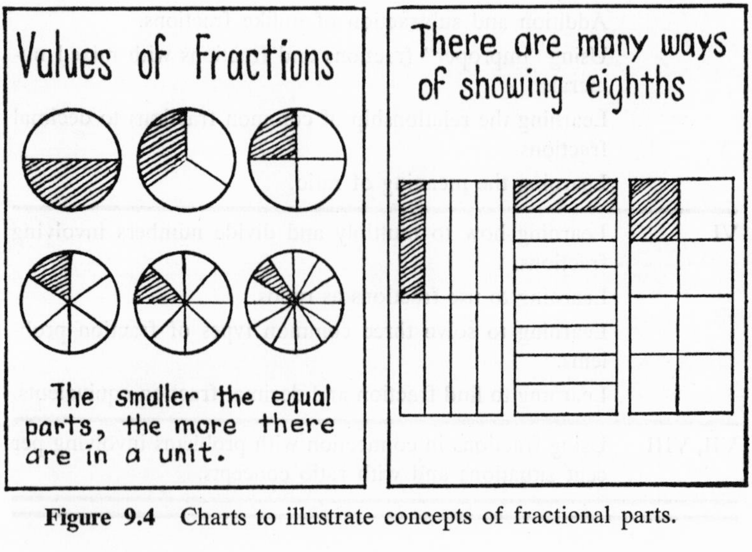

Figure 9.4 Charts to illustrate concepts of fractional parts.

Fractions of groups. When the child is ready, he may be led to realize that the new unit fractions which he has learned, such as $\frac{1}{6}$, $\frac{1}{8}$, or $\frac{1}{12}$, may also be applied to groups as well as to whole objects. Through the use of discs or other counters he may perceive that a group, such as twelve, may be made up of a number of smaller equal groups, and that each of these smaller groups may then be considered to be a fractional part of the larger group. This concept of a fractional part of a group is closely connected with the concept of partition in division. In a partition situation in division, when we think of a group being divided into a number of equal parts, each of these parts would be a fractional part of the whole group, and this could be expressed in writing by using a numeral of a unit fraction. Charts such as those shown in Figure 9.5 would help illustrate this concept.

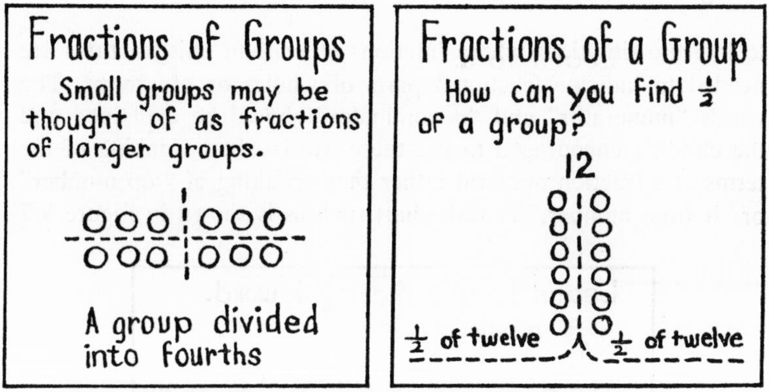

Figure 9.5 Charts to illustrate fractional parts of groups.

Fractions with Numerators Greater than One

Through using sectors of circles and other manipulative materials, the pupil may understand quite readily the meaning of fractions such as "three-fourths," "two-thirds," and other fractions which are not unit fractions. Diagrams, charts, and arrangements of materials such as are shown in Figure 9.6 could be used to illustrate these concepts.

The pupils should have experience in writing fraction numerals

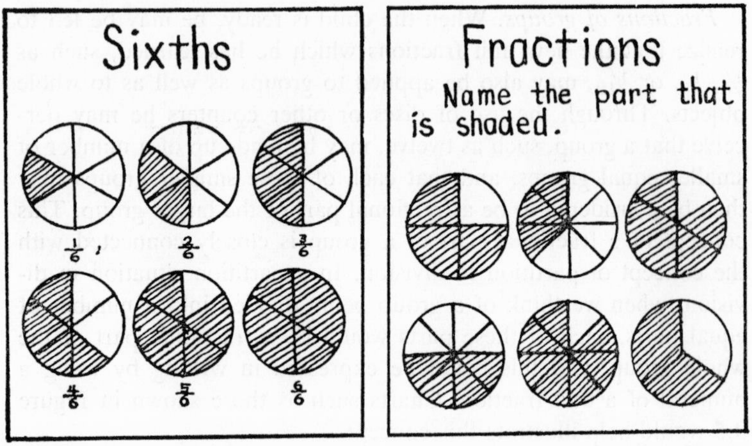

Figure 9.6 Charts used to develop concepts of fractional parts.

to indicate situations where fractions other than unit fractions are needed to indicate fractional parts of wholes or of groups. The words "numerator" and "denominator" should be explained and the children encouraged to use these words when speaking of the terms of a fraction numeral rather than speaking of "top number" or "bottom number." A wall chart such as is shown in Figure 9.7

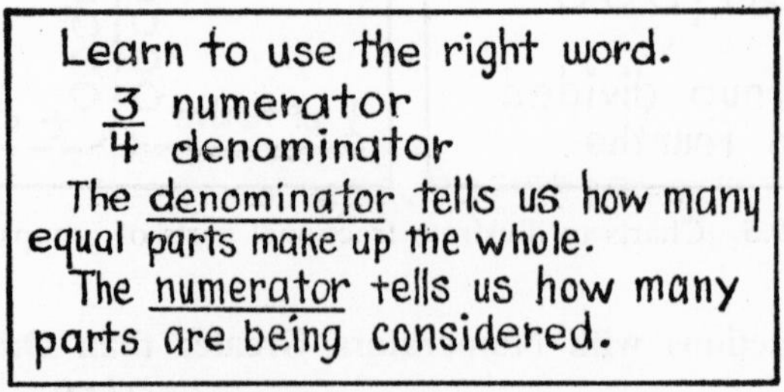

Learn to use the right word.
3 numerator
4 denominator
The denominator tells us how many equal parts make up the whole.
The numerator tells us how many parts are being considered.

Figure 9.7 A chart used to develop vocabulary.

will help remind children to use the proper words while they are becoming familiar with the terms.

The meaning of "proper fractions," "improper fractions," and "mixed numerals" should be clarified by using manipulative materials, diagrams, and charts, such as are shown in Figure 9.8.

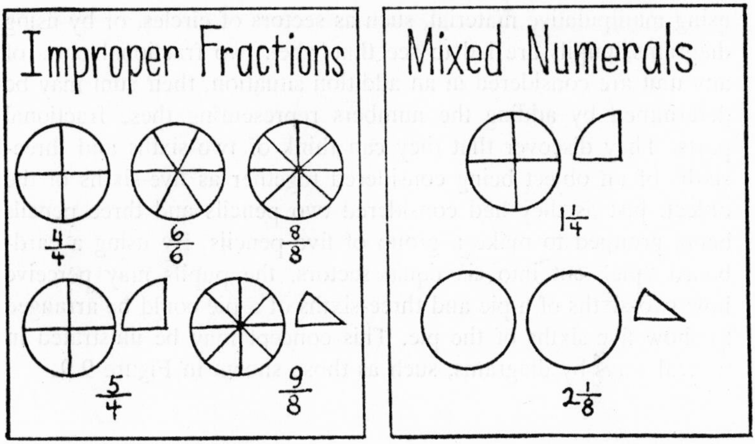

Figure 9.8 Charts used to clarify the meaning of the terms "improper fraction" and "mixed numeral."

Experience with manipulative materials while the pupil is solving various problems involving the use of fractions is very helpful at this stage of learning. The written symbols for fractions have little meaning for pupils until they can associate them with parts of a group or with parts of wholes. The abundant experience with manipulative materials, diagrams, and charts will make this visualization of fraction situations much easier. Pupils should have considerable practice in using symbols to express what they see represented with materials, or with diagrams, and they should also have experience in showing with materials or diagrams what is expressed in written symbols, until the written symbols for a fraction have definite and clear meanings for the pupils.

Addition and Subtraction of "Like" Fractions

The term "like fractions" has been used traditionally to refer to two or more fractions which have numerals with the same denominators, e.g., $\frac{1}{4}$, $\frac{3}{4}$, $\frac{7}{4}$.

The general procedure for illustrating the meaning of adding and subtracting like fractions resembles that used for illustrating the meaning of the addition and subtraction of whole numbers. By using manipulative material, such as sectors of circles, or by using diagrams, pupils are led to see that when two fractional parts of any unit are considered in an addition situation, their sum may be determined by adding the numbers representing these fractional parts. They discover that they can think of two-sixths and three-sixths of an object being considered together as five-sixths of the object, just as they had considered two pencils and three pencils being grouped to make a group of five pencils. By using a cardboard "pie" cut into six equal sectors, the pupils may perceive how two-sixths of a pie and three-sixths of a pie could be arranged to show five-sixths of the pie. This concept may be illustrated in several ways by diagrams, such as those shown in Figure 9.9.

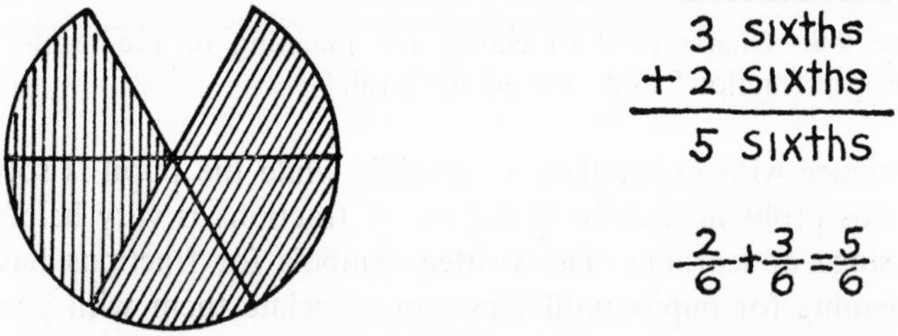

Figure 9.9 Combined use of sectors of cardboard circles and the chalkboard to illustrate the addition of like fractions.

As the pupils are being introduced to the meaning of the addition and subtraction situations through the use of manipulative materials, they should be shown how to write the numerical expressions in both vertical and horizontal form, as shown in Figure 9.9.

The subtraction of like fractions may be illustrated quite easily at the same time by showing five-sixths of the cardboard pie and then removing two-sixths of the pie to show that three-sixths of a pie would remain.

The similarity between the meaning of subtraction of fractions and the subtraction of whole numbers should be brought out. The use of symbols for expressing the subtraction of fractions is similar to their use for expressing the subtraction of whole numbers, as shown in Figure 9.10.

$$\frac{5}{6} \quad - \quad \frac{2}{6} \quad = \quad \frac{3}{6}$$

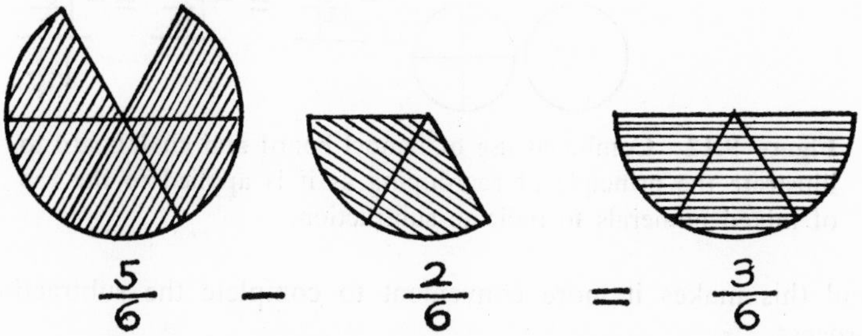

Figure 9.10 Combined use of sectors of cardboard circles and the chalkboard to illustrate the subtraction of like fractions.

Mixed numerals involving like fractions. The term "mixed number" has been used traditionally by teachers to refer to a number of which the numeral is made up of the numeral of an integer along with the numeral for a fraction, e.g., $3\frac{4}{5}$, $2\frac{1}{5}$. We shall use the term "mixed numeral" to refer to this type of compound numeral. In adding two numbers represented by mixed numerals, the pupils should understand that the principle of regrouping is employed so that the sum may be expressed in a convenient form. In Figure 9.11, the mixed numeral $3\frac{6}{4}$ has the same value as $4\frac{2}{4}$ or $4\frac{1}{2}$, but

$$2\frac{3}{4} \quad + \quad 1\frac{3}{4} \quad = \quad 3\frac{6}{4} \quad = \quad 4\frac{2}{4} \quad = \quad 4\frac{1}{2}$$

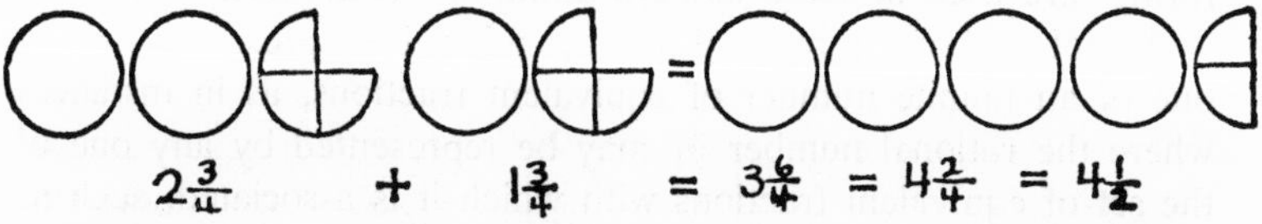

Figure 9.11 Combined use of flannel board and chalkboard to illustrate the principle of regrouping as it is applied to the use of mixed numerals to indicate addition.

is expressed as a fraction in its simplest form as a matter of convenience and convention.

Similarly, when mixed numerals are used in a subtraction situation, a unit may be changed to an improper fraction without changing the value of the mixed numeral, as shown in Figure 9.12,

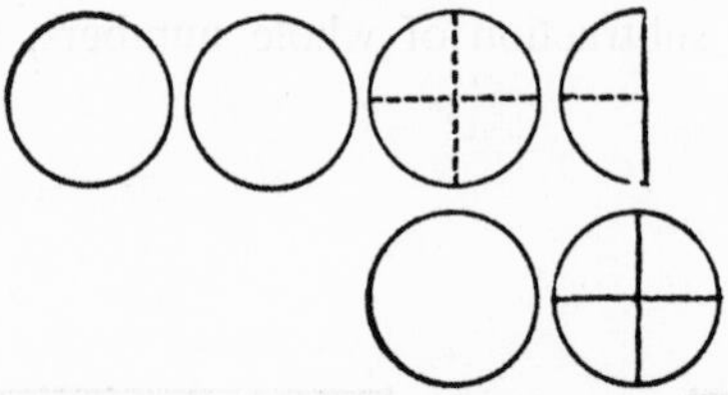

$$3\tfrac{1}{2} = 3\tfrac{2}{4} = 2\tfrac{6}{4}$$
$$\underline{-1\tfrac{3}{4}} = \underline{-1\tfrac{3}{4}} = \underline{-1\tfrac{3}{4}}$$
$$1\tfrac{3}{4}$$

Figure 9.12 Combined use of flannel board and chalkboard to illustrate the principle of regrouping as it is applied to the use of mixed numerals to indicate subtraction.

and this makes it more convenient to complete the subtraction process.

The pupils should be given ample practice in solving many verbal problems involving the use of mixed numerals in addition and subtraction situations in order to enable them to gain facility in using this type of algorism.

Changing to Other Terms

The *reduction of fractions* is a term which has been used traditionally in the elementary school to refer to a situation where one equivalent fraction has been selected to replace another in representing a rational number. The more meaningful expressions, "changing to lower (or higher) terms" or "expressing in simplest form," are used in some modern children's textbooks.

As noted above, a rational number might be represented by any one of an infinite number of equivalent fractions, as in instances where the rational number $3/4$ may be represented by any one of the set of equivalent fractions with which it is associated, such as $3/4$, $6/8$, $9/12$, and so on. A computational procedure for finding a fraction equivalent to a second fraction is based on the principle that we do not change the value of a number when we multiply it by one. The identity element for the operation of multiplication on rational numbers is the rational number $1/1$, which might also be represented by any fraction from the set $2/2$, $3/3$, $4/4$, ... While applying the principle that $a \times 1/1 = a$, we also remember that the rational number $1/1$ could be represented by any fraction in the set $1/1$, $2/2$, $3/3$, . . . , and we conclude that $a \times 2/2 = a$, $a \times 3/3 =$

a, $a \times \frac{4}{4} = a$, and so on; e.g., $\frac{3}{4} \times \frac{2}{2} = \frac{3}{4}$, $\frac{3}{4} \times \frac{3}{3} = \frac{3}{4}$, $\frac{3}{4} \times \frac{4}{4} = \frac{3}{4}$.

Thus the computational procedure for finding a fraction equivalent to $\frac{3}{4}$ consists of multiplying the numbers represented by the numerator and denominator of $\frac{3}{4}$ by the particular number which is needed to produce the given term in the fraction we are seeking, e.g., $\frac{3}{4} = ?/16$ is solved as $\frac{3}{4} \times \frac{4}{4} = \frac{12}{16}$. By this procedure we have identified a particular member in a set of equivalent fractions, any one of which could have been used to represent the rational number $\frac{3}{4}$. The rational number itself has not been changed by this procedure, but another equivalent fraction to represent it has been determined.

The mathematical principles basic to the procedure for reducing or changing fraction numerals are important, and the rationale for the computational procedure should be emphasized as important in its own right and not thought of as being merely a readiness activity to prepare children for the addition and subtraction of unlike fractions. While the average achiever in the fifth grade may not be expected to grasp all the implications involved in the reduction of fractions when he is first introduced to the process, the teacher should have a clear idea of the principles implicit in the process so that the language he uses will be precise and the concepts which he assists the pupils to develop will be compatible with those which he hopes they will develop later.

Addition and Subtraction of Unlike Fractions

When two or more fractions have different denominators in their numerals they are said to be *unlike* fractions, e.g., $\frac{2}{4}$ and $\frac{2}{6}$, $\frac{1}{2}$ and $\frac{2}{3}$.

Before teaching the procedure for adding or subtracting unlike fractions, the teacher should guide the pupils to an understanding of what is meant by equivalent fractions and then ensure that they understand the computational procedure for determining fractions which are equivalent to a given fraction.

Sectors of circles or diagrams may be used to illustrate how a fractional part, such as $\frac{1}{2}$, may be represented by other fractions which are equivalent to $\frac{1}{2}$, such as $\frac{2}{4}$, $\frac{3}{6}$, $\frac{4}{8}$, and so on. For instance, sectors of circles may be used on the flannel board, as shown in Figure 9.13, to show how two-fourths, or three-sixths,

Figure 9.13 Use of a flannel board to illustrate the concept that $\frac{1}{2}$, $\frac{2}{4}$, $\frac{3}{6}$, and $\frac{4}{8}$ are equivalent fractions.

of a unit circle will cover the sector which is one-half of the unit circle. A diagram or a chart such as is shown in Figure 9.14 will reinforce this concept.

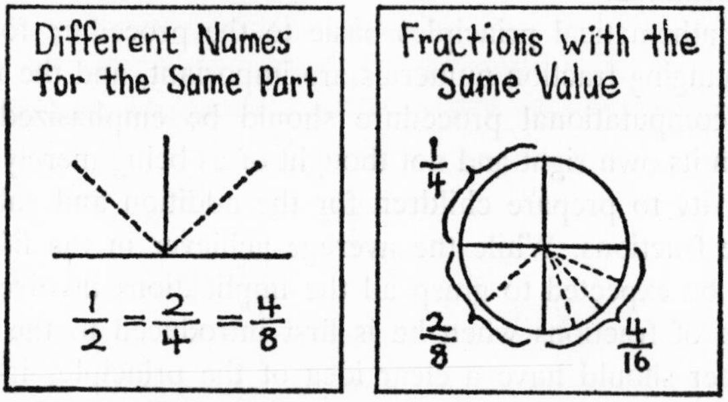

Figure 9.14 Charts to illustrate the concept that a fraction is equivalent to other fractions.

A measuring cup which has been half filled with sand could also be shown to be $\frac{2}{4}$ filled or $\frac{4}{8}$ filled. This helps the pupils perceive that, although the name of the fraction has been changed, its value remains the same, as illustrated in Figure 9.15.

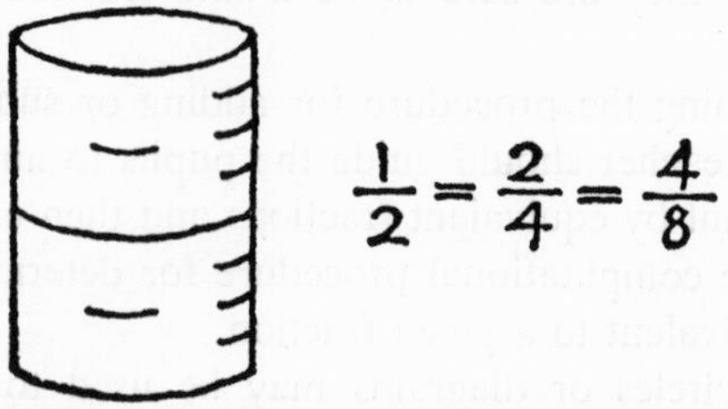

Figure 9.15 Using sand in a measuring cup to illustrate the concept of fractions having the same value.

A problem such as the following could be used to illustrate the need for employing equivalent fractions in a particular instance. "John's mother had one-half of a pie on one plate and one-third of a pie on another plate of the same size. If she put it all on one plate, how much pie would there be altogether?"

Sectors of circles could then be arranged on the flannel board to show how sectors representing ½ and ⅓ could be put together, but that to find a name for the fraction represented by the total amount it would be necessary to express each of the fractions, ½ and ⅓, in such a way that their denominators would be the same. Various ways of expressing ½ and ⅓ with equivalent fractions should be drawn from the class, until the pupils discover that by selecting fractions equivalent respectively to ½ and ⅓ which have the same denominators, they could solve the problem. The pupils should note that there are various ways of expressing the computation in writing, as in Figure 9.16, and that the selec-

$$\begin{array}{ccccccccc}
\frac{1}{2} & = & \frac{3}{6} & = & \frac{6}{12} & = & \frac{9}{18} & = & \frac{18}{36} \\
+\frac{1}{3} & = & +\frac{2}{6} & = & +\frac{4}{12} & = & +\frac{6}{18} & = & +\frac{12}{36} \\
\hline
 & & \frac{5}{6} & = & \frac{10}{12} & = & \frac{15}{18} & = & \frac{30}{36}
\end{array}$$

Figure 9.16 Chalkboard arrangement to illustrate the use of equivalent fractions in computations involving unlike fractions.

tion of the lowest of these common denominators is a matter of convention and convenience.

The subtraction of unlike fractions could be illustrated in a similar manner. A suitable problem would be, "If Joyce's mother had half a pie on a plate and from this she gave Joyce one-sixth of the whole pie, how much would be left?"

Sectors of circles could be used to illustrate the half of a pie, and then the pupils led to understand that by thinking of the one-half pie as three-sixths, they could solve the problem. The algorism expressing the required subtraction process should then be written by the pupils, as in Figure 9.17.

$$\begin{array}{rcl} \frac{1}{2} & = & \frac{3}{6} \\ -\frac{1}{6} & = & \frac{1}{6} \\ \hline & & \frac{2}{6} \text{ or } \frac{1}{3} \end{array}$$

Figure 9.17 An algorism used in subtraction involving fractions with different denominators.

The pupils should solve many verbal problems involving the addition and subtraction of unlike fractions. Proper fractions, improper fractions, and mixed numerals should be used until the pupils have facility in using the necessary written symbols with understanding. Figure 9.18 shows arrangements of sectors of

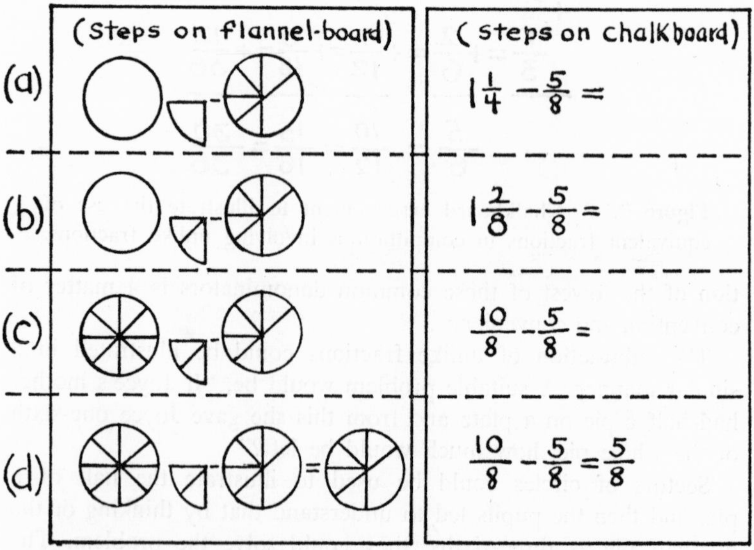

Figure 9.18 Arrangements on flannel board to illustrate steps in subtraction.

circles on a flannel board to illustrate a subtraction process in various steps.

Multiplication of Fractions

Traditionally, the multiplication of fractions has been introduced to elementary school children by showing them how to "multiply" a fraction by a whole number, e.g., $3 \times \frac{3}{4}$. Mathematically, we think of multiplication as a binary operation on two numbers in the same set which results in a unique number in the same set, and consequently such a definition does not enable us to multiply a number from the set of rational numbers by a number from the set of whole numbers.

By thinking of the rational number which is the *image* of the whole number, and writing $\frac{3}{1} \times \frac{3}{4}$ instead of $3 \times \frac{3}{4}$, we are indicating the multiplication of a rational number by a rational number and this is permitted by a definition of multiplication which is in terms of an operation on members of the same set.

A large proportion of the verbal problems with which children deal involve whole numbers in multiplication and division situations, but the pupils should be encouraged, at first, to write these whole numbers as if they were rational numbers during any computational procedure involving their multiplication or division with fractions; e.g., write 3 as $\frac{3}{1}$, 5 as $\frac{5}{1}$, and so on. Later, when pupils gain skill in computation, they may develop shortcuts by omitting numerals which do not affect the results of the computations.

The child's understanding of the meaning of the multiplication of whole numbers is used to enable him to understand the multiplication of fractions. He has learned to think of multiplication as a process in which he uses the basic facts of multiplication to find a number which is equal to the sum of several equal numbers. He knows that the answer could also be found by using the addition facts and the addition process rather than multiplication, although this would be a slower and more tedious procedure.

The teacher should review with the class this meaning of the multiplication of whole numbers, and then introduce the multiplication of fractions to the class by using some problem within the child's social experience, such as "John's father had three packages of seeds. If each package weighed ¾ pound, how many pounds of seeds were there altogether?"

This problem could be illustrated by using diagrams on the chalkboard and also by using sectors of circles on the flannel board, as shown in Figure 9.19.

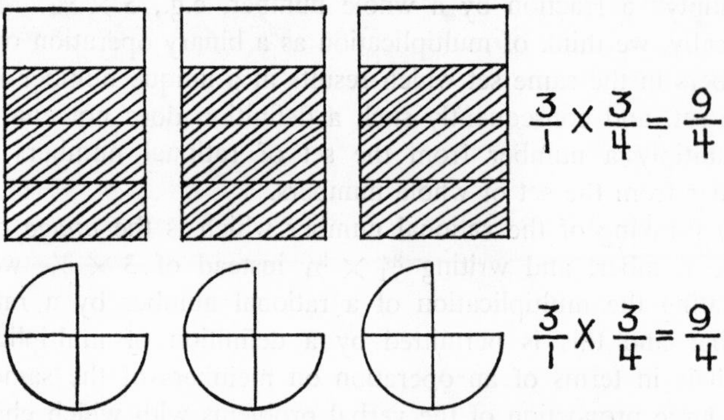

Figure 9.19 Chalkboard and flannel board arrangements to introduce situations involving the multiplication of fractions.

The teacher should lead the pupils to understand that the problem could be solved either by multiplication or by addition, and help them to recall that multiplication provides a quicker way of solving certain problems than does addition. In this instance, the children should think of the solution, 3 fourths plus 3 fourths plus 3 fourths, as a way of obtaining the answer by addition. They should note that they could also use their knowledge of the multiplication fact $3 \times 3 = 9$ and think, "Three times three is nine, so three times three-fourths should be nine-fourths." The teacher then should write the expression $3/1 \times 3/4 = 9/4$ on the chalkboard, point out to the children that the number 3 has been expressed in this instance by the numeral "$3/1$," and then give an explanation such as "Here we are expressing the number three as the fraction $3/1$, so that we may follow the rule for multiplying fractions." Incidentally, the teacher will find that the pupils discover the rule for multiplying fractions much more readily in situations where a fraction numeral is used in place of the numeral for a whole number.

By solving many similar problems, using small numbers and illustrating each situation with sectors of circles and diagrams, pupils may soon be led to "discover" the rule for multiplying fractions. As noted on page 233, the teacher should be aware of the fact that the meaning of the multiplication of fractions lies within the definition itself and not in instances drawn from the physical world. The procedure suggested above makes use of instances drawn from the pupils' experiences to help them feel that the rule for multiplying fractions is "reasonable," but these instances drawn from the physical world should not be thought of as *proofs*.

In the traditional elementary school program, the "multiplication" of a fraction by a whole number has been followed by the "multiplication" of a whole number by a fraction. As pointed out above, when multiplication is defined in terms of a binary operation on two numbers within the same set, it does not make provision for the multiplication of a whole number by a rational number. In a situation arising from a verbal problem where the pupil has a need for multiplying a whole number by a fraction, e.g., $3/4 \times 4$, he should be taught to express the whole number as a rational number, e.g., $3/4 \times 4$ expressed as $3/4 \times 4/1$, and then follow the rule for multiplying fractions. The difficulty here for the teacher is not that of teaching the children to use this procedure, but it is one of helping them feel that the results they obtain are "reasonable." They may ask, "How can this really be multiplication when the product is *less* than the multiplicand?"

The pupils in grade 3 are introduced to the meaning of multiplication of whole numbers through situations in which they may use either addition or multiplication to find the answer. Because they think of 3×4 as another way of finding the value of $4 + 4 + 4$, they might have in mind some informal definition of multiplication such as "Multiplication is a quick way of doing addition where the several addends are all the same." When the pupils come to the place where they need to "multiply" a whole number by a fraction, e.g., $3/4 \times 4$, they find that this informal definition does not apply because in this instance there are not "several addends" and, furthermore, the answer or product is less than the multiplicand itself, and consequently it could not be obtained by addition as they had formerly thought of this process.

The difficulty here is that a new definition of multiplication is needed which is sufficiently general to include the multiplication of fractions as well as the multiplication of whole numbers. A broader concept of the meaning of multiplication must be grasped by the pupils if the results obtained by multiplying by a fraction are to seem "reasonable" to them.

One informal definition of multiplication which is broad enough to include the case of multiplying by a fraction is as follows. "Multiplication is finding a number which has the same ratio to the multiplicand that the multiplier has to 1." [3]

Helping sixth grade pupils to understand this new and broader definition of multiplication will be very rewarding to the teacher as it will provide an opportunity to give the pupils new and deeper insight into arithmetic. As the pupils have to replace their former concept of multiplication, or at least rearrange it to some extent through a new "discovery," they should be prepared carefully for this new step by having them review their earlier concept of multiplication and then by showing them in what respects the new definition is similar to their former definition and in what respects it is different.

The following steps are suggested as providing a suitable procedure for the teacher to use with an average sixth grade class.

1. Tell the class that as one studies arithmetic it is sometimes necessary to extend and broaden one's earlier definitions in order to include new ideas. Tell them that they have now come to a place where they will learn a broader meaning for multiplication.
2. Review with the pupils their former concept of multiplication as a process of finding a number that has the same value as the sum of several equal groups. For instance, 3×4 is equal in value to $4 + 4 + 4$.
3. By using the algorisms $\begin{array}{r}4\\ \times 3\\ \hline 12\end{array}$, $\begin{array}{r}5\\ \times 3\\ \hline 15\end{array}$, $\begin{array}{r}6\\ \times 3\\ \hline 18\end{array}$, $\begin{array}{r}7\\ \times 3\\ \hline 21\end{array}$, call attention to

[3] Burdette R. Buckingham, *Elementary Arithmetic: Its Meaning and Practice* (Boston: Ginn and Company, 1947), p. 66.

the fact that in each case we are trying to find a number that is as many times the multiplicand as the multiplier, 3, is times 1.

4. By using algorisms with different multipliers, such as $\begin{array}{r}4\\ \times 2\\ \hline 8\end{array}$, $\begin{array}{r}5\\ \times 4\\ \hline 20\end{array}$, $\begin{array}{r}6\\ \times 3\\ \hline 18\end{array}$, $\begin{array}{r}7\\ \times 1\\ \hline 7\end{array}$, help the pupils discover that in each instance we are finding a number which has the same "relationship" to the multiplicand that the multiplier has to 1. Some time should be taken at this point to develop and clarify the manner in which the word "relationship" is being used in this context. For example, in the instance $\begin{array}{r}4\\ \times 2\\ \hline 8\end{array}$, 8 has the same relationship to 4 as 2 has to 1, because just as 2 is twice 1, so 8 is the number that is twice 4. In the instance $\begin{array}{r}5\\ \times 4\\ \hline 20\end{array}$, just as 4 is 4 times 1, so 20 is the number that is 4 times the multiplicand, 5. In the instance $\begin{array}{r}6\\ \times 3\\ \hline 18\end{array}$, just as the multiplier 3 is 3 times 1, so the number 18 is 3 times the multiplicand, 6.

5. Place the algorism $\begin{array}{r}6\\ \times \frac{1}{2}\\ \hline\end{array}$ on the chalkboard, and ask the pupils to see if they can find the number that has the same relationship to 6, the multiplicand, that ½, the multiplier, has to 1. Let the pupils discuss this situation until they discover that because the multiplier is ½ of 1, they will have to find the number that is ½ of 6; in this case it will be the number 3.

6. Have the pupils find the answer in several other instances where the multiplier is ½, ¼, or ⅓. Use instances of this type until the pupils discover that because the name itself of a fraction indicates its relationship to 1, we can determine the product in each case by finding that fraction of the

multiplicand, and the number we find, or the product, thus will have the same relationship to the multiplicand that the multiplier has to one.

The pupils thus are led to feel that it seems reasonable to observe that when a number is multiplied by a proper fraction, the product will be less than the multiplicand.

Experiences to Help Pupils Feel that the Rule for Multiplying Fractions Is "Reasonable"

The rule, which is based upon a *definition* of the multiplication of rational number (page 233), may be stated informally as follows: "To multiply two fractions, multiply the numerators of the fractions to find the numerator of the product, and then multiply the denominators of the fractions to find the denominator of the product."

Using a flannel board. Once a pupil has extended his concept of multiplication to the point where he can think of that process as one of finding a number which has the same relationship to the multiplicand that the multiplier has to one, he is able to understand why finding a fraction *of* a given number will give the same result as multiplying the given number *by* the fraction. Various instances of finding a fraction of a fraction may then be illustrated on the flannel board.

In the example $\frac{1}{2} \times \frac{4}{5}$, he is finding a number which has the same relationship to $\frac{4}{5}$ that $\frac{1}{2}$ has to 1. As the relationship of $\frac{1}{2}$ to 1 is itself $\frac{1}{2}$, he needs to find $\frac{1}{2}$ of $\frac{4}{5}$. It should be noted that there are two different ways of illustrating this procedure and that either of these ways would make it seem reasonable that $\frac{1}{2}$ of $\frac{4}{5} = \frac{2}{5}$.

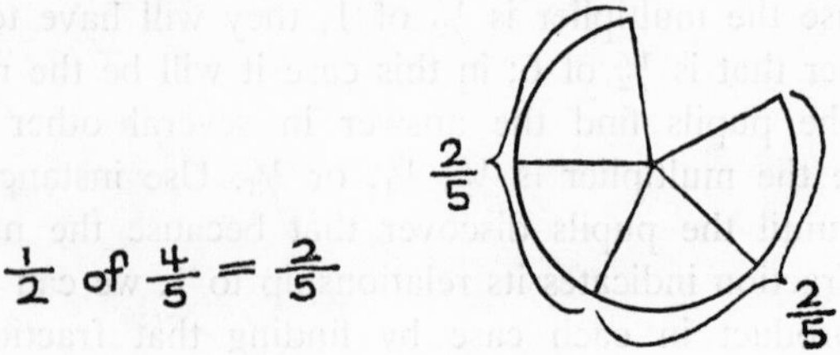

In this instance we have taken ½ of the numerator, which is 4, to find the numerator of the product.

$$\frac{1}{2} \text{ of } \frac{4}{5} = \frac{4}{10} = \frac{2}{5}$$

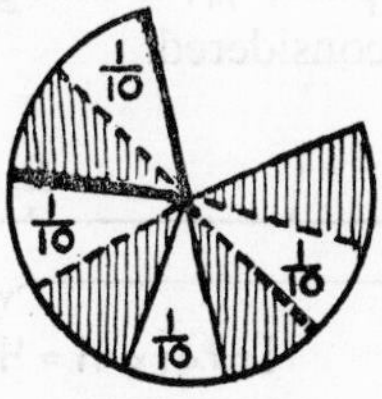

In this instance, each of the fifths has been replaced by two-tenths (two sectors each $\frac{1}{10}$), and one of these tenths taken from each fifth to make up the new fraction.

Using a number line. A number line, shown in Figure 9.20, may be used to illustrate a multiplication situation. Here 3×4

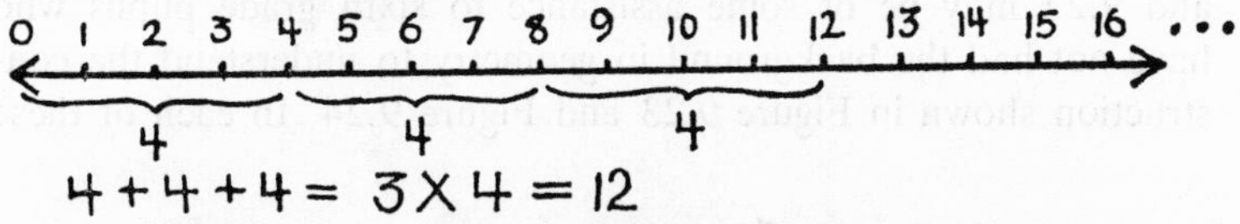

Figure 9.20 A number line used to indicate that $4 + 4 + 4 = 3 \times 4 = 12$. Although the multiplier, 3, is not shown as part of the construction, it is understood to be the number of intervals being considered.

is shown by the multiplicand being represented by an interval of 4, while the multiplier, 3, indicates the number of intervals being considered.

Figure 9.21 illustrates a situation where the interval is ¾ and the multiplier, which is 4, is thought of as indicating the number of intervals being considered.

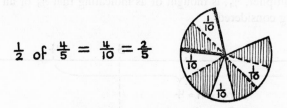

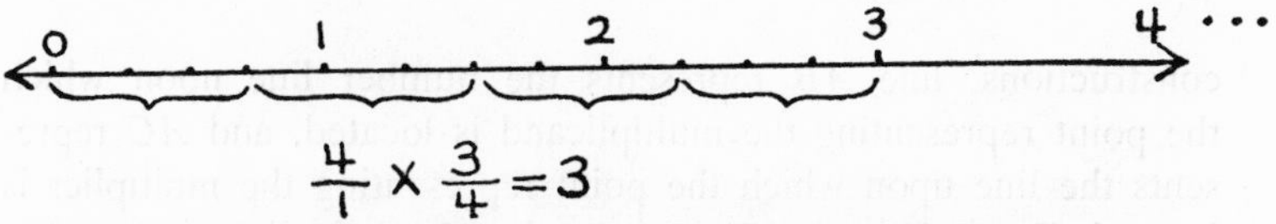

Figure 9.21 A number line used to indicate that $\frac{3}{4} + \frac{3}{4} + \frac{3}{4} + \frac{3}{4} = \frac{4}{1} \times \frac{3}{4} = 3$. The multiplier is thought of in this instance as indicating the number of intervals being considered.

Figure 9.22 shows that in finding the product of $\frac{3}{4} \times \frac{4}{1}$, the multiplicand might be thought of as an interval of 4, while the multiplier, $\frac{3}{4}$, is thought of as indicating that $\frac{3}{4}$ of an interval is being considered.

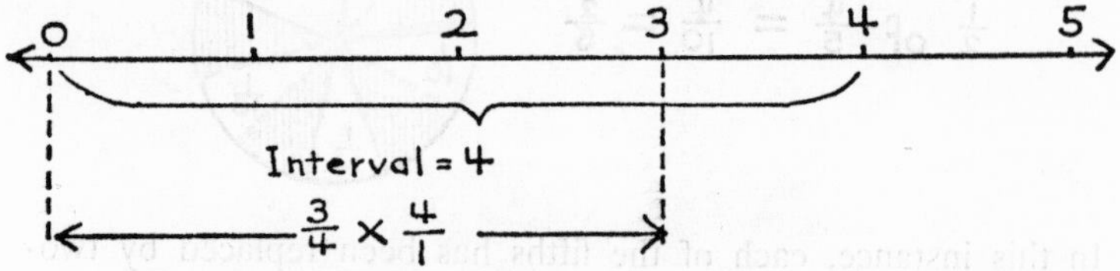

Figure 9.22 A number line used to indicate that $\frac{3}{4}$ of $4 = \frac{3}{4} \times \frac{4}{1}$, as the multiplier, $\frac{3}{4}$, is thought of in this instance as indicating the part of the interval being considered.

The constructions used in the diagrams in Figures 9.20, 9.21, and 9.22 may be of some assistance to sixth grade pupils who have not had the background in geometry to understand the construction shown in Figure 9.23 and Figure 9.24. In each of these

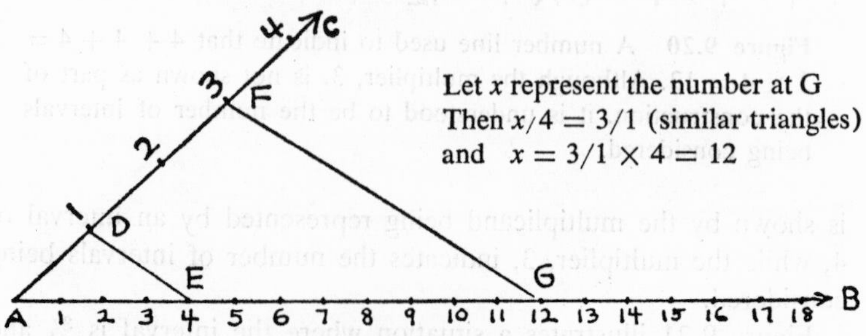

Figure 9.23 A construction on a number line to illustrate the multiplication of 3×4. Note that the unit interval on the line AB need not be equal to the unit interval on AC.

constructions, line AB represents the number line upon which the point representing the multiplicand is located, and AC represents the line upon which the point representing the multiplier is located. From the point D, representing the unit distance on AC, a line is drawn to the point E, which represents the multiplicand.

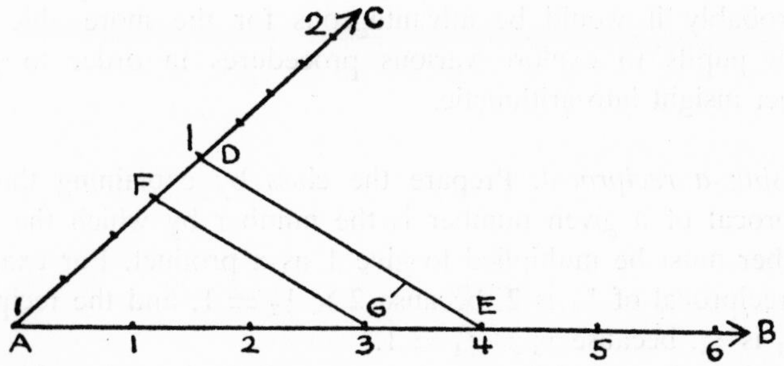

Figure 9.24 A construction on a number line to illustrate the multiplication of $\frac{3}{4} \times \frac{4}{1}$.

From the point *F,* which represents the multiplier, a line is drawn parallel to *DE* to meet *AB* at the point *G,* which represents the product.

Division by a Fraction

Usually, sixth grade pupils are required to learn the following rule to enable them to divide by a fraction: "To divide by a fraction, invert the divisor and multiply." Sometimes the rule is stated as, "To divide by a fraction, multiply by the reciprocal of the fraction." Although either of these rules is easy to apply when the pupil has learned it, rationalizing the rule, or helping the pupil feel that the results he obtains by using the rule are "reasonable," presents a challenge to the teacher.

Several articles have been published suggesting procedures which a teacher might use to rationalize a rule for division by a fraction.[4] These procedures may be classified as follows:

1. Procedures using the concept of a reciprocal.
2. Procedures involving the use of a common denominator for the divisor and the dividend.
3. Procedures making use of ratio concepts.

[4] Edwin Eagle, "Don't Let That Inverted Divisor Become Mysterious," *Arithmetic Teacher,* 1:15–17, October, 1954; Herbert Hannon, "Why Invert the Divisor?" *Arithmetic Teacher,* 4:262–265, December, 1957; and Theodore S. Kolesnik, "The Division of Common Fractions," *Arithmetic Teacher,* 7:133–134, March, 1960.

Probably it would be advantageous for the more able sixth grade pupils to explore various procedures in order to get a deeper insight into arithmetic.

Using a reciprocal. Prepare the class by explaining that the reciprocal of a given number is the number by which the given number must be multiplied to give 1 as a product. For example, the reciprocal of $\frac{1}{2}$ is 2, because $2 \times \frac{1}{2} = 1$, and the reciprocal of $\frac{3}{4}$ is $\frac{4}{3}$, because $\frac{4}{3} \times \frac{3}{4} = 1$.

Review the principle noted on page 243 that when both the numerator and the denominator of a fraction are multiplied by the same number the value of the fraction remains unchanged, e.g., $\frac{3}{4} \times \frac{3}{3} = \frac{9}{12} = \frac{3}{4}$.

Review the concept that when a number is divided by 1 its value is unchanged, e.g., $3 \div 1 = 3$.

When the class is ready for the demonstration of the procedure, start by using an example of a fraction being divided by a fraction, such as $\frac{3}{4} \div \frac{2}{3}$.

STEP 1. Show on the chalkboard that $\frac{3}{4} \div \frac{2}{3}$ may be written as

$$\frac{3}{4} \div \frac{2}{3} = \frac{\frac{3}{4}}{\frac{2}{3}}$$

STEP 2. Show that the denominator of the compound fraction may be changed to 1 by multiplying it by its reciprocal, but that in order to comply with the principle of compensation, it will be necessary to multiply the numerator of the compound fraction by the same number, thus,

$$\frac{3}{4} \div \frac{2}{3} = \frac{\frac{3}{2} \times \frac{3}{4}}{\frac{3}{2} \times \frac{2}{3}}$$

STEP 3. Show that the denominator of the compound fraction is now equal to 1, thus,

$$\frac{3}{4} \div \frac{2}{3} = \frac{\frac{3}{4}}{\frac{2}{3}} = \frac{\frac{3}{2} \times \frac{3}{4}}{\frac{3}{2} \times \frac{2}{3}} = \frac{\frac{3}{2} \times \frac{3}{4}}{1}$$

STEP 4. Have the class recall that when a number is divided by 1, its value is unchanged; therefore,

$$\frac{3}{4} \div \frac{2}{3} = \frac{\frac{3}{4}}{\frac{2}{3}} = \frac{\frac{3}{2} \times \frac{3}{4}}{\frac{3}{2} \times \frac{2}{3}} = \frac{\frac{3}{2} \times \frac{3}{4}}{1} = \frac{3}{2} \times \frac{3}{4}$$

STEP 5. Have the class note that in the expression above, $\frac{3}{4} \div \frac{2}{3} = \frac{3}{2} \times \frac{3}{4}$ and that by the principle of commutation, $\frac{3}{2} \times \frac{3}{4} = \frac{3}{4} \times \frac{3}{2}$, and that we have shown that, in this instance, to divide a number by the given fraction $\frac{2}{3}$ is equivalent to multiplying the number by $\frac{3}{2}$, which is the reciprocal of the fraction $\frac{2}{3}$.

STEP 6. Have the pupils use a similar procedure with several other examples until it seems reasonable to them that such a procedure could be used as a general rule.

Steps 5 and 6 may be expressed generally as:

$$a/b \div c/d = \frac{a/b}{c/d} = \frac{d/c \times a/b}{d/c \times c/d} = \frac{d/c \times a/b}{1} = d/c \times a/b =$$
$$a/b \times d/c.$$

Procedures involving the using of a common denominator for the divisor and the dividend. The following procedure, which employs concrete materials, is simple enough to permit the more able pupils to discover a rule for themselves.

The teacher should begin with a problem within the social experience of the pupils, such as "If Mary can make a glass of orangeade with $\frac{3}{4}$ of an orange, how many glasses of orangeade could she make with three oranges?" The problem could then be illustrated on the flannel board and the solution developed through the following steps.

STEP 1. The forms are arranged on the flannel board to represent the three oranges, as shown in Figure 9.25.

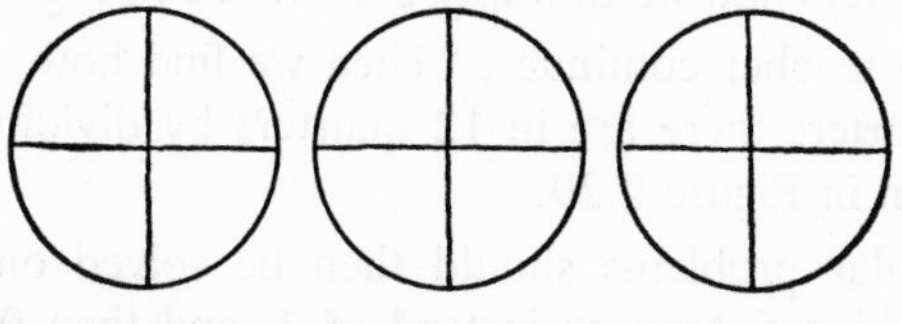

Figure 9.25 Forms arranged on flannel board as first step in illustrating division by a fraction.

STEP 2. Three quarters are then moved down to the corner of the flannel board to illustrate what is needed to make one glass of orangeade, Figure 9.26.

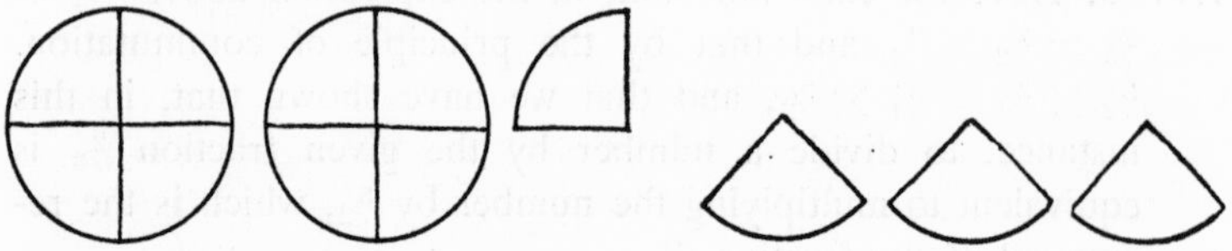

Figure 9.26. Forms arranged as second step in illustrating division by a fraction.

STEP 3. Three more quarters are moved down to illustrate what is needed for the second glass. Three more quarters are moved to illustrate what is needed for the third glass, and the same procedure is repeated for the fourth glass, Figure 9.27.

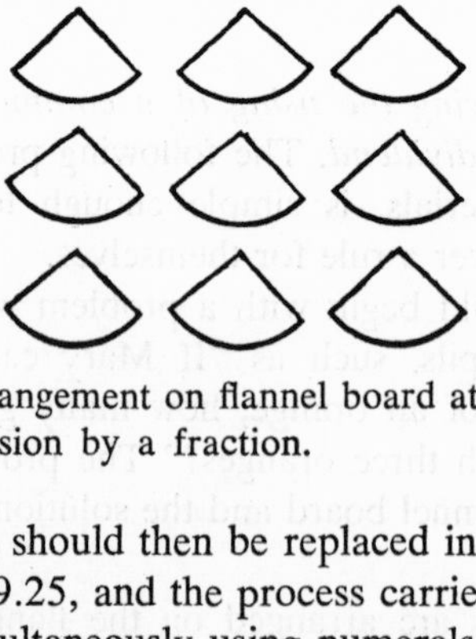

Figure 9.27 Arrangement on flannel board at end of third step in illustrating division by a fraction.

STEP 4. The forms should then be replaced in their original position in Figure 9.25, and the process carried through a second time while simultaneously using numerals on the chalkboard to indicate each step thus, "First we change the three oranges into quarters and we multiply 3 × 4," as in Figure 9.28.

STEP 5. The teacher continues, "Then we find how many groups of 3 quarters there are in 12 quarters by dividing 12 by 3," as shown in Figure 9.29.

STEP 6. Similar problems should then be solved on the flannel board, using 6 oranges instead of 3, and then 9 oranges instead of 3. Each time the problem should be solved by using

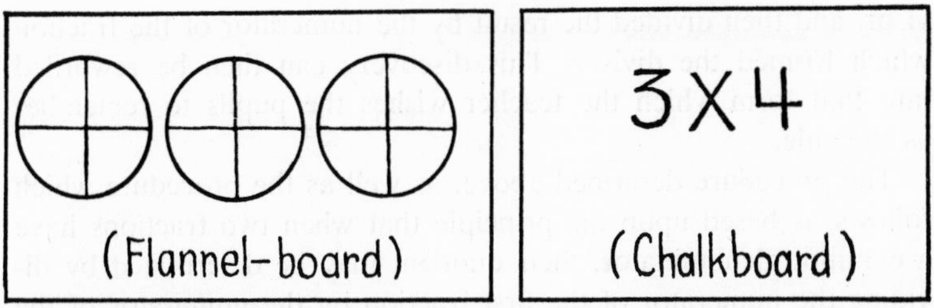

Figure 9.28 Using flannel board and chalkboard simultaneously in the fourth step illustrating division by a fraction.

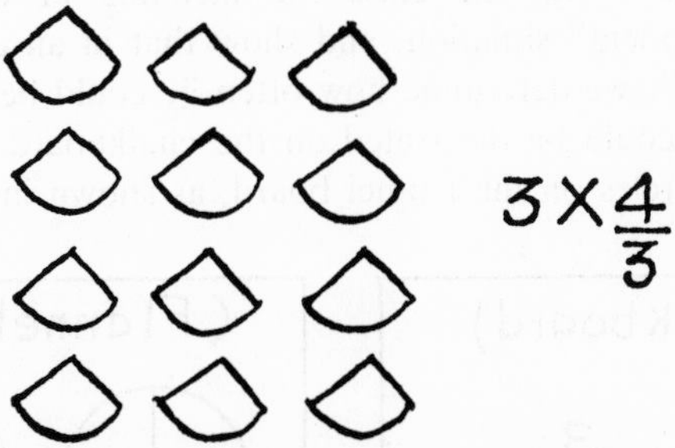

Figure 9.29 Using the flannel board and chalkboard simultaneously in the fifth step illustrating division by a fraction.

the forms while the numerals are used simultaneously on the chalkboard to indicate the solution. The procedure should be discussed by the class until the pupils discover that each time they have multiplied the whole number by the denominator of the fraction in order to change the whole number to fourths, and then they divided the result by the numerator of the fraction in order to find how many groups of three fourths there were.

After the pupils have solved a number of problems, the teacher should ask them if they can discover a "quick way" of finding the answer when we are dividing a whole number by a fraction. As they reexamine the problems they have solved, the more able pupils will discover that in each instance they multiplied the whole number by the denominator of the fraction which formed the divisor, and then divided the result by the numerator of the fraction which formed the divisor. This discovery can then be reworded into that form which the teacher wishes the pupils to remember as the rule.

The procedure described above, as well as the procedure which follows, is based upon the principle that when two fractions have a common denominator, their quotient may be determined by dividing the numerator of the first fraction by the numerator of the second fraction. This principle may be illustrated for sixth grade pupils by using either diagrams or the flannel board and following the steps given below.

STEP 1. Review with the class the meaning of division in a "measurement" situation, and show that in an example such as $3/4 \div 3/8$ we determine how often $3/8$ could be contained in $3/4$. This could be illustrated on the chalkboard, or with sectors of circles on the flannel board, as shown in Figure 9.30.

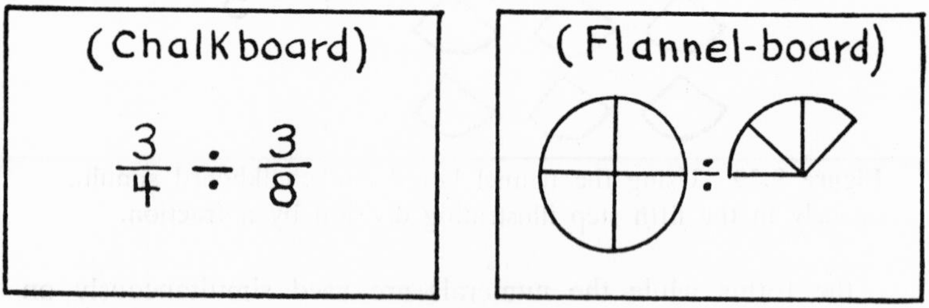

Figure 9.30

STEP 2. Change $3/4$ to $6/8$ and show this as in Figure 9.31.

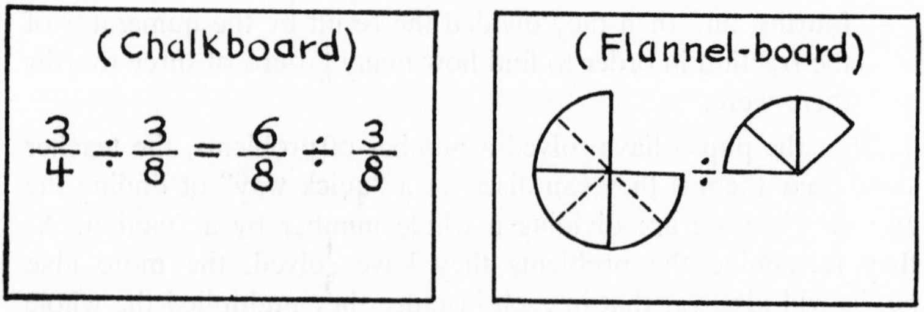

Figure 9.31

STEP 3. By using the diagram, show that $\frac{3}{8}$ may be contained twice in $\frac{6}{8}$, as in Figure 9.32.

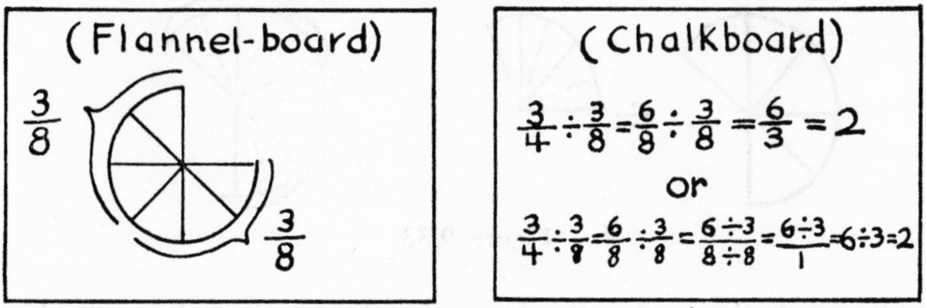

Figure 9.32

STEP 4. Use other examples, such as $\frac{3}{4} \div \frac{3}{16}$, $\frac{4}{5} \div \frac{1}{10}$, and $\frac{5}{8} \div \frac{5}{16}$, and through questions help the pupils to discover that when both fractions have a common denominator, division may be accomplished by dividing the numerator of the fraction that is the dividend by the numerator of the fraction that is the divisor, as shown in Figure 9.33.

$$\frac{3}{4} \div \frac{3}{16} = \frac{12}{16} \div \frac{3}{16} = \frac{12}{3} = 4$$

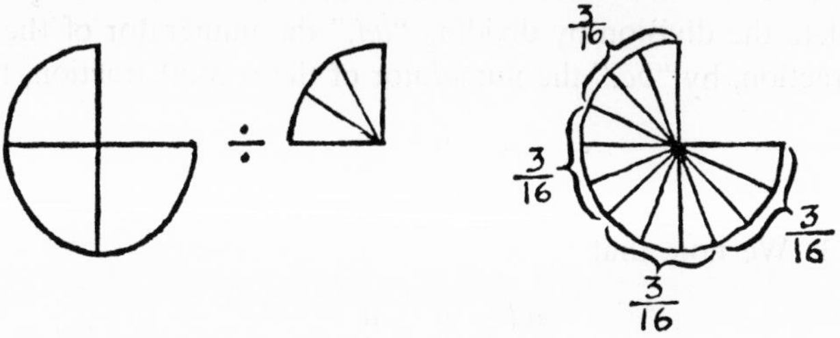

$$\frac{4}{5} \div \frac{1}{10} = \frac{8}{10} \div \frac{1}{10} = \frac{8}{1} = 8$$

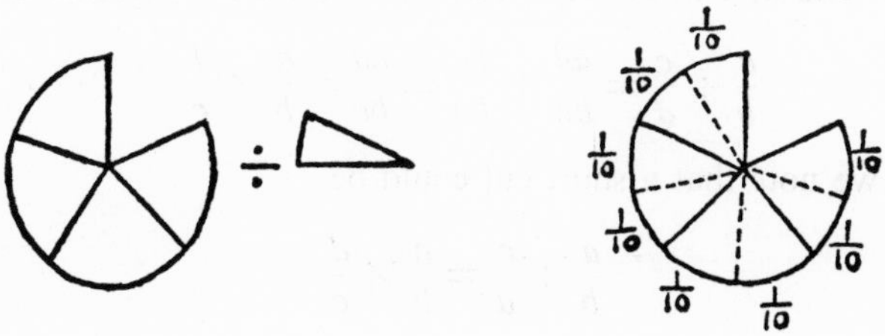

$$\frac{5}{8} \div \frac{5}{16} = \frac{10}{16} \div \frac{5}{16} = \frac{10}{5} = 2$$

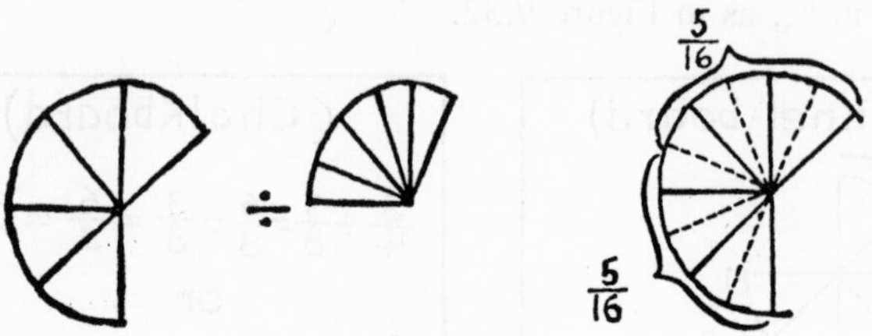

Figure 9.33

It may be interesting for the teacher to note that the principle employed in the process described above provides a basis for the rule "Invert the divisor and multiply." This may be shown algebraically as follows:

STEP 1. We start with the expression $\frac{a}{b} \div \frac{c}{d}$; and to find the common denominator, we could "cross multiply," as follows:

$$\frac{ad}{bd} \div \frac{bc}{bd}$$

STEP 2. As we now have a common denominator, we may complete the division by dividing "*ad*," the numerator of the first fraction, by "*bc*," the numerator of the second fraction, thus:

$$\frac{ad}{bc}$$

STEP 3. We note that

$$\frac{ad}{bc} = \frac{a}{b} \times \frac{d}{c}$$

STEP 4. The first three steps may now be shown together as:

$$\frac{a}{b} \div \frac{c}{d} = \frac{ad}{bd} \div \frac{bc}{bd} = \frac{ad}{bc} = \frac{a}{b} \times \frac{d}{c}$$

Thus we note that a short cut could be

$$\frac{a}{b} \div \frac{c}{d} = \frac{a}{b} \times \frac{d}{c}$$

Suggested Learning Activities

1. Following the definition of equivalent fractions given on page 230, show whether the following pairs of fractions are equivalent: $\frac{1}{3}$ and $\frac{1}{9}$, $\frac{2}{7}$ and $\frac{3}{14}$, $\frac{3}{5}$ and $\frac{6}{15}$, $\frac{3}{4}$ and $\frac{6}{8}$.
2. Tell what is meant by isomorphism; give two examples.
3. At a grade level of your choice, three to eight inclusive, list five social situations (activities or experiences) involving the use of fractions likely to be found in the everyday life of pupils.
4. Make a flannel board and fractional parts. Illustrate their use in teaching the addition of equivalent fractions.
5. Make up a problem to illustrate each of the four basic operations on fractions.
6. Divide $\frac{4}{5}$ by $\frac{3}{8}$, using first the reciprocal and then the common denominator methods. Show the full process in each case.

Guided Supplementary Reading

1. What does Adler mean by the term "family of fractions"? What other name does he give to the family?
2. According to Banks, what is the origin of the word "fraction"?
3. Brueckner, Grossnickle, and Reckzeh point out four meanings of fractions. What are they?
4. Pacioli, as reported by Buckingham, quoted from the Bible to show that multiplying must increase. What quotation was given and in what year did Pacioli make it?
5. What two meanings of fractions do Clark and Eads point out?
6. What kinds of quantitative experiences does Eads consider of most value at grade 5?
7. What mathematical principles does Eads advocate be taught in grade 6?
8. What theorem does Freund use to justify cancellation of common factors which appear in the numerator and denominator of a fraction?
9. What principle of mathematics does Geary demonstrate but not mention?
10. Gibb, Jones, and Junge speak of fractions as "ordered pairs of natural numbers." What do they mean by "ordered pairs"?
11. What criterion do Grossnickle and Brueckner suggest be applied to the selection of fractions to be taught to slow learners?

12. What instructional aid did Hannon invent to help children understand and locate common denominators?
13. Hannon suggests teaching division of fractions in relation to what other process?
14. How does Hibbard suggest $\frac{2}{3}$ of $\frac{3}{4}$ can be taught meaningfully?
15. What instructional aids did Hoffman use in teaching multiplication of fractions?
16. Divide $\frac{7}{8}$ by $\frac{1}{4}$ using the "cross-multiplication" method shown by Kolesnik.
17. What general effects were found by Lankford and Pattishall when pupils were encouraged to find several ways of solving a given problem involving fractions?
18. What device does Lansdown suggest be used to explain cancellation?
19. What four concepts of a fraction do Marks, Purdy, and Kinney identify?
20. How do McSwain and Cooke define a complex fraction?
21. According to Mueller, how would ancient Egyptians have written the fraction three fourths?
22. What procedure does Sister Mary Robertelle suggest for teaching indirect proportion?
23. What two definitions of addition of fractions does Schaaf give? Why does he prefer the first one?
24. Spencer and Brydegaard indicate why "improper fractions" are so called. What reason is given?
25. What procedure is given by Spitzer for initial teaching of fraction division?
26. According to Swain, early Greek mathematicians avoided fractional parts of a unit. Why?
27. Why does Van Engen argue that the study of rate pairs should be introduced into the elementary school?

Suggested Supplementary References

1. ADLER, IRVING, *The New Mathematics,* Chapter 4. New York: The John Day Company, 1958.
2. BANKS, J. HOUSTON, *Learning and Teaching Arithmetic,* Chapter 9. Boston: Allyn and Bacon, Inc., 1959.
3. BRUECKNER, LEO J., FOSTER E. GROSSNICKLE, AND JOHN RECKZEH, *Developing Mathematical Understanding in the Upper Grades,* Chapter 6. Philadelphia: The John C. Winston Co., 1957.

4. Buckingham, Burdette R., *Elementary Arithmetic,* Chapter 9. Boston: Ginn and Co., 1953.
5. Clark, John R., and Laura K. Eads, *Guiding Arithmetic Learning,* Chapter 6. New York: World Book Co., 1954.
6. Eads, Laura K., "Teaching Mathematics in Grade Five," *Grade Teacher,* Vol. 76, p. 49, March, 1959.
7. Eads, Laura K., "Teaching Mathematics in Grade Six," *Grade Teacher,* Vol. 76, p. 38, April, 1959.
8. Freund, John E., *A Modern Introduction to Mathematics,* Chapter 9. Englewood Cliffs, N.J.: Prentice-Hall, Inc., 1956.
9. Geary, C., "Teaching Cancellation," *Instructor,* Vol. 68, pp. 95–96, October, 1958.
10. Gibb, E. Glenadine, Phillip S. Jones, and Charlotte W. Junge, "Number and Operation," *The Growth of Mathematical Ideas,* Twenty-fourth Yearbook. Washington, D.C.: The National Council of Teachers of Mathematics, 1959.
11. Grossnickle, Foster E., and Leo J. Brueckner, *Discovering Meanings in Arithmetic,* Chapter 10. Philadelphia: The John C. Winston Co., 1959.
12. Hannon, Herbert, "Sets Aid in Adding Fractions," *Arithmetic Teacher,* Vol. 6, pp. 35–37, February, 1959.
13. Hannon, Herbert, "Why Invert the Divisor?" *Arithmetic Teacher,* Vol. 4, pp. 262–265, December, 1957.
14. Hibbard, W., "Multiplying Fractions," *Arithmetic Teacher,* Vol. 3, p. 112, April, 1956.
15. Hoffman, Hazel W., "Meaning of Multiplication of Fractions," *Arithmetic Teacher,* Vol. 5, pp. 89–90, March, 1958.
16. Kolesnik, Theodore S., "The Division of Common Fractions," *Arithmetic Teacher,* Vol. 7, pp. 133–134, March, 1960.
17. Lankford, F. G., Jr., and E. G. Pattishall, Jr., *Development of Independence in Adding and Subtracting Fractions.* University of Virginia: Council for Educational Research, 1956.
18. Lansdown, B. C., "From Cake to Cancellation," *Arithmetic Teacher,* Vol. 4, pp. 136–137, April, 1957.
19. Marks, John L., C. Richard Purdy, and Lucien B. Kinney, *Teaching Arithmetic for Understanding,* Chapter 8. New York: McGraw-Hill Book Co., Inc., 1958.
20. McSwain, E. T., and Ralph J. Cooke, *Understanding and Teaching Arithmetic in the Elementary School,* Chapter 7. New York: Henry Holt and Co., 1958.
21. Mueller, Francis J., *Arithmetic, Its Structure and Concepts,* Chapter 5. Englewood Cliffs, N.J.: Prentice-Hall, Inc., 1956.

22. ROBERTELLE, MARY, SISTER, "Indirect Proportion," *Grade Teacher,* Vol. 77, p. 64, November, 1959.
23. SCHAAF, WILLIAM, L., *Basic Concepts of Elementary Mathematics,* Chapter 5. New York: John Wiley & Sons, 1960.
24. SPENCER, PETER L., AND MARGUERITE BRYDEGAARD, *Building Mathematical Concepts in the Elementary School,* Chapter 7. New York: Henry Holt and Co., 1952.
25. SPITZER, HERBERT F., *The Teaching of Arithmetic,* Chapter 7. Boston: Houghton Mifflin Co., 1961.
26. SWAIN, ROBERT L., *Understanding Arithmetic,* Chapter 8. New York: Rinehart and Co., Inc., 1957.
27. VAN ENGEN, HENRY, "Rate Pairs, Fractions, and Rational Numbers," *Arithmetic Teacher,* Vol. 7, pp. 389–399, December, 1960.

CHAPTER *10*

Decimal Fractions

Rational Numbers Expressed as Common Fractions or as Decimal Fractions[1]

In the previous chapter, a rational number was described as a set of ordered pairs of integers in which division of the first component by the second component is implied for each ordered pair, with the exception that the second component cannot be zero in any instance. When a rational number is expressed by a common fraction, this fraction represents the whole set of equivalent fractions which comprise that particular rational number. It may be seen quite readily that a decimal fraction could be used likewise to indicate a rational number because the value of any common fraction may be expressed as a decimal fraction which is either terminating or repeating. For example, as the common fraction ¾ implies the division of 3 by 4, we may carry out the division by writing

[1] Note that in the system of ideas in which a fraction is treated as a numeral, the terms "decimal notation" and "decimal" are used instead of "decimal fraction." See School Mathematics Study Group, *Studies in Mathematics, Volume VI* (School Mathematics Study Group, New Haven: Yale University Press, 1961), p. 138.

$$
\begin{array}{r}
0.75 \\
4\overline{)3.00} \\
2\,8 \\
\hline
20 \\
20 \\
\hline
0
\end{array}
$$

This decimal fraction, 0.75, is said to be a *terminating decimal* because further division would result only in zeros being annexed to the quotient.

If the fraction $\frac{1}{3}$ were converted into a decimal notation, as in the following instance, the division could be carried out as far as we wish; the quotient would then be a *nonterminating decimal.* It may be referred to also as an *infinite decimal* or as a *repeating decimal.*

$$
\begin{array}{r}
0.33333\ \cdots \\
3\overline{)1.00000} \\
9 \\
\hline
10 \\
9 \\
\hline
10 \\
9 \\
\hline
10 \\
9 \\
\hline
1
\end{array}
$$

To indicate that certain digits are repeating, we may use the convention of putting a dot over the digit which repeats. We may write $0.\dot{3}$ instead of $0.3333\cdots$. We place a dot over the first and last digit of the cycle of digits which repeat, as $0.32\dot{6}4\dot{5}$, or we may place a bar over the repeating sequence as $0.32\overline{645}$.

Converting a Decimal Fraction into an Equivalent Common Fraction

When a terminating decimal fraction is expressed as a common fraction, the numerator of the common fraction will consist of the digits to the right of the decimal point in the decimal fraction numeral, and the denominator of the common fraction will be written as some power of ten, depending upon the number of digits to the right of the decimal point in the decimal fraction numeral. For example, $.3 = 3/10$, $.25 = 25/100$, $.125 = 125/1000$.

To express a repeating decimal as a common fraction, a procedure such as the following may be used.

To find the common fraction equivalent to the repeating decimal $.\dot{3}$, first represent this fraction by x and write

$$x = .3333 \cdots$$

Multiply both sides of this equation by 10, and write

$$10x = 3.3333 \cdots$$

Subtract x from the left side of the equation and the equivalent of x, which is $.3333 \cdots$, from the right side, as

$$\begin{aligned} 10x &= 3.3333 \cdots \\ -x &= .3333 \cdots \\ \hline 9x &= 3 \end{aligned}$$

On dividing each side of this equation by 9, we find that $x = 3/9 = 1/3$, and hence the repeating decimal $.3333 \cdots$ is found to be equivalent to the common fraction $1/3$.

When the cycle of digits which repeat consists of two or more digits, both sides of the equation would need to be multiplied by a a suitable power of ten. For instance, in finding the common fraction equivalent to $.242424 \cdots$, both sides of the equation would be multiplied by 100, as

$$\begin{aligned} 100x &= 24.242424 \cdots \\ -x &= .242424 \cdots \\ \hline 99x &= 24 \\ x &= 24/99 = 8/33 \end{aligned}$$

In a situation where the repeating sequence does not start immediately following the decimal point, a suitable power of x would need to be subtracted, as in the example of finding the common fraction equivalent to $.3454545 \cdots$

$$\begin{aligned} x &= .3\dot{4}\dot{5} \\ 1000x &= 345.4545 \cdots \\ -10x &= 3.4545 \cdots \\ \hline 990x &= 342 \\ x &= {}^{342}/_{990} = {}^{19}/_{55} \end{aligned}$$

A Repeating Decimal as an Infinite Series

An important concept in mathematics is that of an infinite series. While a careful study of types of infinite series is considered to be beyond the scope of the elementary school program, the concept may be introduced to children when they are introduced to the idea of a repeating decimal fraction.

If we consider the infinite series $\frac{1}{2} + \frac{1}{4} + \frac{1}{8} + \frac{1}{16} + \cdots$, we note that each term after the first term is obtained by multiplying the term immediately preceding it by $\frac{1}{2}$. A series of numbers such as this, where each term after the first may be found by multiplying the preceding term by a constant (a given number) constitutes a *geometric progression.* The constant by which the term was multiplied is called the *common ratio.*

If we find the sum of any given number of the terms given above by adding the first two, then in turn adding each new term to the sum of all the preceding terms ($\frac{1}{2} + \frac{1}{4} = \frac{3}{4}$; $\frac{3}{4} + \frac{1}{8} = \frac{7}{8}$; $\frac{7}{8} + \frac{1}{16} = \frac{15}{16}$; $\cdots$), we obtain the following sums in turn: $\frac{3}{4}$, $\frac{7}{8}$, $\frac{15}{16}$, $\frac{31}{32}$, and so on. It will be noted that as more terms are added the sum becomes closer and closer to 1. In fact, we may come as close as we wish to 1 by continuing to add more terms of the series. As this series continues to get closer to one, irrespective of how many more terms are added, we may say that the *limit* of this infinite series is 1. A series of this type is called a *convergent series* because its sum comes closer and closer to a given number as more terms are added. By definition, a convergent series is said to represent the number to which it converges, and consequently the infinite series $\frac{1}{2} + \frac{1}{4} + \frac{1}{8} + \frac{1}{16} + \cdots$ is said to represent 1.

On examining repeating decimal fractions it may be seen that each repeating decimal fraction may be expressed in the form of a convergent series. For example, the repeating decimal .3333 · · · may be considered to be equivalent to the infinite series .3 + .03 + .003 + .0003 + · · · or to the infinite series $\frac{3}{10} + \frac{3}{100} + \frac{3}{1000} + \frac{3}{10000} + \cdots$. As each term after the first may be found by multiplying the preceding term by the constant which indicates the common ratio, in this instance $\frac{1}{10}$, the terms of this series form a geometric progression. A formula for finding the sum of the terms of an infinite geometric progression of this type, where the common ratio is between zero and one, is $S = \frac{a}{1-r}$, where "a" represents the first term of the series and "r" represents the common ratio. In this instance, $a = \frac{3}{10}$ and $r = \frac{1}{10}$, so the sum of the infinite series is

$$S = \frac{\frac{3}{10}}{1 - \frac{1}{10}} = \frac{\frac{3}{10}}{\frac{9}{10}} = \frac{3}{10} \times \frac{10}{9} = \frac{3}{9} = \frac{1}{3}$$

This means that the sum of the terms of the infinite series $\frac{3}{10} + \frac{3}{100} + \frac{3}{1000} + \frac{3}{10000} + \cdots$ will approach $\frac{1}{3}$ as a limit, and by definition this infinite series is said to represent $\frac{1}{3}$.

Some infinite series do not converge toward any number as a limit, and consequently they cannot be thought of as representing either a rational or an irrational number. An example of such a nonconvergent series would be $1 + 2 + 4 + 8 + \cdots$.

It may be instructive to note that the number one may be represented by the repeating decimal .9999 · · · . Either of the two procedures described above for finding a number equivalent to a repeating decimal may be used to illustrate this observation. For example, let x represent the common fraction equivalent to the repeating decimal .9999 · · · , then following the procedure mentioned above we find that

$$\begin{aligned} 10x &= 9.999\cdots \\ x &= .999\cdots \\ \hline 9x &= 9 \\ x &= 1 \end{aligned}$$

and we may conclude that the repeating decimal .999 · · · = 1.

A similar result may be obtained by using the formula for finding the sum of the terms of an infinite geometric progression. Using the formula $S = \frac{a}{1-r}$ to find the sum of the series $9/10 + 9/100 + 9/1000 + \cdots$, we may write

$$S = \frac{9/10}{1 - 1/10} = \frac{9/10}{9/10} = 1$$

These two illustrations show that 1 may be represented by the non-terminating decimal .999 · · · . It will be noted that the *terminating* decimal .99999 would represent $\frac{99999}{100000}$, a number which is less than 1.

A generalization which may be noted at this point is that every terminating decimal has an equivalent nonterminating decimal expression, e.g., $.235 = .2349999 \cdots = .234\dot{9}$.

Infinite Decimals Representing Irrational Numbers

As has been stated, some infinite decimals may neither terminate nor repeat. Such would be the case in each instance where an infinite decimal represents an irrational number. As noted in Chapter 6, an irrational number cannot be expressed as the quotient of two integers. The discovery that there are numbers which are not rational is credited to Pythagoras. The following line of reasoning shows that if we assume as a premise that the square root of 2 is a rational number, it would lead to a conclusion which would be inconsistent with this premise.

If $\sqrt{2}$ were a rational number it could be expressed as a fraction in its lowest terms. Let this fraction be represented by a/b.

Then $a/b = \sqrt{2}$. Square both sides of this equation and $(a/b)^2 = 2$, and $a^2/b^2 = 2$. Multiplying both sides of this equation by b^2 we find that $a^2 = 2b^2$, and, therefore, a^2 must be an even number. Consequently "a" must be even, because it can be shown that if the square of a number is even then the number itself must be even.

If a is an even number, it must be twice some other number, which we will call r. Consequently $a = 2r$.

Substituting $2r$ for a in the equation $a^2 = 2b^2$, we see that $4r^2 = 2b^2$, and consequently $2r^2 = b^2$. Then b^2 is seen to be an even number and, therefore, b is an even number. As both a and b are even numbers, it follows that the fraction a/b is not in its lowest terms. We are thus led to the conclusion that $\sqrt{2}$ cannot be represented by a fraction in its lowest terms, and as such a conclusion is inconsistent with the premise with which we started when we said that $\sqrt{2}$ would be represented by the fraction a/b and that this fraction would be expressed in its lowest terms, we must conclude further that $\sqrt{2}$ is not a rational number.

Expressed in decimal form, the irrational number $\sqrt{2}$ is the infinite decimal 1.4142135 · · · which neither repeats nor terminates. Another well-known irrational number which children meet in the elementary school program is π (pi), which represents the ratio of the circumference of a circle to its diameter. This number is represented by the infinite decimal 3.141592 · · · . Some other examples of irrational numbers,[2] of which there are infinitely many, are $\sqrt{5}$, $\sqrt{7}$, and $\sqrt[3]{4}$.

Although irrational numbers cannot be expressed exactly either by terminating or by repeating decimals, there are convergent infinite series which may be used to express irrational numbers. By employing the concept of a converging infinite series, we are provided with a way for defining real numbers, as each real number may be thought of as a set of converging infinite series which may be expressed as an infinite decimal. If the infinite series converges to a number which may be expressed as the quotient of two integers, then that series is equivalent to a rational number, and the corresponding infinite decimal will end in an endless chain of zeros or as some repeating decimal. If the infinite series converges to a number which cannot be represented by the quotient of two integers, then that series represents an irrational number which may be expressed as an infinite decimal which neither terminates nor repeats.

As noted above, a subset of the real numbers is isomorphic [3]

[2] To answer some of the questions raised in the preceding would require a mathematical discussion beyond the scope of this book. Such questions might involve: the process of finding a rational approximation to an irrational number, why π is irrational, why some irrational numbers are algebraic ($\sqrt{2}$) whereas others are transcendental (π, e, log 2), etc.

[3] For an explanation of isomorphism see Chapter 9, p. 231.

to the rational number system, and it is in this sense that we may think of the rational numbers being "included," along with the irrational numbers, to make up the real number system.

When pupils in the elementary school are introduced to the concept of repeating decimals and learn how to convert them to common fractions, they may be told that there are infinite decimals which neither terminate nor repeat, and that these decimals represent irrational numbers, but a study of the real number system should be left to higher grade levels.

Introducing Decimal Fractions to Children

When pupils are learning about money in the second grade, usually they are shown how a decimal point is used to mark off the cents from the dollars in written material. During the third grade, they learn how to add or subtract numbers which are indicating sums of money, and they learn to keep the decimal points in the numerals under each other in order to separate the columns showing cents from those showing dollars. During the fourth grade, they learn to multiply or to divide a number which indicates dollars and cents by another number, and to mark off the "cents" columns by a decimal point. These early experiences give the pupils a certain degree of familiarity with the appearance of a decimal point in a numeral, but they do not introduce children to the real meaning of a decimal fraction. This is because an expression such as $3.25 is read as "Three dollars and twenty-five cents" and not as "Three decimal two five dollars" or as "Three and twenty-five hundredths of a dollar."

When introducing the meaning of a decimal fraction to fifth grade children, often it is convenient to refer to the speedometer of an automobile, and call their attention to how the last digit on the odometer, or trip mileage indicator, shows the tenths of a mile. At this grade level, many of the children have already learned that this last digit indicates tenths of a mile. A cardboard "speedometer" such as is shown in Figure 10.1 is easily prepared. If the last two or three digits of the odometer are made moveable, problems based upon various settings and involving the addition and subtraction of decimal fractions may be illustrated.

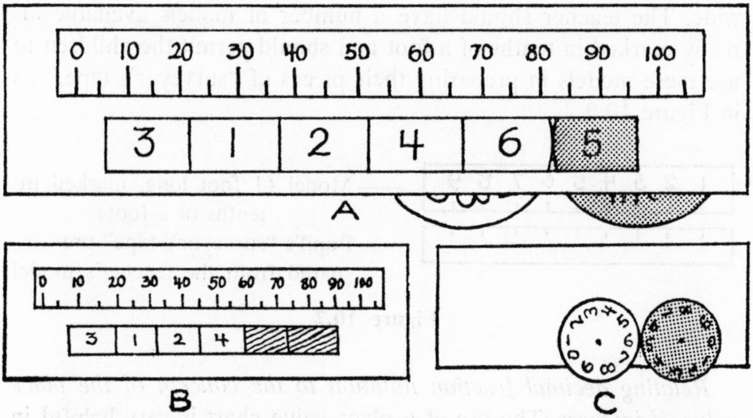

Figure 10.1 Make C to fit back of B so that one numeral at a time shows in each of the "windows" of the ones place and of the tens place. When placed together, they should look like A.

The children should be asked to explain why the last digit of the odometer may be read as "tenths" although it is not written as a common fraction. Through questions, they should be led to understand that when we have agreed that the last digit of the odometer will always indicate tenths, it is unnecessary to write the denominator each time. They should then be told that there is also an agreement that the first digit to the right of the decimal point will always indicate tenths, and that for this reason we may indicate a fraction which has ten for a denominator by merely writing the numerator in the first place after the decimal.

At this point, in order to give the pupils practice in using decimals to indicate tenths, it is suggested that each pupil prepare a piece of "surveyor's tape" and measure the length and width of various objects. Through measuring the length and width of his textbook or desk and then expressing the dimensions to the nearest tenth of a foot as a decimal fraction, the pupil learns, through practice, how a decimal fraction may be used and expressed.

Before preparing the "surveyor's tape" the children should be told that surveyors use measuring tapes marked in tenths of a foot instead of in inches. The teacher should then supply each pupil with a piece of cardboard a foot long and approximately an inch wide. The teacher should have a number of models available already marked in tenths of a foot and should permit the children to use these models in preparing their pieces of "surveyor's tape," as in Figure 10.2.

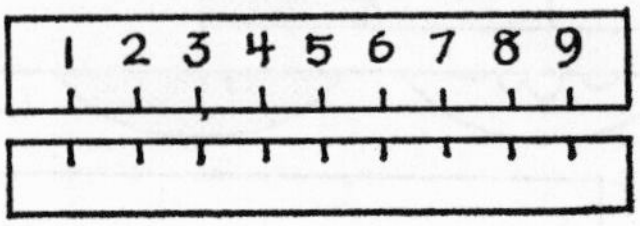

←Model (1 foot long, marked in tenths of a foot)

←Pupil's "surveyor's tape" prepared from the teacher's model

Figure 10.2

Relating decimal fraction notation to the concept of the place value of integers. The use of a place-value chart is very helpful in assisting the pupil to extend his concept of the place value of integers to include the place-value of decimal fractions. In Figure 10.3 the place-value chart with which the pupil is already familiar

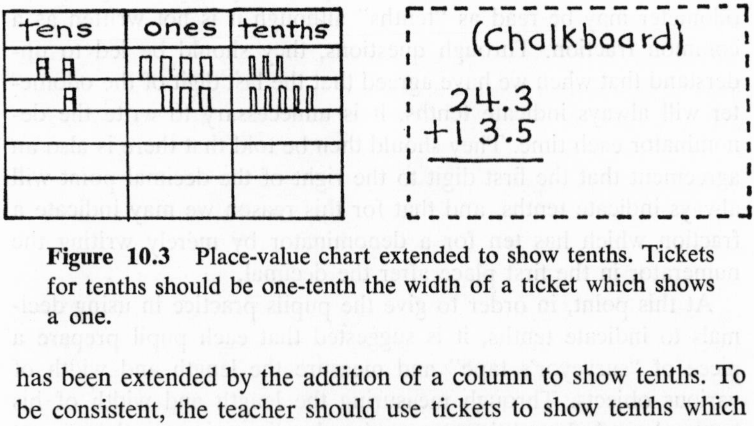

Figure 10.3 Place-value chart extended to show tenths. Tickets for tenths should be one-tenth the width of a ticket which shows a one.

has been extended by the addition of a column to show tenths. To be consistent, the teacher should use tickets to show tenths which are one-tenth the width of the tickets being used to show one. For this reason, the tickets indicating ones should be wider than those usually used, in order to permit the tickets showing tenths to be made wide enough to be easily handled. For this particular lesson, a few tickets that are wider than usual should be prepared to show ones, and some of these cut into tenths. Once the tickets have been prepared, the chart may be used to illustrate the place value of a decimal fraction, and later used to show that the processes of addition and subtraction for decimal fractions follow the same rules as do the similar processes for integers.

To help the pupils discover that it is reasonable for the first place to the right of the decimal point to be the place which shows tenths, the following procedure is suggested.

Numerals may be arranged on the chalkboard, as in Figure 10.4, and the pupils asked to note that each number in this ar-

10,000.
1 000.
100.
10.
1.
.1

Figure 10.4 An arrangement indicating that it is reasonable to consider the place to the right of the decimal as the one which shows tenths.

rangement is one-tenth of the number above it. When they consider .1 in relation to the number above it, they will understand that it is reasonable to think of it as one-tenth.

At this time, the pupils could be asked what they would expect the place to the right of the tenths' place to represent, and they should be encouraged to discover that this place would indicate one-tenth of one-tenth, or a hundredth.

When the pupils read or write decimal fractions indicating hundredths, such as .01, they may feel that there is an inconsistency here because there is only one zero used for a hundredth (.01) while there are two zeros used to express a hundred (100). Their attention should be directed to the fact that the ones' place, not the decimal point, is the center of our system of notation, and that if the zero for the ones' place were included, as in 0.01, the seeming inconsistency would disappear. The zero is omitted as it is not needed in the ones' place in writing a number such as 0.01, but it is included if it is necessary to "hold" a place to the left of the decimal point in writing a number such as 100.

A place-value abacus may also be used to advantage to reinforce the concept of place value in indicating tenths, hundredths, thousandths, and other denominators which are powers of ten. In Figure 10.5 a place-value abacus has the third wire marked to indicate the ones' place. It may then be shown that it is consistent to use the places to the right of the ones' place to indicate tenths, hundredths, and thousandths, respectively.

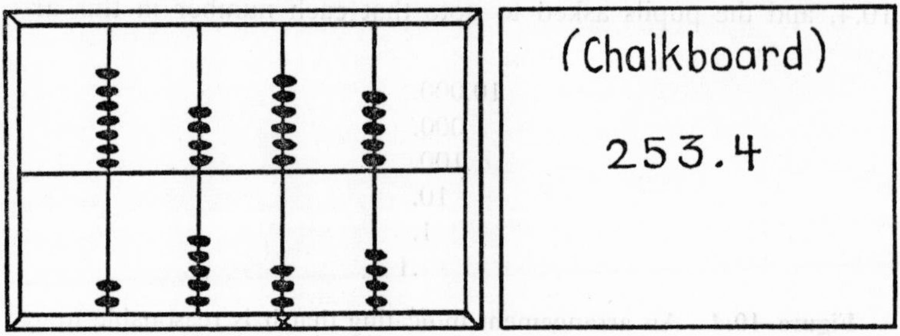

Figure 10.5

When the pupils have discovered the place value of the second place to the right of the decimal point, the teacher should have them recall how a decimal point is used in our monetary system to show dollars and cents, and how this practice is consistent with our system of notation for decimal fractions.

Expressing a decimal fraction as a common fraction. Once the pupil understands the notation used for expressing decimal fractions it will not be difficult for him to understand how decimal fractions may be expressed as common fractions. He will understand that the numerator of the common fraction will consist of the digits to the right of the decimal point in the decimal fraction, and that the denominator of the common fraction will be determined by counting out the places to the right of the decimal point, starting at tenths, and continuing to hundredths, thousandths, and so on. He will find that frequently it is necessary to reduce the fraction thus obtained in order to use the lowest denominator possible.

At this stage, the pupil should be shown how he can change certain common fractions to decimal fractions in instances where the common fraction may be expressed quite easily in tenths, hundredths, or thousandths. At a later time, when he has learned how to divide a decimal number [4] by an integer and how to annex zeros to the multiplicand, he may be shown the formal division procedure used in converting a common fraction to a decimal fraction, as described on pages 267–8.

Addition and Subtraction of Decimal Fractions

When the principle underlying the system of notation for decimal fractions is understood to be similar to that used for integers, the pupil should have no difficulty in adding or subtracting decimal numbers and in understanding the meaning of addition and subtraction as applied to decimal numbers. A place-value chart which has been extended to include a column for the tenths' place, Figure 10.3, may be used to illustrate that the same procedure is used in adding and subtracting decimal numbers that is used for adding and subtracting integers. The only new element in the situation is the use of an extra column, or columns, to show the digits to the right of the decimal point. While the pupil was in the lower grades he had practice in adding and subtracting numbers indicating dollars and cents. The rule he learned at that time, relative to keeping the decimal points in the numerals under each other while adding or subtracting, will have the same application when using decimal numbers in grade 5.

The teacher should make use of many verbal problems within the social experience of the pupils to provide them with practice in applying their knowledge of decimal numbers in social settings. The pupils should be encouraged also to prepare problems of their own that require the addition and subtraction of decimal numbers for their solution. Some of the situations which may be used to give practice in using decimal fractions are those involving the mileage on trips, measurements with the surveyor's tape, comparisons of temperature or rainfall records, and comparisons of speed records or gasoline consumption. Other situations in which

[4] As in this development a fraction is treated as a number, as described on page 230, Chapter 9; the terms "decimal number" and "decimal fraction" are used interchangeably.

the pupil may be interested and which provide suitable practice may be found in any modern series of pupils' textbooks.

Multiplication with Decimal Fractions

Since multiplication has the same meaning when multiplying decimal numbers as it has for multiplying integers, the meaning of the process itself does not have to be explained. The concept that the pupils need to develop at this stage concerns the placing of the decimal point in the product. The rule for placing the decimal point in the product is not difficult to learn or to apply, and may be stated as, "Place the decimal point so that there will be as many decimal places in the product as there are altogether in the multiplier and the multiplicand."

Although it is desirable for children to learn to use this rule correctly, it is suggested that the understanding of another procedure should be developed before the pupils are taught to use this rule mechanically.

Using an estimate to determine the position of a decimal point in a product. By teaching the pupil how to determine the position of a decimal point by an estimate, the teacher ensures that the pupil will understand the meaning of what is being done and is not using the rule without proper insight into the problem situation. Furthermore, once having learned how to fix the position of the decimal point by an estimate, the pupil is able to continue to use this procedure later as a check on the result he obtained when he used the formal rule.

The procedure may be introduced to the pupils through the use of a verbal problem such as, "How far could a car go on three gallons of gasoline, if it can go 19.7 miles on each gallon?" The numbers are first multiplied without regard to the decimal point, and then the need for placing the decimal point in the product, 591, is discussed. The pupils are asked to think of the meaning of the problem, and to make an estimate of the distance the car would travel. A convenient estimate in this instance would be 20 miles per gallon, so the car would go about 3×20, or 60 miles. On examining the product of 3×19.7, or 591, it would be noted that it would be necessary to place the decimal point so that the product would be 59.1, as this is the only place where the result would be near the estimated number 60. This procedure permits the placing of the decimal point with considerable accuracy, as an estimate would have to be very bad indeed to be ten times too much or ten times too little. Such an extremely poor estimate would be the only reason for misplacing the decimal point.

After the children had learned to determine the position of the decimal point by estimation in instances where the multiplicand was a decimal number, the procedure would be extended to cover instances where both the multiplier and the multiplicand were decimal numbers. An exercise requiring the pupil to find the product of 2.6 × 23.4 would be such an instance. Here estimates would be used for both the multiplier and the multiplicand, and it would be seen that the decimal point could be placed quite accurately in the product. An estimate of the product in this instance would be 3 × 20, or 60. A decimal point would have to be placed in the product of 26 × 234, or 6084, to show 60.84, because this is the only way that the product could be made to approximate 60.

Changing the value of a numeral by moving the decimal point. Before introducing a formal rule for placing the decimal point in a product, the teacher should lead the pupils to understand why moving the decimal point in a numeral one place to the right is equivalent to multiplying the number by ten, while moving the decimal point one place to the left is equivalent to dividing the number by ten. This dependence of the value of a numeral upon the position of the decimal point may be illustrated by numerals arranged on the chalkboard as in Figure 10.6.

It should be shown that as the decimal point identifies the position of the ones' place in a numeral, we are, in effect, changing the position of the ones' place when we move a decimal point to the right, and consequently each digit must assume a value that is ten times its previous value.

Following somewhat similar reasoning, it may be shown that the value of a numeral is divided by ten when a decimal point is

.001
.01
.1
1.
10.
100.
1000.

Figure 10.6

moved one place to the left, as may be seen when 25 becomes 2.5. The pupils should understand that the reason why the value of the numeral is multiplied by ten or divided by ten each time the decimal point is moved one place resides in the fact that the base of our system of notation is ten.

Developing a rule for placing the decimal point in a product. The teacher may use an example requiring the multiplication of an integer by a decimal number, such as 1.5 × 25, and by questioning the class lead the pupils to understand that when we disregard the decimal point in the multiplier, 1.5, we are, in effect, using 15 as a multiplier. In this instance, the multiplier we are using is thus ten times as large as it should be and consequently the tentative product, 375, must be ten times as large as it should be. In order to find the correct product, it will be necessary, therefore, to divide the tentative product by ten, and we may do this by moving the decimal point one place to the left. In this instance, the correct product would be 37.5.

An example involving the multiplication of a whole number by a number with two decimal places will illustrate how in this instance disregarding the decimal point will be equivalent to using a multiplier that is one hundred times as large as it should be. The tentative product will also be one hundred times as large as it should be. By moving the decimal point two places to the left, we divide the tentative product by one hundred, and thus find the correct product.

Another example, such as 1.5 × 2.5, will illustrate that in this instance, by first disregarding the decimal points, the multiplier will be ten times too large and the multiplicand will also be ten times too large. The tentative product, 375, must be ten times ten, or one hundred times, too large. To find the correct product, the tentative product, 375, must be divided by one hundred, and this may be done by moving the decimal point two places to the left.

By using other examples of a similar type, the teacher should lead the pupils to understand that when we disregard decimal places in either the multiplier or the multiplicand, or in both, we will first get a tentative product that is larger than it should be. To compensate for this, we must divide the tentative product by ten for each of the decimal places which were disregarded when we found the tentative product.

Division with Decimal Fractions

Introducing the process of dividing a decimal number by a whole number. The use of a place-value chart to show the division of 24.6 by 2 is illustrated in Figure 10.7. The pupil should note

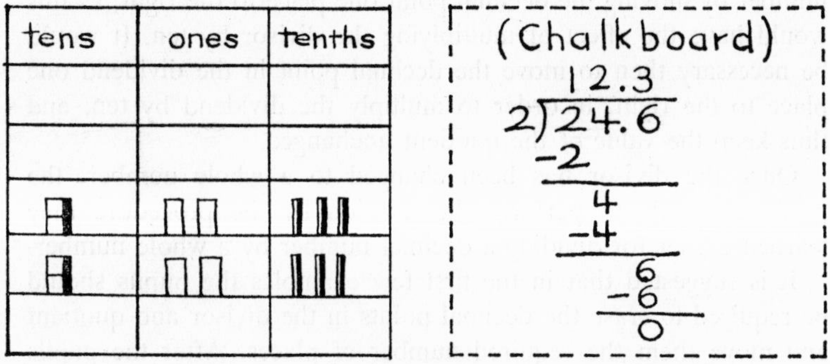

Figure 10.7

that the general procedure used to divide a decimal number by a whole number resembles that used to divide a whole number by a whole number, but that another column is needed on the chart to show the "tenths" place of the numerals. The pupil should note that as the quotient digit in each instance is placed in the proper position to indicate its place value, the "3" in the quotient, which indicates the number of "tenths," must be located in the "tenths" place of the quotient, as shown in Figure 10.7.

A number of similar examples will enable the pupil to discover that in each instance he must use a decimal point in the quotient to indicate the position of the digit showing "tenths" as he comes to the "tenths" place in the dividend during his computation.

Dividing a decimal number by a decimal number. Before introducing the procedure used for dividing a decimal number by a decimal number, the teacher should have the pupils recall the following two concepts which they learned earlier. First they should recall the concept that when a decimal point is moved to the right in a numeral it has the effect of multiplying the original value of the numeral by ten for each place it is moved. Secondly, the pupils should recall the concept that in a division situation, when both the divisor and the dividend are multiplied by the same number the value of the quotient is unchanged.

Through using an example such as $.2\overline{)4.86}$, the pupils may be led to understand that the divisor may be changed to a whole number by moving the decimal point one place to the right, as this would have the effect of multiplying the divisor by ten. It would be necessary then to move the decimal point in the dividend one place to the right, in order to multiply the dividend by ten, and thus keep the value of the quotient unchanged.

Once the divisor has been changed to a whole number, the pupils are able to perform the division by the procedure they learned earlier for dividing a decimal number by a whole number.

It is suggested that in the first few examples the pupils should be required to erase the decimal points in the divisor and quotient and move them the required number of places. After the pupils have understood the principle involved and the procedure, they should then be shown how to use a caret in the dividend to mark the number of places the decimal point should be moved. The use of carets renders it unnecessary to erase the decimal points and actually move them on the paper.

Annexing zeros to the dividend. Before introducing problems that necessitate the annexing of zeros to the dividend, the teacher should help the pupils to recall the fact that when zeros are annexed to the right of the decimal point, the value of the number involved is not changed. The quotient may thus be determined to tenths, to hundredths, or to as many decimal places as desired.

The use of an expression such as $1/10 = 10/100 = 100/1000$ will help illustrate that $.1 = .10 = .100$, and so on. The pupils should understand that when we annex a zero to a decimal number we are, in effect, multiplying both the numerator and the denominator of the equivalent common fraction by ten, and thus we are not changing its value.

Once the pupils have learned that they may annex zeros to the right of the decimal point in a division situation, they will be able to change a common fraction to a decimal fraction by dividing the numerator of the common fraction by its denominator, and they should be given practice in carrying out this procedure.

Estimating the position of the decimal point in the quotient. Quite often the correct position of the decimal point in the quotient may be checked easily by using estimates for the divisor and the dividend, and performing the division mentally. If in the example $2.34_{\wedge}\overset{353}{\overline{)82.61_{\wedge}3}}$ the pupil wishes to check the correct position for the decimal point in the quotient, he should note that, as $80 \div 2$ is 40, the decimal point in the quotient would have to be placed so as to give a value of approximately 40, or in other words, to give the value of a whole number of two digits. This procedure enables the pupil to check the position of the decimal point by noting whether or not his answer seems to be a reasonable one.

Introducing repeating decimals. After elementary school pupils have learned the procedure of annexing zeros to the dividend during the division of decimal numbers, they should be introduced to repeating decimals by discovering that when converting certain fractions, such as $1/3$, to decimal fractions, they will find that the quotient becomes a repeating decimal, such as $.33333 \cdots$. The pupils then should be taught to use the procedure described on pages 268–270 to enable them to convert a repeating decimal to a common fraction, but a more extensive study of infinite decimals should be reserved for higher grade levels.

Suggested Learning Activities

1. Write two common fractions which may be expressed as terminating decimals. Continue with two examples of common fractions which may be expressed as infinite decimals.
2. Show how to convert .6 to a common fraction. Follow with .1.
3. Give two examples of geometric progression different from that in your text.
4. Give two examples of converging series different from those in your text.
5. Show by using a formula that $.6666 \cdots = \frac{2}{3}$. Assume that $.6666 \cdots = \frac{6}{10} + \frac{6}{100} + \frac{6}{1000} \cdots$
6. Use two methods to show that $.4999 \cdots = \frac{1}{2}$.
7. Give five examples of real-life situations involving the use of decimal fractions likely to be encountered by fifth and sixth grade children.
8. Using a pocket-chart, show how you might explain the following addition and subtraction examples to fifth or sixth grade pupils:

(a)	(b)	(c)	(d)
4.7	8.6	8.4	32.3
+2.6	+5.5	−3.6	−4.6

9. Write three problems involving addition of decimals and suitable to sixth grade pupils. Do the same for subtraction of decimals.
10. Tell what would be the approximate whole number products of the following: 8.3×29.7, 5.7×30.19, 27.8×24.32.
11. If the decimal points in the following are disregarded, tell how many times too large the answer would be: 1.3×4, 1.42×300, 2.72×32.5, $4.63 \times .862$.
12. Using a pocket-chart, demonstrate the placing of decimal points in dividing: 46.4 by 2 and 3.69 by 3.

Guided Supplementary Reading

1. Through what illustrations does Benz argue that some teaching of adding "ragged decimals" might well be profitable?
2. How do Brueckner, Grossnickle, and Reckzeh recommend "ragged decimals" representing measurements be modified?
3. Write 43.8621 using the symbolism of Simon Stevin as reported by Buckingham.

4. What method for placing the decimal point in the quotient proved most successful in Flournoy's study?
5. What term is used by Gibb, Jones, and Junge to illustrate your authors' use of "converging" as applied to irrationals?
6. Historically, in the United States, what has been the order of teaching decimal and "vulgar" (common) fractions?
7. Write 86.321 using each of six historical devices for showing decimal fractions as reported by Larsen.
8. What two procedures do Marks, Purdy, and Kinney describe to illustrate how to use estimation to determine a reasonable answer in multiplication of decimals?
9. What did Mazzei conclude regarding the prevention of errors in arithmetic?
10. Why does Mueller suggest that the decimal point be regarded as a "designator"?
11. What test does Swain give to use in determining whether a given common fraction can be converted to a decimal fraction?
12. Why does Swart suggest that pupils should be taught to move the numeral rather than the decimal point in multiplying or dividing by a power of ten?
13. What method of locating the decimal point in division of decimals is recommended by Whittenburg? Why?

Suggested Supplementary References

1. BENZ, HARRY E., "Note on the Teaching of Ragged Decimals," *Arithmetic Teacher,* Vol. 5, pp. 149–151, April, 1958.
2. BRUECKNER, LEO J., FOSTER E. GROSSNICKLE, AND JOHN RECKZEH, *Developing Mathematical Understanding in the Upper Grades,* Chapter 6. Philadelphia: The John C. Winston Company, 1957.
3. BUCKINGHAM, BURDETTE R., *Elementary Arithmetic,* Chapter 10. Boston: Ginn and Company, 1953.
4. FLOURNOY, FRANCES, "Consideration of Pupils' Success with Two Methods for Placing the Decimal Point in the Quotient," *School Science and Mathematics,* Vol. 59, pp. 445–455, June, 1959.
5. GIBB, E. GLENADINE, PHILLIP S. JONES, AND CHARLOTTE W. JUNGE, "Number and Operation," *The Growth of Mathematical Ideas,* 24th Yearbook. Washington, D.C., The National Council of Teachers of Mathematics, 1959.
6. JONES, EMILY, "Historical Conflict—Decimal *vs.* Vulgar Fractions," *Arithmetic Teacher,* Vol. 7, p. 4, April, 1960.

7. LARSEN, HAROLD D., *Arithmetic for Colleges,* Chapter 8. New York: The Macmillan Company, 1958.

8. MARKS, JOHN L., C. RICHARD PURDY, AND LUCIEN B. KINNEY, *Teaching Arithmetic for Understanding,* Chapter 9. New York: McGraw-Hill Book Company, Inc., 1958.

9. MAZZEI, RENATO, "A Technique for the Prevention of Errors in Arithmetic," *School Science and Mathematics,* Vol. 59, pp. 493–497, June, 1959.

10. MUELLER, FRANCIS J., "The Neglected Role of the Decimal Point," *Arithmetic Teacher,* Vol. 5, pp. 87–88, March, 1958.

11. SWAIN, ROBERT L., *Understanding Arithmetic,* Chapter 9. New York: Rinehart and Co., Inc., 1957.

12. SWART, WILLIAM L., "Don't Move the Point, Move the Number," *Arithmetic Teacher,* Vol. 7, pp. 204–205, April, 1960.

13. WHITTENBURG, C. T., "Experiencing Arithmetic—V: Decimal Fractions," *American Childhood,* Vol. 42, pp. 28–31, May, 1957.

CHAPTER 11

Teaching Per Cent and Its Applications

Gradation of topics involving per cent. With some exceptions, topics involving per cent usually have been delayed in the elementary school program until the pupils have reached the seventh grade. By the time pupils have become familiar with the concepts and the computation involved in using common fractions and decimal fractions in the sixth grade, they should be capable psychologically of dealing with topics in per cent. Where time is available, they should be introduced to per cent topics before they reach the seventh grade. One reason which is given for delaying topics in per cent until the seventh grade is that there is frequently a need to restrict the sixth grade program in order to prevent it from becoming too heavy for some pupils. Another reason which is given is that the topics dealing with per cent are concerned largely with the business world of adults, and they will hold more interest for children when they are more mature than they are in the sixth grade.

Purposes of teaching topics in per cent. An important reason for teaching per cent and its applications is that this area of arithmetic has very high value as "consumer education." When a pupil reads newspapers, periodicals, or textbooks, he will meet references to per cent very frequently. Many business advertisements contain references to per cent. Newspaper items refer often to increases or decreases in terms of per cent. Comparisons in population growth, national income, building conditions, steel production, defense spending, and so on, are stated usually in terms of per cent. Without an understanding of the major concepts relating to per cent, a reader would be handicapped in understanding many of the implications in his daily reading.

Another reason for teaching per cent and its applications is to enable adults to perform the calculations needed in their own business dealings. Often decisions have to be made on the basis of comparisons and it becomes convenient to express the data in the form of per cent when making the comparisons. The ability to employ computations involving the use of per cent is needed in many financial transactions in the business world and in the daily life of the average citizen.

Organizing the program for teaching per cent. In order to facilitate learning the concepts involved in the social applications of per cent, it is often convenient to organize the pupils' program into units such as banking practices of calculating interest and discount, installment buying, profit and loss, increase and decrease, insurance, budgeting, and similar topics. This makes it easier for the pupils to grasp the relationships involved in the social settings in which the problems are placed.

In order to enable the pupils to understand better the mathematical concepts underlying the calculations in per cent problems, the teacher may introduce them to per cent by relating it to the pupils' knowledge of common fractions and decimal fractions as well as to concepts of ratio and proportion. The latter concepts are discussed on page 298. The teacher may then lead them to see how their former knowledge may be employed in the calculations needed to solve problems in areas of installment buying, insurance, simple and compound interest, and so on. The pupils thus get practice in using the computational procedures in per cent problems at the same time that they are learning the social applications of per cent in daily living.

Introducing the topic of per cent to children. One way to introduce per cent to pupils and to emphasize its frequent use in daily reading is for the teacher to select items referring to per cent from an issue of a daily newspaper and display them on a chart or a bulletin board. Through discussion, the pupils may be led to note that per cent is used in many of the business advertisements, and is used also very frequently in news items in a wide variety of instances where comparisons are being made.

After a discussion regarding common applications of per cent, and when the pupils have recognized the value of understanding the meaning of per cent, they should be told that per cent refers to the rate per hundred, and that as fractions are used in calculating a percentage, they will find that they will use common fractions or decimal fractions in solving many problems involving per cent.[1] In this respect, the term 6% means six per hundred, and consequently the percentage that this rate would yield when applied to a given base could be found by using the common fraction $\frac{6}{100}$ and finding $\frac{6}{100}$ of the base or by using the decimal fraction .06 instead of the common fraction $\frac{6}{100}$.

Pupils should be given a clear understanding of the terms *rate, base,* and *percentage.* The *rate* is stated as a per cent. For instance, 8% means a rate of 8 per 100. The *base* is the number to which the rate is applied, while the *percentage* is the number obtained by applying the rate to the base. For example, in a problem such as "Find 8% of $250," the base is 250, the rate is 8%, and the percentage is 20 in this instance.

A *hundred-board,* such as is shown in Figure 11.1, may be used to illustrate the meaning of per cent as so many per hundred, and to develop the concept that in the instance where we are using a rate of 8%, eight per hundred would correspond to the

[1] The School Mathematics Study Group treat an expression in per cent as another way of expressing a rational number, and consequently are able to write 71% = 71/100 = .71. See School Mathematics Study Group, *Number Systems* (Vol. VI of Studies in Mathematics; New Haven: Yale University Press, 1961), p. 151. For an alternative development, in which a per cent is not considered to be a fraction, see Henry Van Engen, "Rate Pairs, Fractions, and Rational Numbers," *Arithmetic Teacher,* 7:389–399, December, 1960.

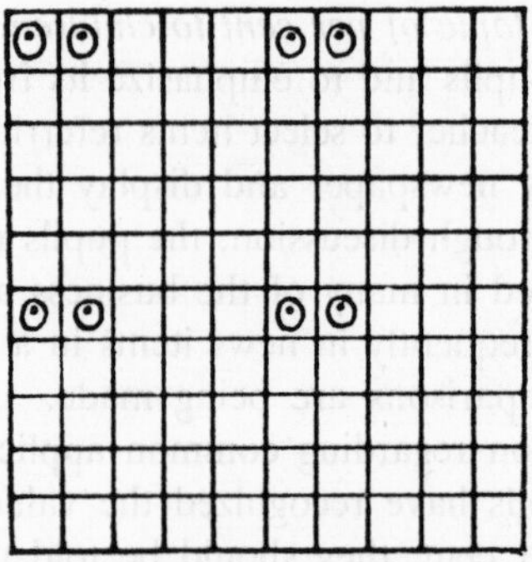

Figure 11.1 An arrangement on the hundred-board to illustrate how a rate of 8% may refer to 8 per 100, 4 per 50, or 2 per 25.

rate of four per fifty or two per twenty-five. A chart such as is shown in Figure 11.2 may be used to indicate the relationships among the fractions of a given base and the percentages obtained by applying various rates to the same base.

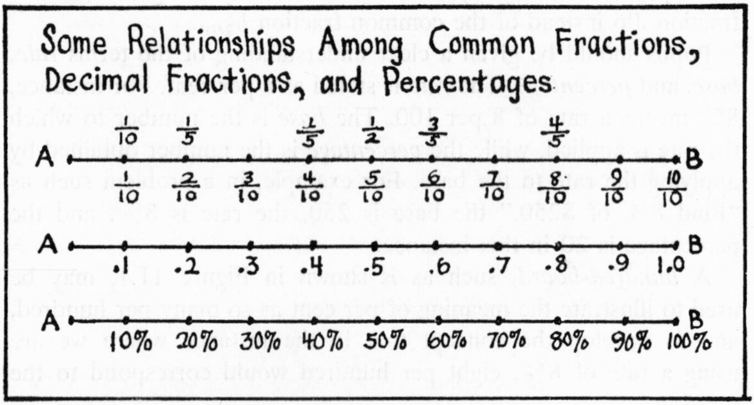

Figure 11.2 Chart showing some relationships among common fractions, decimal fractions, and percentages.

Two Approaches to Teaching Per Cent

There are two common effective approaches available to the teacher in teaching the calculations needed in solving problems involving per cent.

The more traditional approach makes use of three formulae which are used in the three "cases," or types, of per cent problems. In this approach the pupils are taught to identify the case to which a certain per cent problem belongs, and then to carry out the computations indicated by the formula which is suitable for solving the problem in that particular case.

A second approach involves the use of ratio and proportion and the solving of an equation. The pupils are taught to state the information given in the problem as a mathematical sentence in the form of an equation. Once the pertinent information has been stated as an equation, the equation may be solved by following a routine procedure. Probably the second approach would be preferred in situations where the class had been taught the use of equations and how to write mathematical sentences in earlier grades, as then the equation approach would be a new application of a procedure which had been learned previously. This approach is discussed later.

The formula approach. When a formula approach is used, it is convenient for the teacher to organize the pupils' work in per cent into three sections which are referred to traditionally as the three "cases" of per cent, though some prefer to speak of three "types" or "usages" of per cent.

The first usage of per cent problems refers to that type of problem in which the pupil is given the rate and the base, and is asked to determine the percentage, as in the problem "Find 6% of $200." This is a very common use of per cent in business in connection with problems involving interest, discount, profit and loss, installment buying, insurance, and in many other instances.

The second usage of per cent is the type in which the pupil is asked to find what per cent one number is of another, as in the problem "Thirty is what per cent of forty?" This usage of per cent includes many common instances in which comparisons are being made between rates in various situations which arise in daily living.

The third usage of per cent is not met as frequently in daily living as are the other two types. The third usage refers to the type of problem in which the pupil is required to find a number when a percentage of it, along with the rate, is known. An example would be, "Thirty is 75% of what number?"

As noted above, during the time the pupils are learning the computations needed to solve problems in per cent, they usually are instructed in the general purpose and nature of the common types of business transactions involving each usage. For instance, topics dealing with simple and compound interest and with bank discount are discussed in relation to the purpose of banks and their value to the community. The common types of bank forms and business forms used in transactions involving the lending of money are also examined. When calculations involved in installment buying are discussed, the nature and purposes of installment buying are considered, along with the advantages and disadvantages of such transactions.

The first type of per cent problem. Calculations involving the first usage of per cent are introduced often by problems requiring the calculation of simple interest. The teacher may use a question such as "What is the simple interest on $200 at 5% for one year?" in order to introduce the terms "base," "rate," and "percentage." The pupils then should be led to discover that they can find the answer to the question in more than one way. They could think of the rate of 5% as yielding a percentage of 5/100 or 1/20 of the base, and consequently they could determine the percentage by finding the number that was 1/20 of $200. The pupils could find the answer also by multiplying 200 by .05, because this procedure also would yield a number which is 5/100 of the base.

Once the pupils have understood the reasons for the calculations, they should discuss the formula $p = rb$ (percentage = rate × base), and be given practice in using the formula to calculate the percentage in various problems where the rate and the base are known.

In order to become familiar with the use of a formula in solving problems in per cent, the pupils should be encouraged to use the formula in calculating their answers to problems in the first usage of per cent. The use of a formula in the third usage of per cent is particularly helpful, and the practice the pupils receive in using the formulae in the first and second usages, where the meanings of the formulae are easily grasped, will prepare them to employ it in the third usage, which pupils often find more difficult.

The second type of per cent problem. As noted above, the second usage of per cent is exemplified by problems in which the pupils are finding what per cent one number is of another number. A problem such as the following could be used. "If a pupil had 6 questions correct out of 8 questions, what per cent of the total number would this be?" The pupils should be led to understand that in this instance the number correct would be $6/8$ of the total number of questions, and that this would indicate a rate of 75%. The form of the formula for solving problems in the second usage of per cent is $r = \frac{p}{b}$ $\left(\text{rate} = \frac{\text{percentage}}{\text{base}}\right)$, where it is understood that the rate is expressed as so many per hundred. In this instance, the rate $= 6/8 \times 100 = 75\%$. Here the percentage is 6, the base is 8, and we multiply by 100 because per cent refers to a rate per hundred.

While studying the meaning of the second usage of per cent, the pupils should note that per cent notation is particularly useful in making comparisons where rates are involved. Sometimes it is difficult to compare rates which are expressed in the form of two fractions without the calculations needed to bring them to a common denominator, but when each rate is expressed as a per cent the comparison is made quite easily. For example, a pupil can compare a score of 19 out of a possible 25 marks on a certain test with a score of 18 out of a possible 24 marks on another test by comparing the rate in each case, i.e. 76% and 75%.

The third usage of per cent. The third type of per cent problem is often more difficult for the pupils to understand than are the first and second types. By using a diagram to illustrate a rather easy problem involving the third type of per cent, the teacher may help the pupils to visualize the relationships in this type of problem.

The pupils may be asked to solve a problem such as the following. "At a sale, the price of an article was reduced to 75% of its former marked price. If it then sold for $300, what was its former marked price?" The relationships involved in this problem may be illustrated on the chalkboard by a diagram such as is shown in Figure 11.3. Here the pupils are being asked to find the former marked price which is represented by the line segment *AB*. As the sale price was 75% of the former marked price, the sale price would be ¾ of the former marked price, and the line segment *AB* could be divided into four equal parts so that three of these parts, *AE*, would represent the sale price. As the question tells us that the sale price is $300, this would also be shown as represented by the line segment *AE*. Using a questioning procedure, the teacher may now lead the pupils to understand that as each ¼ of the line must represent $100, the whole line segment, *AB*, would represent $400. Statements indicating this line of reasoning would be expressed as follows:

¾ of the former sale price is $300.
¼ of the former sale price is $300 ÷ 3 = $100
4/4 of the former sale price is 4 × $100 = $400

The pupils should be shown that the same answer would result from similar reasoning but without using common fractions as follows:

75% of the marked price is $300.
1% of the marked price is $300 ÷ 75 = $4
100% of the marked price is 100 × $4 = $400

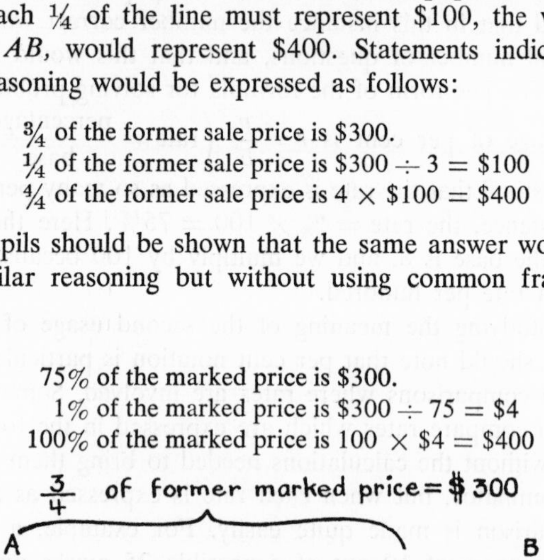

Figure 11.3 Diagram to illustrate certain relationships in a problem involving the third case in per cent.

After the pupils understand the nature of the third usage of per cent and the reasoning involved in the solution of problems of this type, they should discuss the form of the formula, $b = \frac{p}{r}$, $\left(\text{base} = \frac{\text{percentage}}{\text{rate}}\right)$, and note that in using this form they are carrying out computations similar to those made when using the diagram in Figure 11.3. The use of a formula may then, and only then, become the usual procedure for solving problems in the third usage of per cent, because trying to apply a formula without first understanding how it is derived often may lead to confusion.

Although traditionally teachers have spoken of three formulas for these three usages, it should be brought to the attention of the pupils that they are employing three different forms of the same formula.

The Equation Approach

In the procedure described above, the pupils are taught how to utilize each of the three forms of the formula needed to solve problems in the three usages of per cent. Another procedure, one which involves expressing the conditions of the problem in the form of a proportion and then solving the resulting equation, may be taught either in place of, or along with, the procedure using the formula. The teacher should note that more than one approach to solving a problem may be taught to children providing that the mathematical implications in each approach are understood.

The use of proportion in solving problems in per cent has an advantage over the use of the formula because the same general procedure may be followed for all three usages, and thus the pupils are not required to memorize a form of the formula for each usage. Once the pupils have succeeded in expressing the problem in equation form, the steps in the computational procedure may be followed more or less mechanically. An understanding of the equation approach to solving per cent problems must be based, however, upon an understanding of the concept of proportion.

Ratio and proportion. The concepts of ratio and proportion have a wide application in solving many types of arithmetic problems, and some understanding of these concepts as they are used to solve simple problems is well within the capabilities of many pupils in the fifth and sixth grades. These concepts also provide very effective readiness for understanding per cent and its applications.

A *ratio* may be described as an ordered pair of numerals which is used to symbolize a correspondence between two numbers. For example, if a man paid \$3.10 for ten gallons of gasoline, the ratio 310/10 would indicate the rate in terms of cents and gallons at which he bought the gasoline. This ratio may be read as "Three hundred ten to ten."

Two ratios, a/b and c/d, are considered to be equivalent when $ad = bc$. This may also be expressed by saying that two ratios are equivalent when their cross-products are equal.[2]

An equation expressing the fact that two equivalent ratios are equal is called a *proportion*. For example, $310/10 = 31/1$ is a proportion.

It should be noted that each ratio belongs to a set of equivalent ratios. For instance, the ratio 3/4 (read "Three to four") belongs to the set of equivalent ratios 3/4, 6/8, 9/12, · · · , so the rate expressed by the ratio 3/4 is the same as that expressed by each of the ratios 6/8, 9/12, 12/16 and by any one of infinitely many equivalent ratios. If in a problem we are told that a man paid \$3.10 for ten gallons of gasoline, we know that the same rate is indicated by each member of the set of equivalent ratios of which 310/10 is a member, e.g., {31/1, 62/2, 93/3, · · · }. If we know one member of a set of equivalent ratios, e.g., 310/10, and if we know one component of a second member of the same set, by making use of the knowledge that the cross-products of equivalent ratios are equal, we can find the other component of the second member. For example, if we know that 310/10 is a member of the set and that the first component of another member is 93, then we may find the second component of the other member by the following steps.

$$\frac{310}{10} = \frac{93}{x}$$

$$310x = 930 \quad \text{(cross-products are equal)}$$

$$x = 3$$

[2] Although usually pupils are not given the mathematical rationale for this statement until they reach higher grade levels, it is permissible for them to use it as a device for checking the equivalence of ratios.

The procedure employed when using equations to solve problems in per cent is based upon the principle that as a per cent expresses a ratio of some number to one hundred, any problem in per cent may be resolved into one in which we are required to equate the two ratios, $\frac{\text{per cent}}{\text{one hundred}} = \frac{\text{percentage}}{\text{base}}$.

In the first usage of per cent, we are required to determine the percentage, and thus we need to equate the ratios $\frac{\text{per cent}}{\text{one hundred}} = \frac{x}{\text{base}}$, where "$x$" indicates the unknown percentage.

In the second usage of per cent, we are required to determine the rate, and thus equate the ratios $\frac{x}{\text{one hundred}} = \frac{\text{percentage}}{\text{base}}$, where "$x$" would indicate the unknown per cent.

In the third usage, we are determining the base, and the ratios to be equated would be $\frac{\text{per cent}}{\text{one hundred}} = \frac{\text{percentage}}{x}$, where "$x$" indicates the unknown base.

In each usage, after the pupil has stated the pertinent information in the form of a proportion, by making use of the principle that the cross-products of equivalent ratios are equal he may convert the problem to one of solving an equation. For example, in solving the problem "Find 6% of \$200" the information would be expressed first in the form of the two equal ratios

$$\frac{6}{100} = \frac{x}{200}$$

By cross-multiplication, $6 \times 200 = 100x$, and we find that

$$x = \frac{6 \times 200}{100} = 12$$

To take an example of the second usage of per cent, the question "30 is what per cent of 40?" would be expressed first as the two equal ratios $\frac{x}{100} = \frac{30}{40}$.

By cross-multiplication, $40x = 30 \times 100$, and then

$$x = \frac{30 \times 100}{40} = 75$$

The question "30 is 75% of what number?" is an example of the third usage of per cent. This information could be expressed by the two equal ratios $\frac{75}{100} = \frac{30}{x}$. By cross-multiplication, $75x = 30 \times 100$, and we find that

$$x = \frac{30 \times 100}{75} = 40$$

It will be observed that in following the procedures indicated above, the main difficulties which the pupils will experience will lie probably in stating the information in the problem in the form of a proportion. Once the information has been stated thus as a mathematical sentence, the calculations are quite similar in all three types of problems.

A limitation on the use of the cross-multiplication procedure to solve equations, as suggested above, should be noted. This procedure may become rather mechanical for the pupils at this grade level as they have not been instructed yet in the normal procedure for solving equations, and consequently they may not understand the rationale for the "short cut" used in cross-multiplication. Later, when the pupils begin a more systematic study of algebra, it will be necessary for the teacher to emphasize the reasons why the cross-multiplication procedure is valid. As pupils usually are introduced to per cent problems before they study equations of the type used in solving these problems, the cross-multiplication procedure is defended here on the grounds that it is a simpler way to solve problems which traditionally have presented considerable difficulty to pupils using a formula approach.

Calculations where the rate is not expressed as a whole number. After learning how to determine a percentage of a number in instances where the rate is expressed as a whole number, the pupils should be given practice in computations where the rate is given as a mixed numeral, for example, "Find 6½% of $200." The pupils should be led to understand that as $6\frac{1}{2}\% = \frac{13}{2}\% = \frac{13}{200}$, the answer in this instance may be determined by finding $\frac{13}{200}$ of \$200. The pupils should learn also that the answer may be found by first expressing $6\frac{1}{2}\%$ as 6.5% and multiplying \$200 by .065. When the rate is expressed as a mixed numeral, the pupils should become familiar with both procedures for computing the percentage and be able to select the more efficient procedure for solving a certain problem.

In instances where the rate is expressed as less than one per cent, the pupil should be shown how to use two steps in his computation by first finding 1% of the base, and then taking the required fraction of this percentage. This procedure will assist him in checking whether or not the answer is a reasonable one, and is particularly helpful where the base has been expressed in both dollars and cents. Errors in such instances are frequently caused by the incorrect placement of the decimal point. When the pupils have become accustomed to computations involving rates of less than 1%, they should be shown how to complete the computation in one step. Even at this stage it is helpful for them to check their answers to see whether or not they are reasonable by mentally calculating 1% of the base, and then assuring themselves that the decimal point has been located so that the answer is less than this amount.

Learning to use rates larger than 100%. A pupil is required often to use computations involving a rate that is larger than one hundred per cent in problems involving the calculation of increases. At first, it may be difficult for the pupil to grasp the meaning of a rate greater than 100% because he may have become accustomed to thinking mistakenly that 100% is the largest possible rate.

Through class discussion of problems placed in familiar social settings and involving calculations of increases, such as noting the increase in population growth or in school enrollment, the pupil may be helped to visualize relationships where the rate is greater than 100%. He should be led to understand that in an instance where the enrollment of a school is being compared to a smaller enrollment at an earlier date, and when the smaller enrollment figure is being used as the base, the present enrollment would be more than 100% of the earlier enrollment.

He should note that in such instances the comparison might be made in two ways. We might speak of the new enrollment as an increase over the former base, or we might speak of the new enrollment as a percentage of the former base. As an increase equal to the base would indicate an increase of 100%, an increase greater than the base would indicate an increase of over 100%. The pupil should note also that in situations where it is necessary to calculate per cent of increase or decrease, the rate of increase or decrease is applied to the original measure.

Teaching Social Applications of Per Cent

As noted above, an important reason for having children learn per cent and its applications, apart from the value of their learning the mathematical relationships involved, is to acquaint them with socially significant aspects of the business world, and thus give them a better understanding of the society in which they live. Although this particular objective may be considered to pertain more directly to the social studies program than to the mathematics program, the nature of the material makes it economical in terms of the pupils' time to develop an understanding of the social settings of per cent in its everyday applications at the same time that pupils are learning the mathematical relationships involved.

As children live today in a very complex society, they need considerable help in order to understand it. Their normal daily activities bring them into brief contacts with the business world, but not to the extent that will enable them to grasp any but the most obvious patterns and structures. A study of the social settings of topics such as simple and compound interest, profit and loss, installment buying, commissions, taxes, and increase and decrease thus may be thought of rightly as having a place in the mathematics program of children at this age level. Motivation for learning mathematics is increased also as the children are able to appreciate its usefulness in everyday life.

As the modern textbooks for pupils include detailed examples of the mathematical calculations needed in dealing with each of the various topics in per cent, the discussion here is confined to suggestions for increasing the pupils' understanding of the social implications involved in these topics. The following outline for developing an understanding of the social settings of simple and compound interest situations will indicate procedures which may be adapted for introducing other topics. The extent of the class discussions and the scope of activities provided would depend upon the age and experience of the pupils in the class as well as upon the community resources available and upon the time allotted in the mathematics program for each topic.

Outline of a Teaching Procedure for Developing an Understanding of the Social Settings of Transactions Involving Applications of Per Cent

Simple and Compound Interest

I. Class discussion to determine the children's knowledge of common situations involving interest, and to introduce the topic.
   A. Institutions, organizations, and individuals often need to borrow money at interest in order to finance projects.
      1. Governmental borrowing at federal, state, and local levels through bonds which draw interest.
      2. Borrowing by business enterprises to initiate or to enlarge operations.
      3. Personal borrowing for a variety of purposes.
   B. Many institutions depend upon lending money for their revenue.
      1. Banks and finance companies
      2. Insurance companies

II. The nature of simple interest
   A. Definition of terms used
      1. Principal (base)
      2. Rate (rate)
      3. Interest (percentage)
      4. Time (days, months, years)
   B. Business forms used
      Examining samples of real forms from business establishments and noting the essential features.

C. Derivation of a formula for computing simple interest where different time intervals are involved.
   1. Years
   2. Months
   3. Days
   4. Sixty days rule

III. The nature of compound interest
   A. Comparisons of situations involving simple and compound interest.
   B. Derivation of formula for computing compound interest where time involves periods of years, half years, quarter years, and combinations of these.
   C. Use of tables for computing compound interest.

At appropriate places during the development of the topic, use may be made of films, filmstrips, field trips, resource persons, and the like. In instances where the topic has some bearing upon the immediate experiences of the pupils, such as in school banking, examples should be drawn from these sources.

Other suggestions for developing pupils' understanding of the social settings of business transactions are given in Chapter 13, where the development of problem-solving ability is discussed. Modern teachers' manuals accompanying children's textbooks are rich sources of suggestions in this area.

Suggested Learning Activities

1. Examine three of the most recently published arithmetic series available to you and note at what level and in what way per cent is introduced in each. At what level is the bulk of teaching on this topic recommended?
2. Clip from a newspaper six items (news stories as well as advertisements) the reading of which requires an understanding of per cent. How would you explain the meanings involved to a group of average seventh graders?
3. Make up a problem requiring a calculation involving per cent for each of the following: interest on savings, discount for cash payment, installment buying, profit on sales, increase in school enrollment, automobile insurance, family budget.
4. Make a chart illustrating how per cent is related to decimals and common fractions.

5. Make a chart to which pupils may refer as they are learning to use the terms "rate," "base," and "percentage."
6. Make up two problems, likely to be within the experience of pupils, which illustrate each of the three usages of per cent.
7. Write a plan for teaching a lesson in which pupils are to learn how the equation, or formula, $b = \frac{p}{r}$ is used when solving problems of the third common type of per cent problems.
8. Write a plan for teaching pupils how to solve a problem of the second usage of per cent by the ratio method. Consult the teacher's manual or edition of a school textbook for suggestions.
9. Make an outline for developing an understanding of the social settings of a per cent topic of your choice.

Guided Supplementary Reading

1. What dual use of the term "percentage" does Banks identify?
2. How do Brueckner, Grossnickle, and Reckzeh suggest one proceed in using per cents less than 1%?
3. How does Buckingham differentiate "equation" and "formula"?
4. Dutton and Adams recommend that the teaching of the three commonly occurring types of per cent problems should not be too routinized. Why?
5. Gibb, Jones, and Junge recommend that a study of common fractions, decimal fractions, and per cent terminate in an understanding of the algebraic sentence $xy = z$. Why?
6. According to Larsen, how did the familiar per cent sign (%) evolve?
7. What computational skills do Marks, Purdy, and Kinney designate as especially important in working per cent problems?
8. What does Mueller give as the rationale for the solution of percentage problems?
9. By what means does Rappaport suggest that we can eliminate confusion over the use of the word "percentage"?
10. Why does Riedesel argue that teaching of bank discounts should be removed from the eighth grade arithmetic program? Does the editor completely agree?
11. What does Spitzer mean by "the unitary analysis method" of solving per cent problems?
12. In Van Engen's article he says that a per cent is not a fraction. What does he say it is?
13. What would Wendt substitute for "cases" in teaching per cent?

Suggested Supplementary References

1. BANKS, J. HOUSTON, *Learning and Teaching Arithmetic,* Chapter 11. Boston: Allyn and Bacon, Inc., 1959.
2. BRUECKNER, LEO J., FOSTER E. GROSSNICKLE, AND JOHN RECKZEH, *Developing Mathematical Understanding in the Upper Grades,* Chapter 7. Philadelphia: The John C. Winston Company, 1957.
3. BUCKINGHAM, BURDETTE R., *Elementary Arithmetic,* Chapter 12. Boston: Ginn and Company, 1953.
4. DUTTON, WILBUR H., AND L. J. ADAMS, *Arithmetic for Teachers,* Chapter 12. Englewood Cliffs, N.J.: Prentice-Hall, Inc., 1961.
5. GIBB, E. GLENADINE, PHILLIP S. JONES, AND CHARLOTTE W. JUNGE, "Number and Operation," *The Growth of Mathematical Ideas,* 24th Yearbook. Washington, D.C.: The National Council of Teachers of Mathematics, 1959.
6. LARSEN, HAROLD D., *Arithmetic for Colleges,* Chapter 9. New York: The Macmillan Company, 1958.
7. MARKS, JOHN L., C. RICHARD PURDY, AND LUCIEN B. KINNEY, *Teaching Arithmetic for Understanding,* Chapter 10. New York: McGraw-Hill Book Company, 1958.
8. MUELLER, FRANCIS J., *Arithmetic, Its Structure and Concepts,* Chapter 5. Englewood Cliffs, N.J.: Prentice-Hall, Inc., 1956.
9. RAPPAPORT, DAVID, "Percentage—Noun or Adjective?" *Arithmetic Teacher,* Vol. 8, pp. 25–26, January, 1961.
10. RIEDESEL, A., "Why Teach Bank Discount?" *Arithmetic Teacher,* Vol. 4, p. 268, December, 1957.
11. SPITZER, HERBERT F., *The Teaching of Arithmetic,* Chapter 8. Boston: Houghton Mifflin Company, 1961.
12. VAN ENGEN, HENRY, "Rate Pairs, Fractions, and Rational Numbers," *Arithmetic Teacher,* Vol. 7, pp. 389–399, December, 1960.
13. WENDT, A., "Per Cent Without Cases," *Arithmetic Teacher,* Vol. 6, pp. 209–214, October, 1959.

CHAPTER 12

Extending Concepts of Measurement

Procedures for introducing concepts of measurement to children in kindergarten and in the first and second grades were suggested in Chapter 5. A sequence of topics was outlined, along with several activities which children could carry on at these grade levels in order to become acquainted with various concepts and some of the vocabulary related to measurement. In the intermediate and upper grades these concepts should be extended to enable pupils to grasp the meaning of many technical terms such as "precision," "accuracy," "relative error," "tolerance," "tolerance interval," and "significant digits." They also should learn the procedures needed for making computations involving numbers which arise from approximations in measurement situations. The interest of the pupils in studying the various topics involving measurement would be stimulated and they would have a greater appreciation for this part of their social heritage if they were given some understanding of the history of how units of measurement came to be adopted and then standardized over a period of several centuries.

There is little need for reminding a teacher of the various uses of measurement in everyday life and the extent to which the work of the world depends upon the use of measuring instruments. A teacher will have no difficulty in drawing abundant illustrations of the importance of measurement from any class of pupils in the intermediate or upper grades of the elementary school. Pupils recognize very readily the important role played by measurement in the modern world. Many interesting activities are available to children through which they may gain skill in using instruments of measurement and in expressing their findings in mathematical terms. Measurement activities are particularly rich in opportunities to provide practice in using and extending the meaning of common fractions and decimal fractions.

The Approximate Nature of Measurement

When we measure something, we are carrying on a process which associates a number with some physical or geometrical concept such as length, temperature, weight, or capacity. In counting we associate a number with a group of discrete elements; but when we measure in order to associate a number with a quantity, the quantity being measured is continuous. We assume that its true measure cannot be determined exactly, because, however small the divisions of the scale we are using might be, still smaller divisions are conceivable. The number we obtain through measuring the quantity of an object is thought of as being an approximation to the true measure of the quantity. For example, if the height of a child is stated to be 54 inches when measured to the nearest inch, this means that the height of the child is nearer 54 inches than to either 53 inches or 55 inches, and that his actual height must be, therefore, between 53½ inches and 54½ inches. If the measurement had been taken to the nearest quarter inch, a recorded height of 54 inches would mean that his actual height was between 53¾ inches and 54¼ inches. When we are measuring to the nearest inch, we say that the *precision of measurement* is one inch, but when we are measuring to the nearest quarter-inch the precision of measurement is one-quarter inch. Thus we note that the precision of measurement usually depends upon the size of the unit of measurement we are using. When a smaller unit of measurement is employed, we say that the precision of measurement is greater.

In Figure 12.1, the length of the line segment AB is measured by a scale marked off in one-half inch divisions. To the nearest half-inch, the line segment is $4\frac{1}{2}$ inches long. Any difference between the actual length of the segment AB and the recorded measure of $4\frac{1}{2}$ inches is called the *error of measurement.* It will be seen that in this instance the error of measurement could be any length up to one-quarter inch, and the length of AB still would be reported as $4\frac{1}{2}$ inches because the measurement is being made to the nearest half-inch. The *greatest possible error,* or *tolerance,* in this example is one-quarter inch, and the interval between $4\frac{1}{4}$ inches and $4\frac{3}{4}$ inches is known as the *tolerance interval.* The greatest possible error, or tolerance, is sometimes stated along with a reported measurement. For instance, a measurement might be recorded as $4\frac{1}{2}$ in. $\pm$ $\frac{1}{4}$ in. This may be read as "Four and one-half inches, plus or minus one-quarter inch."

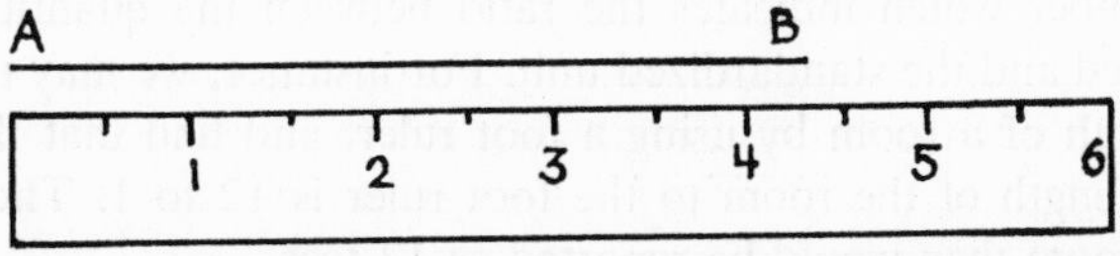

Figure 12.1 The recorded measure of the line segment AB is $4\frac{1}{2}$ inches when the segment is measured to the nearest half-inch. The difference between the actual length of the segment and $4\frac{1}{2}$ inches is the *error of measurement.* In this instance, the *greatest possible error,* or *tolerance,* is $\frac{1}{4}$ inch, and the tolerance interval is the interval between $4\frac{1}{4}$ inches and $4\frac{3}{4}$ inches.

The term *relative error* refers to the ratio between the greatest possible error and the recorded measurement. It may be expressed also either as a decimal fraction or as a per cent. For example, if a recorded measure were 50 inches and the greatest possible error were one-half inch, then the ratio of one-half to fifty would be the relative error and this may be expressed either as .01 or as 1%. The term "accuracy" has a technical meaning when used in connection with measurement, and refers to the size of the relative error. A measurement is said to be more accurate than another measurement if its relative error is less. When used in this way, the word "accuracy" does not refer to the care with which the measurement was made nor to the correct use of the measuring instrument. When a measurement is recorded it is assumed that care has been taken in making it and that the measuring instrument was used properly.

Because the numbers obtained from measurements are approximations only of the true measures, certain modifications are necessary in our calculations with these numbers. Procedures for calculating with numbers arising from approximations will be discussed later.

Direct and Indirect Measurement

To measure a quantity, we employ some process which will enable us to associate a number with the quantity being measured. Often this consists in comparing some standardized unit to the quantity being measured and then reporting the measurement as the number which indicates the ratio between the quantity being measured and the standardized unit. For instance, we may measure the length of a room by using a foot ruler, and find that the ratio of the length of the room to the foot ruler is 12 to 1. The length of the room then would be reported as 12 feet.

When a unit is being applied directly to the quantity being measured, as in the example above, we are said to be employing *direct measurement*. At times we measure a certain quantity by using numbers obtained from the direct measurement of other quantities. In such instances we are said to be measuring that certain quantity by *indirect measurement*. For example, when we use a thermometer to measure heat, we are using the numbers obtained by noting the length of the column of liquid in the thermometer, and thus using indirect measurement to measure the degrees of heat. Formulas too are used often to obtain numbers by indirect measurement. Rather than count the number of square feet in the floor of a room, we may use the formula $A = lw$ (area = length $\times$ width), and after measuring the length and the width of the room by direct measurement, we calculate the area of the floor by using a formula and thereby determine the area of the floor by indirect measurement.

Other common examples of indirect measurement are noted in

the use of a clock to measure time, a gasoline pump to measure gallons, spring scales to measure weight, and a speedometer to measure speed. In each of these instances the numbers we associate with the quantity being measured have been obtained from a scale upon which an indicator moved in response to forces transmitted through gears or other mechanical means. In none of these instances have we applied a standardized unit directly to the quantity being measured, and consequently the numbers we associate with the quantities have been obtained indirectly.

Standard Units of Measurement

Linear units. Historical records show that at one time parts of the body were used commonly as linear units. The cubit, which was the length from the tip of the middle finger to the point of the elbow, had widespread use in many countries for centuries although the length of the cubit varied from about 17½ inches in the Roman cubit to about 20½ inches in the Babylonian cubit. Other units used commonly were the width of the finger, which is approximately one inch, and the width of the palm, approximately four inches. The ell was the length from the middle of the chest to the tip of the middle finger when the arm was outstretched. The girth was the length around the chest. Both the ell and the girth corresponded roughly to our yard. The fathom, which was the length between the fingertips of both hands when the arms were outstretched, was also in common use.

Short distances on the ground were measured in feet, using the length of the foot, or in paces, which in some countries meant the length of a step and in Roman measure meant the length of a double step, or approximately five feet. Greater distances were reported sometimes in terms of a day's journey or in some similar manner.

The systems of weights and measures used in England, and which were brought to the United States by the colonists, had been adopted earlier from the Romans and the Saxons. Over a period of centuries, from the time of William the Conqueror to the very important Weights and Measures Act of 1824, the girth (yard), the gallon, the pennyweight, and the bushel were defined in various ways. As a result of international agreements and the availability of better measuring instruments, other more recent statutes have defined units of measurement more precisely.

The colonists in this country, arriving from England at different times, brought with them the definitions of units which were used in England at various times, and consequently units of measurement often were defined differently in different parts of the country. In order to fix standards of weights and measures, the Senate in 1817 asked the Secretary of State (John Quincy Adams) to prepare a report on the situation. The report was very well done, but action on it was delayed as it was thought desirable for trade purposes to get some common agreements with France and England. In 1830 the Senate directed the Treasury to check on weights and measures used at customs houses. Following an inquiry, the Treasury Department adopted certain definitions for the more common units. The yard was set at 36 inches and the pound at 7000 grains. These definitions agreed with the imperial standards for these units in Great Britain. The gallon was set at 231 cubic inches and the bushel at 2150.42 cubic inches. These units represented the wine gallon and the Winchester bushel respectively, which were legal in Great Britain before that time but which were different from the imperial gallon and the imperial bushel which were later made the legal units in that country.

In 1870, the French government took steps which resulted in a series of international conferences and in the establishment of a permanent International Bureau of Weights and Measures. In time, the international meter and the international kilogram were defined by the bureau. In 1893, the Superintendent of Weights and Measures, with the approval of the Secretary of the Treasury, decided that the international meter and kilogram would be considered as the fundamental standards of length and mass in the United States, and consequently the yard was defined as 0.9144 meter and the pound as 0.4536 kilogram.

Measures of Capacity

The problem of developing standard units of measurement for capacity in this country has been even more difficult than that of developing standard units for measuring length. Some confusion has resulted from terms such as "pint" and "quart" having meanings when used in dry measure which are different from their meanings when used in liquid measure. The root of the problem lies in the train of historical events connected with the effort to standardize the units of capacity in England.

Liquid measure. In England, the idea of measuring capacity developed from the practice of using weight, rather than volume, to define units of capacity. This idea is expressed traditionally in the saying "A pint's a pound the world around." A gallon of a substance was considered to be eight pounds of it, and consequently a gallon differed according to the specific gravity of the substance being measured. Thus a wine gallon was smaller than an ale gallon, and an ale gallon was smaller than a corn (wheat) gallon. After several centuries, two types of gallons were given legal recognition in England: the wine gallon of 231 cubic inches, and the corn gallon of 270 cubic inches.

The Weights and Measures Act of 1824 did much to remedy this situation by repealing all relevant laws pertaining to the size of a gallon and setting up a new unit, the *imperial standard gallon,* which was defined as having a volume equal to the volume of ten pounds of distilled water at a temperature of 62 degrees Fahrenheit and a barometric pressure of 30 inches. This definition set the volume of the imperial gallon at 277.274 cubic inches.

Using this imperial gallon as the standard unit for measuring capacity, the sizes of the other units, used for either liquid or dry measure, are determined.

During the colonial period in this country, gallons of various sizes were used for measuring liquids in different localities. This practice persisted until about 1830 when the Treasury Department recommended the use of a gallon of 231 cubic inches, which corresponded to the wine gallon which had been used in England. This gallon became the standard gallon for measuring liquids in this country. Other units for measuring liquids were defined in terms of this gallon of 231 cubic inches.

Dry measure. Before the Weights and Measures Act of 1824, the problem of finding a suitable unit for dry measure in England led to bushels of various sizes being used. In theory, eight gallons or 64 pounds of any substance constituted a bushel of that substance, but of the many possibilities, two bushels which were defined differently were recognized legally. The Winchester bushel was defined in terms of volume, and was considered to be equivalent to the volume of a cylinder 18.5 inches in diameter and eight inches in height. This is equivalent to 2150.42 cubic inches. The London bushel was based upon weight as it was defined as a volume equal to the volume of corn which was equivalent in weight to eight gallons of wine. In theory, the London bushel was slightly larger in volume than the Winchester bushel, but in practice it too was set at a volume of 2150.42 cubic inches.

After the Weights and Measures Act of 1824 the bushel was redefined in terms of the imperial gallon. This meant that its volume would be equivalent to the volume of 80 pounds of water, and consequently a volume of 2218.19 cubic inches.

In the United States, following the recommendations of the Treasury Department, the bushel was defined by volume as being 2150.42 cubic inches, and consequently it corresponded to the Winchester bushel which had been used previously in England. In practice, however, the size of a bushel varied considerably, and depended upon the material being measured. Three types of bushels came into common use. The *struck bushel* for measuring grain and small objects referred to a standard bushel measure of material which had been leveled off. The *heaped bushel,* which was sometimes defined as 1¼ standard bushels, meant that the vegetables or other contents had been heaped as high as possible on a standard bushel measure. The *rounded bushel* was never defined legally, but referred to a volume somewhere between that of the heaped bushel and that of the struck bushel.

To facilitate the handling of large quantities of farm products, various states from time to time have defined a bushel of each of the common farm commodities in terms of weight. The definitions have been made often without common agreement among states, and consequently there is considerable variety among the states with regard to the definition of a bushel in terms of weight for each particular commodity. A result of these differences in the definition of a bushel has been the increasing tendency to buy and sell many commodities by weight rather than by dry measure.

In the United States the bushel of 2150.42 cubic inches is the standard bushel, and other units of dry measure have been defined in terms of this unit. It should be noted that as the liquid pint and the liquid quart are smaller than the pint and quart used in dry measure, it is illegal to use the liquid pint or quart for selling commodities which are not liquids.

Measures of Weight

When we weigh a substance we are measuring the attraction of gravity on the mass of that substance. The attraction of gravity between two objects is in direct proportion to the product of the masses of those objects and in inverse proportion to the square of the distance between their centers. Consequently when we weigh an object, although its mass does not change, its weight will vary as its distance from the center of the earth increases. This phenomenon will present certain problems to the space traveler of the future which are not encountered on the surface of the earth.

For practical purposes, we consider we are measuring the mass of an object on the earth's surface by measuring the effect of gravity upon it, or in other words, by measuring its weight, even though we know that the weight of an object at sea level would differ from its weight at a greater distance from the earth's center.

In England the pound unit was adopted from the Romans, who in turn had based their pound, or *libra,* upon the weight of a sixtieth part of a *talent.* The talent was a unit which corresponded to the weight of a cubic foot of water, and had been developed by the Babylonians. During the centuries the pound was defined in many different ways and consequently it varied somewhat in weight. The Romans divided the pound into twelfths. The word "ounce" is said to have come from the Roman word *uncia,* meaning one-twelfth.

During the Middle Ages, a heavier pound known as the *merchant's pound* and equivalent in weight to about 5/4 of the earlier pound, or 15 ounces, gradually became popular as a unit. This merchant's pound was made legal in England for weighing things other than precious metals or drugs. The lighter pound of twelve ounces became known as the *troy pound.* A still heavier pound of sixteen ounces, known as the *avoirdupois* pound, became popular for measuring heavy goods such as coal, and for a time three kinds of pounds were in use at the same time for measuring the weight of different types of material.

By the Weights and Measures Act of 1824, the avoirdupois pound was established legally, along with the troy pound, and still later, in 1855, it was redefined as the imperial standard pound of 7000 grains.

In England, as in many other countries, the names of certain coins or monetary units were used also to name units of weight. A pound weight of silver was divided into 240 pence, or pennies, and the shilling was made equal to 12 pence. The terms "penny" and "shilling" were used to indicate both monetary units and weight units. The present English monetary unit of a pound thus was derived from the weight of a pound of silver. The table for both the monetary and weight units was as follows.

12 pence	= 1 shilling
20 shillings	= 1 pound

The pound was first considered to weigh 5400 grains, but later the 12-ounce troy pound of 5760 grains became the legal pound; and still later, as mentioned above, the heavier imperial standard pound of 7000 grains was made the legal pound.

In the United States, the Treasury Department recommended the use of the avoirdupois pound of 7000 grains, and this recommendation was followed. The relationships between troy weight, apothecaries' weight, and avoirdupois weight are illustrated in the following tables. In all instances, the weight of the grain is the same.

TROY WEIGHT

24 grains	= 1 pennyweight
20 pennyweights	= 1 ounce (480 grains)
12 ounces	= 1 pound (5760 grains)

APOTHECARIES' WEIGHT

20 grains	= 1 scruple
3 scruples	= 1 drachm (60 grains)
8 drachms	= 1 ounce (480 grains)
12 ounces	= 1 pound (5760 grains)

AVOIRDUPOIS WEIGHT

16 drams	=	1 ounce (437½ grains)
16 ounces	=	1 pound (7000 grains)

Measures of Time

The difficult problem of measuring time has been one of concern to man since the days of ancient Babylonia and Egypt. The problem was one of concern to man because the movements of the moon and the planets held a religious significance for him, and the seasonal changes were of economic importance. The problem was difficult because the three units which appear to be the most natural to use—the day, the month as seen in recurring phases of the moon, and the year—were units which were difficult to fit into a single system. The month did not consist of an integral number of days, nor did the year consist of an integral number of either months or days. A further difficulty arose from the fact that the length of the day varies at different times of the year. The efforts to solve the problem of making a workable calendar were an important factor in stimulating the study of astronomy and mathematics in the days of Babylonia and ancient Egypt.

Our system of measuring time had its origin in the work of the Babylonians and Egyptians, but several changes have been necessary in the calendar to allow for errors which have arisen during the intervening centuries.

The year. If we think of the year as the time taken for the sun to pass from one equinox to the same position again on a succeeding revolution of the earth, it will consist of 365 days, 5 hours, 48 minutes, 46.43 seconds. This is called a *solar year,* or a *tropical* or *equinoctial* year. It is the year in common use and the one by which our clocks are regulated. For a more precise determination, astronomers use either a *sidereal year,* which is determined from the relation of the earth to fixed stars, and is about twenty minutes longer than the solar year, or they use the *anomalistic year,* determined from the position of the earth when it is nearest the sun on successive revolutions. The anomalistic year is about 25 minutes longer than the solar year.

The Babylonian year was calculated from twelve recurring

similar phases of the moon. It was called a *lunar year*. The *lunar month* was taken to be 29½ days, and consequently a lunar year was made up of 354 days. To allow for the extra days, a thirteenth month was added to the length of certain years at irregular intervals according to the decisions of the priests. The lunar year sufficed for a number of centuries among people of eastern countries.

The Egyptians used a solar year of 365 days, and thus their calendar gradually lost time, but was more accurate than that of the Babylonians. At first, the Romans followed the Babylonian plan of using a lunar year, but in 46 B.C. Julius Caesar fixed the length of the year at 365¼ days, thus basing it upon the solar year. He arranged for every fourth year to have 366 days, while common years should have 365 days. This Julian calendar resulted in a year's being about eleven minutes too long, and was revised in 1582 under the direction of Pope Gregory XIII. It was decided that the common year would consist of 365 days but that when the number indicating the date of the year was divisible by four the year would consist of 366 days with the exception that centenary years such as 1600, 1700, 1800, and so on, would not consist of 366 days unless the numbers were divisible by 400. Other adjustments were made to allow for days omitted by the early calendar due to inaccuracies, and this Gregorian calendar is the one we now use.

The day, the hour, and the month. The *solar day* is the period taken from noon to noon, and its length varies more than 50 seconds at different times of the year. The lengths of the solar days of the year are averaged to obtain the *mean solar day* of 24 hours, 3 minutes, 56.56 seconds. The ordinary clock divides this unit of time into 24 hours. Following the Babylonian practice, we divide the hour into sixty parts which we call minutes, and the minute is divided into sixty parts called seconds.

The *lunar month,* or *synodical month,* is the average period between conjunctions, or nearest approaches, of the moon and the sun. This period of approximately 29½ days is rounded to 30 days for a calendar month. In order to obtain a year of twelve calendar months, extra days were added to certain months. In organizing the Julian calendar, a day was taken from February, which was considered to be the last month of the year by the old Roman calendar, in order to make alternate months of 31 days. When the sixth month of the year by the old Roman calendar was renamed August, in honor of Emperor Augustus Caesar, another day was added to give it a number of days equal to July, which had been named in honor of Julius Caesar. This extra day was taken also from February. The names September, October, November, and December come from Latin words meaning seventh, eighth, ninth, and tenth, respectively, and referred to the position of these months in the old Roman calendar. The Julian calendar set the first month of the year as January rather than as March, which formerly had been considered to be the first month of the year.

The present system commonly used for measuring time is based on the solar year, and is summarized in the following table.

60 seconds	=	1 minute
60 minutes	=	1 hour
24 hours	=	1 day
7 days	=	1 week
28, 29, 30, or 31 days	=	1 calendar month
12 calendar months	=	1 year
365 days or	=	
52 weeks 1 day	=	1 common year
366 days	=	1 leap year
365 days, 5 hours,	=	
48 minutes, 46.43 seconds	=	1 solar year

The Metric System

As a result of acts passed by the French government in 1793, 1795, and 1799 a system of weights and measures known as the *metric system* legally replaced the system of weights and measures which had been used prior to that time in France. A new calendar was introduced which attempted also to decimalize the table of units of time.

The metric system was not received well at first by the people of France, who were rather persistent in their use of the old system, and by 1806 the new calendar was abandoned. In 1812 acts were passed which permitted aspects of the old system to be reintroduced, and for a time the use of decimal divisions in the system of weights and measures was abandoned to a large extent. In 1837, a law was passed which made illegal the use of any system of weights and measures other than the metric system, and this law has prevailed in its essential form in France until the present date.

The metric system of weights and measures has been adopted in other countries of Europe and South America for common use with varying degrees of reluctance by the people, although it was adopted very readily for scientific purposes.

The metric system has been permitted by law in the United States since 1866, and in Great Britain since 1897. In 1903 the meter and the kilogram were made fundamental standards in the United States, and consequently the legal definitions of the yard and the pound are now in terms of the meter and the kilogram in this country. The yard is defined as 0.9144 meter and the pound as 0.4536 kilogram.

It has been the intention of those who devised the metric system to make the meter one ten millionth of the distance between the equator and the North Pole of the earth, but due to inaccuracies in measurement this was not accomplished, and the meter was defined as the distance between two lines on a certain platinum-iridium rod which is kept in the Archives of State in France. This distance is equal to 39.3702 of our inches.

The following tables show the relationships among various units of the metric system.

LINEAR UNITS OF THE METRIC SYSTEM

10 millimeters	=	1 centimeter	=	0.01	meter
10 centimeters	=	1 decimeter	=	0.1	meter
10 decimeters	=	1 meter	=	1	meter
10 meters	=	1 decameter	=	10	meters
10 decameters	=	1 hectometer	=	100	meters
10 hectometers	=	1 kilometer	=	1000	meters
10 kilometers	=	1 myriameter	=	10000	meters

A unit of area, especially designed for measuring land, is the *are,* which is an area of 100 square meters.

UNITS OF CAPACITY OF THE METRIC SYSTEM

10 milliliters	= 1 centiliter	=	.01	liter [1]
10 centiliters	= 1 deciliter	=	.1	liter
10 deciliters	= 1 liter	=	1	liter
10 liters	= 1 decaliter	=	10	liters
10 decaliters	= 1 hectoliter	=	100	liters
10 hectoliters	= 1 kiloliter	=	1000	liters
10 kiloliters	= 1 myrialiter	=	10000	liters

Another unit of capacity is the *stere,* especially designed for measuring firewood, and this unit has a volume of one cubic meter.

UNITS OF WEIGHT OF THE METRIC SYSTEM

10 milligrams	= 1 centigram	=	.01	gram
10 centigrams	= 1 decigram	=	.1	gram
10 decigrams	= 1 gram	=	1	gram
10 grams	= 1 decagram	=	10	grams
10 decagrams	= 1 hectogram	=	100	grams
10 hectograms	= 1 kilogram	=	1000	grams
10 kilograms	= 1 myriagram	=	10000	grams

The gram is the weight of a cubic centimeter of water at 4 degrees centigrade.

Another unit designed for measuring heavy weights is the *metric ton,* which is one million grams, and is about 200 pounds heavier than the ton used in our measures.

The following table shows some relationships between certain units in the metric system and some common units used in this country.

CONVERSION CONSTANTS

1 meter	= 39.37 inches
1 yard	= 0.9144 meter
1 kilometer	= 0.621 mile (statute)
1 mile (statute)	= 1.609 kilometers

[1] The liter was intended to be equivalent to the volume of one kilogram of water at a pressure of 76 centimeters of mercury and at a temperature of 4 degrees centigrade. Actually one kilogram of water under these conditions equals 1.000027 cubic decimeters.

CONVERSION CONSTANTS

1 liter	= 0.908 dry quart
1 liter	= 1.0567 liquid quarts
1 dry quart	= 1.101 liters
1 liquid quart	= 0.9464 liter
1 kilogram	= 2.2046 pounds
1 pound	= 0.4536 kilogram
1 hectare	= 2.471 acres
1 acre	= 0.4046 hectare
1 metric ton	= 2204.6 pounds
1 ton	= 0.9072 metric ton

As a result of the increasing emphasis on science and on trade and communication with countries using the metric system of weights and measures, probably more attention will be given in the elementary school program to the study of the metric system.

Teaching Procedures for Developing Concepts Relating to Measurement

Concepts regarding the nature of the measuring process. Many activities were described in Chapter 5 dealing with procedures for introducing children to the concepts of measurement. The suggestions for these activities were based upon the principle that young children should have direct experience in using common measuring instruments for measuring length, time, capacity, temperature, and weight. These activities supply the children with some of the concepts and vocabulary needed in understanding the situations they meet in daily living. The activities also provide readiness for understanding the more complicated concepts regarding measurement to which the children will be introduced in the intermediate and upper grades.

While they are still in the intermediate grades, pupils should grasp the concept that in the measuring process we are able to associate a number with a physical or geometrical quantity by applying a known unit to this quantity. The teacher should direct the attention of the pupils to children's books which give a historical account of how the techniques to carry out measuring processes were developed, and how the various units in common use were developed and standardized in order to make these units more useful over wider areas.

Payne and Seber [2] describe an activity in which the pupils of a class construct a *class cubit* by finding the average of the lengths of the distances from each pupil's elbow tip to his fingertips, and then use sticks of this average length to measure various objects. Such an exercise will give the teacher an opportunity to emphasize the idea that a standard unit is defined arbitrarily and that other units for measuring larger or smaller quantities may be defined in terms of the unit which has been agreed upon as the basic unit. The importance of developing suitable units and the importance of choosing suitable units for the work being done also may be made meaningful to the children by an activity of this nature.

Through discussions it is easy to lead the pupils to see the value of having standard units defined legally so that the business and scientific work of the nations of the world are facilitated.

As mentioned in the first part of this chapter, another very important concept related to measurement is that the numbers arising from measurement situations are approximations to the real value of the ratio between the standard unit and the quantity being measured. An effective procedure which is used commonly by teachers to help pupils appreciate the approximate nature of measurement is as follows.

The teacher asks the pupils to measure a line segment, such as is shown in Figure 12.2, by using a scale marked in inch units and to record the measurement to the nearest inch. They then measure the same line segment with separate scales marked in units of ½ inch, ¼ inch, ⅛ inch, and $\frac{1}{16}$ inch respectively, and each time record their answer to the nearest unit. The pupils are led thus to understand that as smaller units are used, the recorded measure is in each instance a closer approximation to the real value of the

[2] Joseph N. Payne and Robert C. Seber, "Measurement and Approximation," *The Growth of Mathematical Ideas,* Twenty-fourth Yearbook of the National Council of Teachers of Mathematics (Washington: National Council of Teachers of Mathematics, 1959), pp. 193–194.

length of the line segment, and that although a high degree of precision could be attained by using a suitable measuring instrument, we should think of the recorded measurement as only an approximation to the number we are seeking. By employing the concepts of "error of measurement," or "tolerance," and "tolerance interval," we are able to state with varying degrees of precision the limits within which the true measure lies. During an activity such as this the pupils are able also to develop a better understanding of the implications of the various terms related to measurement.

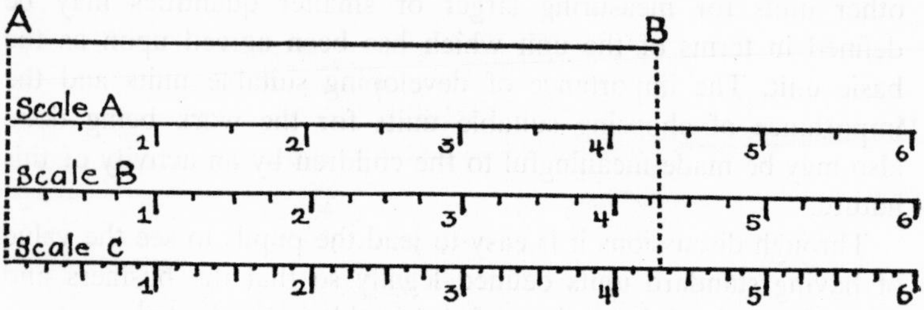

Figure 12.2 Illustrating how the recorded measure of the line segment *AB* is a closer approximation to the actual length of the segment *AB* when a smaller unit is employed. The scales A, B, and C are marked in units of $\frac{1}{2}$ inch, $\frac{1}{4}$ inch, and $\frac{1}{8}$ inch respectively. The length of the line segment *AB* is recorded as $4\frac{1}{2}$ inches by scale A, $4\frac{1}{4}$ inches by scale B, and $4\frac{3}{8}$ inches by scale C.

Pupils are aided also in clarifying the meaning of approximation and the terms related thereto in situations in which the teacher encourages pupils to make estimates before making measurements. Some of these situations should include those in which the pupils are required to estimate the limits between which a true measure lies.

Teaching Pupils How to Compute with Numbers Arising from Approximations

When using formulas in direct measurement, often it becomes necessary to apply operations such as addition, subtraction, multiplication, division, and the extraction of roots upon numbers which are approximations to other numbers. As noted above, pupils should understand that the numbers arising from approximations, such as those obtained through measurement, are numbers which are close to the real value of a measurement and do no more than indicate the limits between which the true value of a measurement lies. They then may be led to understand that specific techniques for computing with approximations are necessary. Making use of examples similar to the following will be found helpful in this respect.

Adding and subtracting numbers arising from measurement. In Figure 12.3, the length of the line segment AB is reported as $3\frac{1}{4}$

Figure 12.3 As the line segment AB is recorded to the nearest $\frac{1}{4}$ inch as $3\frac{1}{4}$ inches, its actual length is between $3\frac{1}{8}$ inches and $3\frac{3}{8}$ inches. The actual length of the segment BC, which is recorded to the nearest sixteenth of an inch as $2\frac{3}{16}$ inches, is between $2\frac{5}{32}$ inches and $2\frac{7}{32}$ inches. The actual length of AC is between $3\frac{1}{8} + 2\frac{5}{32}$ and $3\frac{3}{8} + 2\frac{7}{32}$, or between $5\frac{9}{32}$ and $5\frac{19}{32}$ inches.

inches when measured to the nearest quarter inch. The line segment BC is reported as $2\frac{3}{16}$ inches when measured to the nearest sixteenth of an inch. Consequently the *actual length* of the line segment AB is between $3\frac{1}{8}$ inches and $3\frac{3}{8}$ inches, while the actual length of the line segment BC is between $2\frac{5}{32}$ inches and $2\frac{7}{32}$ inches.

The actual length of the line segment AC is, therefore, between $3\frac{1}{8} + 2\frac{5}{32}$, or $5\frac{9}{32}$ inches and $3\frac{3}{8} + 2\frac{7}{32}$, or $5\frac{19}{32}$ inches. If, however, we add the two numbers reported for the measurement, $3\frac{1}{4}$ and $2\frac{3}{16}$, the sum, which is $5\frac{7}{16}$, implies that the true length of AC lies only between $5\frac{13}{32}$ and $5\frac{15}{32}$, and we have seen in the preceding paragraph that this is not the case. It assumes a degree of precision not justified.

For the above reason, the general procedure for adding numbers arising from measurement is to round the reported measurements to the same degree of precision which is indicated by the *least* precise of the measurements before adding them. By using this procedure in the example given above, we would add $3\frac{1}{4}$ and $2\frac{1}{4}$, and the sum $5\frac{2}{4}$ would imply that the true length would lie between $5\frac{3}{8}$ and $5\frac{5}{8}$.

Although this is a rough rule, it is more conservative than adding the numbers arising from measurements as they are reported and without regard to the precision of the measurements involved, as the resulting sum is less likely to imply a degree of precision which does not exist.

By using somewhat similar examples, pupils may be led to discover rules for computing with decimal numbers arising from measurement. On adding 12.4 and 3.21, the sum 15.61 would imply a degree of precision to the nearest hundredth, while we see that one of these measurements, 12.4, indicates a degree of precision to the nearest tenth only. As another example, in subtracting 5.21 from 14.4, a difference of 9.19 implies a precision of measurement to the nearest hundredth, while we see that one of the numbers implies a degree of precision to the nearest tenth. Class discussion of examples such as these should lead pupils to formulate some such rule as the following. *When adding or subtracting numbers arising from approximations, round all numbers to the degree of precision indicated by the number used in the least precise measurement.*

Significant digits. Before leading pupils to develop a rule for multiplying or dividing numbers arising from approximations, a teacher should ensure that they understand the meaning of the term *significant digits* and that they understand how a consideration of significant digits should affect computational procedures.

After the pupils have learned that the relative accuracy of a measurement is the ratio between the greatest possible error, or tolerance, and the reported measured value, they should be told that the term "significant digits" is used to refer to those digits which affect the relative accuracy of a measurement. Examples, such as the following, may be used to illustrate various situations in measurement requiring the pupils to identify the digits in computations which would affect the relative accuracy of a measurement, and thus be considered to be significant digits.

When a measurement is reported, we assume generally that it is precise to the smallest unit indicated. For instance, a recorded measurement of 2.5 feet is assumed to be correct to the nearest tenth of a foot, while a measurement of 2.51 feet is assumed to be correct to the nearest hundredth of a foot. In the first instance, the greatest possible error, or tolerance, would be ½ of $\frac{1}{10}$ foot, or .05 foot, and the relative accuracy would be the ratio of .05 to 2.5, or .02 when this ratio is expressed as a decimal. In the second instance, the tolerance would be ½ of $\frac{1}{100}$ foot, or .005 foot, and the relative accuracy would be the ratio of .005 to 2.51, or approximately .002 when this ratio is expressed as a decimal. Examples such as this would illustrate that all nonzero digits are significant as they affect the relative accuracy of the measurement.

The pupils should then be given examples of the type which illustrate that sometimes zeros affect the relative accuracy of a measurement and sometimes they do not. For example, when zeros are between other digits in a numeral of a whole number the relative accuracy is affected, and consequently they are significant digits along with the nonzero digits. The relative accuracy of a measurement reported as 305 feet would be affected by the zero, and consequently the numeral 305 has three significant digits.

An example of a measurement reported as 15,000 feet would illustrate that the number of significant digits would depend upon whether or not the number had been rounded. If the number had been rounded to thousands, the numeral would contain two significant digits, as none of the zeros would affect the relative accuracy of the measurement. If the number had been rounded to hundreds, then the numeral would contain three significant figures, as the first zero as well as the nonzero digits would affect the accuracy of the measurement. If the number had not been rounded, and reported to the nearest foot, then all the zeros would be considered as significant digits along with the nonzero digits.

Determining the relative accuracy of measurements involving

the use of decimal numbers, such as 5.05 feet or 5.20 feet, would indicate that zeros in positions such as these would affect the relative accuracy of the measurements and be significant, while the zeros in a numeral such as .005 would not be significant, as they do not affect the relative accuracy of the measurement.

Through computing the relative accuracy of measurements in examples such as those given above, pupils soon learn the reason why some digits are considered to be significant in numbers arising from approximations, and why these numbers need to be given special consideration in computations.

Multiplying numbers arising from measurements. After the pupils have grasped the implications in determining the number of significant digits in a numeral, their attention may be directed to observing how these implications lead to a rough rule for determining the number of significant digits in the product when we multiply two numbers arising from measurements. For example, if the measurements of the sides of a rectangle were reported as 5.25 feet and 4.5 feet, the area of the rectangle as determined by the formula $A = lw$ should not be reported as 23.625 square feet, because this would imply a precision of measurement which is not justified.

As the reported measurement of 5.25 feet is precise to the nearest hundredth of a foot, while the measurement 4.5 feet is precise to the nearest tenth of a foot, the true area of the rectangle might lie anywhere between 4.45×5.245 square feet and 4.55×5.255 square feet, or between 23.34025 square feet and 23.91025 square feet. It is seen easily that the indirect measurement of 23.625 square feet obtained through using the formula should not be considered to be precise to $\frac{1}{1000}$ square foot.

Through working with examples similar to the above illustration, the pupils may be led to develop a guide worded in some manner such as "When multiplying two numbers which arise from measurements, there should be no more significant digits in the product than in the factor with the fewer significant digits."

Dividing numbers arising from measurement. While the children are in the intermediate grades they learn that by annexing zeros to the right of the decimal point in the dividend they may extend a computation involving division to get more digits in the quotient. While they are learning to use procedures for computing with numbers arising from measurements, it should become clear to them that they cannot increase the precision of the number in the quotient by adding zeros to the dividend, because these numbers have arisen from approximations.

Through working with suitable exercises and also by remembering that division is the inverse of multiplication they should be able to formulate some guide for determining the number of significant digits to be retained in the quotient. The need for such a guide should become evident to the pupils through computations being carried out to determine the relative accuracy of measurements, and through class discussion the pupils should be able to arrive at some wording for a guide such as "In dividing numbers arising from measurement, the number of significant digits in the quotient should be the same as that of the numeral which has the fewer significant digits in the divisor or the dividend."

The Importance of Understanding Measurement Concepts

In the traditional elementary school program in arithmetic the principal objectives for teaching measurement concepts have been determined by the social utility of arithmetic in the life of a child or an adult. Although the social objectives of the program should not be neglected, a modern arithmetic program should go beyond these traditional objectives. It should treat the study of measurement as an extension of mathematical concepts and thus develop readiness for further concepts to be met in the area of approximation and the idea of a limit as employed in the calculus. For this reason, time should be taken to permit pupils to explore and discover important concepts of measurement through controlled discovery, thus encouraging them to accomplish much more than the memorization and application of common rules of measurement.

The concepts involved in measurement may be made very interesting to the pupils by a creative teacher, as this area enables pupils to associate many abstract elements of mathematics with concrete objects and meaningful diagrams. The abundant use of concrete illustrations should not be permitted to overshadow the abstract nature of number, however, and the pupils should be reminded that the concrete materials are used as a way of representing mathematical ideas.

Introducing Pupils to Procedures for Finding the Square Root of a Number

Pupils should be led to think of the operation of finding a square root of a number as the inverse of the operation of finding the square of a number. They should understand that $\sqrt{a^2} = a$ because $a \times a = a^2$. For example, $\sqrt{4} = 2$ because $2 \times 2 = 4$.

Pupils should learn that there are tables available which give the squares and square roots of numbers, but that the square root of a number may be found also by computational procedures.

Using estimates to find a square root. It is suggested that pupils should learn to use a division procedure, along with estimates, to find the square root of a number before they learn the square root algorism. This is because through using division and estimations their attention is being focused upon the fundamental nature of the operation of taking a root as being the inverse of the operation of squaring a number.

An example of a procedure for finding the square root of a number by using estimates is as follows:

To find the square root of 54, the pupils should recognize first that the square root must be between 7 and 8, because 7^2 is less than 54 while 8^2 is greater than 54. First step, divide 54 by 7:

$$\begin{array}{r} 7.7 \\ 7\overline{)54.0} \\ \underline{49} \\ 5\;0 \\ \underline{4\;9} \\ 1 \end{array}$$

It should be noted now that as the square root of 54 must be between 7 and 7.7, a suitable second estimate could be the average of these numbers, or $\frac{7 + 7.7}{2} = 7.35$. Second step, divide 54 by 7.35:

```
          7.34
7.35)54.00
     51 45
      2 550
      2 205
        3450
        2940
         510
```

As the square root of 54 is seen now to be between 7.35 and 7.34, we have an approximation of the root correct to one decimal place. If a closer approximation is desired, we may proceed to the third step, which is to divide 54 by the average of 7.35 and 7.34, or $\frac{7.35 + 7.34}{2} = 7.345$. By proceeding with other steps in a similar manner, the pupil may obtain an approximation of the square root of 54 which is correct to as many decimal places as desired.

Introducing a square root algorism. Although the use of a square root algorism is within the capabilities of most pupils in the upper elementary school grades, the teacher may have difficulty in helping them rationalize the procedure so that they understand why the algorism yields the desired results. The following procedure, in which a geometrical construction is employed while developing the algorism, will be found helpful.

The pupils first should be led to discover that by grouping the digits of a numeral of a given number in twos from the right, or in *periods,* they can determine the number of digits in the numeral of the square root of the given number. They may be led to make the discovery by noting that the largest natural number of one digit when squared will yield a number of two digits, i.e., $9^2 = 81$, while the smallest natural number of two digits when squared will yield the smallest natural number with a three-digit numeral, i.e., $10^2 = 100$. Furthermore, the smallest number with a three-digit numeral when squared will yield the smallest number with a five-digit numeral, i.e., $100^2 = 10{,}000$. Further experiments should lead the pupils to conclude that when the numeral of a given number is marked off in periods of two digits each, from the right, there is one period for each digit found in the square root of the given number, i.e., 3|45|67 indicates that the square root of this number has three digits.

To use the square root algorism for finding the square root of 625, arrange the numeral as follows, and mark it off into periods of two digits each, starting from the right.

$$\overline{)6|25}$$

As there are two periods shown in this numeral, the pupils know that the square root of 625 will be shown by a two-digit numeral. The first digit of this numeral is that of the largest number which when squared will not exceed 6, so in this instance it is 2, and consequently "2" should be written in the answer bracket.

$$\begin{array}{l} \quad 2 \\ \overline{)6|25} \end{array}$$

To help the pupils discover the next step of the square root algorism, a figure such as that shown in Figure 12.4 may be drawn on the chalkboard and marked off. At this point, the pupils know that the digit in the tens' place of the numeral they are trying to find is "2", and that the next step is one of finding a suitable number to replace "x" in the ones' place which will yield a number which when squared will be 625. The pupils may then see that they can find the number of hundreds, which is the measure of the shaded portion of Figure 12.4, by squaring the 2 in the answer bracket.

The measure of the area of the two unshaded rectangles in the figure, along with the unshaded square, could now be found by subtracting the measure of the area of the shaded square, 400, from the measure of the original figure. This is shown in the algorism as

2
6|25
−4 00
2 25

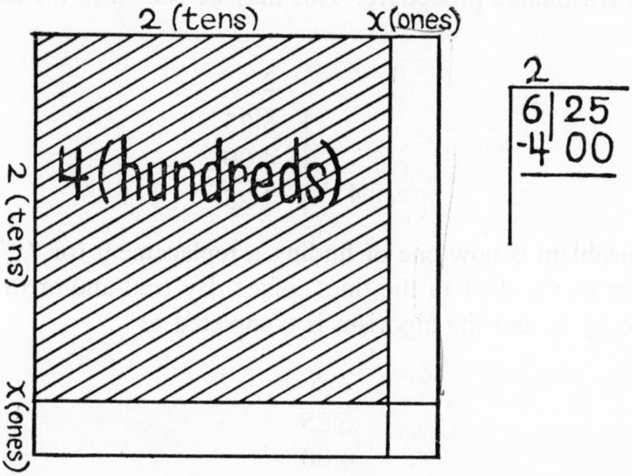

Figure 12.4 Using the chalkboard and a diagram to help children discover the square root algorism (Step 1).

To get an indication of what number is needed to replace *"x"* as the ones' digit, the unshaded portions of the square could be rearranged as in Figure 12.5.

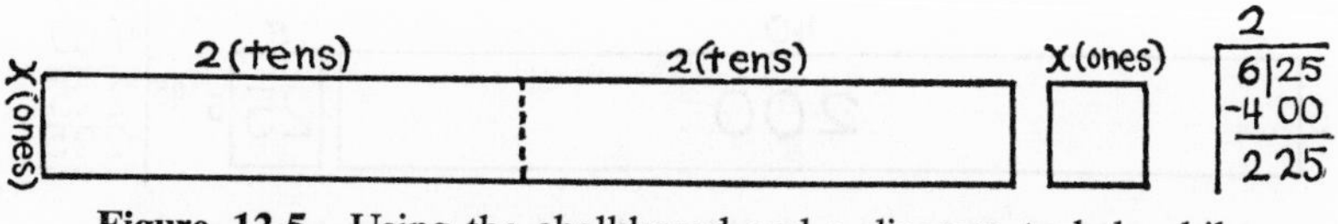

Figure 12.5 Using the chalkboard and a diagram to help children discover the square root algorism (Step 2).

The measure of the area of this new figure may be thought of as equivalent to the measures of the areas of a rectangle and a small square. The length of the rectangle is seen to be twice the number of tens indicated by the digit in the tens place of the answer bracket, and the width of the rectangle is the number replacing "*x*" as the digit in the ones' place of the answer. The measure of the side of the small square is also the number needed to replace "*x*." This diagram should help the pupils discover that the next step in the algorism, that of doubling the number in the answer bracket and using this for the tens digit of the divisor of 225 is a reasonable procedure. This may be shown in the algorism as

```
      2
    ------
   | 6|25
   |-4 00
   |------
 4 | 2 25
```

The problem is now one of finding a replacement for "*x*" which will serve as the digit in the ones' place. By trial-and-error this is found to be 5, and the algorism is completed as

```
      2 5
    ------
   | 6|25
   | 4 00
   |------
45 | 2 25
   | 2 25
```

Replacing "*x*" in the diagram with "5" will help to clarify the procedure, as in Figure 12.6.

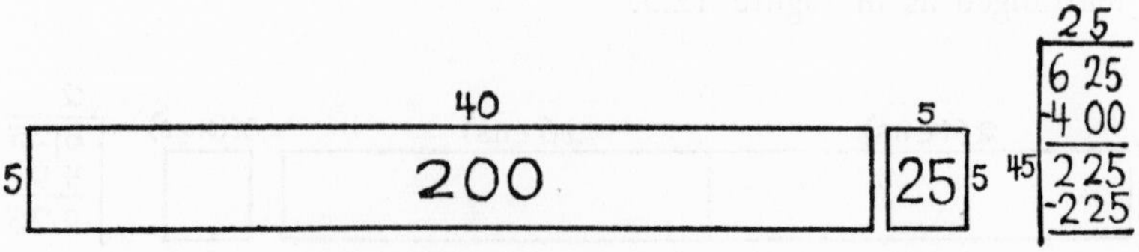

Figure 12.6 Using the chalkboard and a diagram to help children discover the square root algorism (Step 3).

The algebraic proof that the algorism provides a valid procedure for finding the positive square root of a number will not be available to the pupils until they reach a higher grade level. The diagram will help the pupils feel that the procedure is a reasonable one for finding the square root of a number when the root is a number of two digits. By experimenting, the pupils will find that they can extend the procedure to serve as an algorism for finding the square roots of numbers whose numerals contain more than three or four digits, and that the algorism may also be applied to decimal numbers.

Suggested Learning Activities

1. At a grade level of your choice, make a list of measuring needs likely to be encountered by the children in out-of-arithmetic-class situations.
2. Write a plan to show how you might help children learn that all measurements are approximate.
3. State the maximum amount of error in each of the following measurements according to the convention used by scientists and mathematicians. What is the tolerance interval for each? (a) 15.21 inches; (b) 3.6 pounds; (c) 74 miles; (d) 3.70 kilometers.
4. Argue pro and con for adoption by the United States of the metric system of weights and measures.
5. Make a chart showing the historical development of current units of measure in an area of measurement of your choice.
6. Convert the following measures to units in the metric system: (a) 2 feet 7 inches; (b) 4.3 miles; (c) 7 pounds 4 ounces; (d) 5½ gallons (liquid).
7. Your fourth grade class is about to begin a study of the ton as a unit of measure. List some experiences suitable for helping the pupils develop concepts of this measuring unit.
8. Under what circumstances might the use of 4.30 be more desirable than 4.3?
9. Remove nonsignificant digits from the numerals showing the answers in the following computations: (a) $72 + 1.82 = 73.82$; (b) $97.63 - 12.2 = 85.43$; (c) $7.125 \times 3 = 21.375$; (d) $82.404 \div 2.02 = 40.79406$.

Guided Supplementary Reading

1. Banks gives some guidelines regarding the matter of having children memorize tables of measure. What are they?
2. What do Grossnickle and Brueckner mean by "levels of measurement"?
3. Why does Buckingham refer to denominate numbers as irrational?

4. What readiness activities do Clark and Eads recommend before children use standard measures?
5. When, according to DeVore, is a good time to teach boys and girls about the metric system?
6. What sex differences did Corle find in his study of fifth and sixth grade pupils' ability to estimate measures?
7. Compare the opening statement of Chapter 6 in Dutton and Adams with the discussion by Osborn and others on pages 166–167.
8. What are some of the advantages Hauck ascribes to the measurements laboratory?
9. How does Hess suggest one begin the work of teaching pupils how to approximate answers to computations?
10. How does Jenkins recommend that the formula for circle area be taught?
11. As a result of his experiment involving teaching a given area of arithmetic to fifth and sixth graders through the use of teaching machines, what did Keislar conclude as to the effectiveness of the plan?
12. What measuring instrument did McKeen find especially interesting in his seventh grade class?
13. Differentiate "reduction" and "conversion" as Larsen applies them to measures.
14. What is the source of the word "furlong" as reported by Mueller?
15. Osborn and others point out that some qualities of things can be measured in units which can be added, subtracted, or otherwise treated much as we do our real number scale. Name three qualities of things that cannot be so treated.
16. What school activity did Parker exploit for teaching various aspects of arithmetic—especially measurement?
17. Payne and Seber suggest that children early learn a concept of betweenness. What do they mean by this and what is its significance mathematically?
18. What distinction does Schaaf draw between "things" and their "properties"?
19. Scott used the number line to show measurements involving fractions of units. What is this called?
20. What desirable qualities of the English system of measures does Spitzer point out?
21. What does Sueltz suggest one needs to do if he is to understand arithmetic?
22. Swain points out the difference between "mass" and "weight." How does he describe each?
23. What were the four weights used in Williams's puzzle?

Suggested Supplementary References

1. BANKS, J. HOUSTON, *Learning and Teaching Arithmetic,* Chapter 12. Boston: Allyn and Bacon, Inc., 1959.
2. GROSSNICKLE, FOSTER E., AND LEO J. BRUECKNER, *Discovering Meanings in Arithmetic,* Chapter 14. Philadelphia: The John C. Winston Company, 1959.
3. BUCKINGHAM, BURDETTE R., *Elementary Arithmetic,* Chapter 13. Boston: Ginn and Company, 1953.
4. CLARK, JOHN R., AND LAURA K. EADS, *Guiding Arithmetic Learning,* Chapter 8. New York: World Book Company, 1954.
5. DEVORE, M. C., "Two Ways to Measure," *Grade Teacher,* Vol. 74, p. 54, March, 1957.
6. CORLE, CLYDE G., "A Study of the Quantitative Values of Fifth and Sixth Grade Pupils," *Arithmetic Teacher,* Vol. 7, p. 7, November, 1960.
7. DUTTON, WILBUR H., AND L. J. ADAMS, *Arithmetic for Teachers,* Chapter 6. Englewood Cliffs, N.J.: Prentice-Hall, Inc., 1961.
8. HAUCK, E., "Measurements Laboratory for Arithmetic; Linear Measurements," *California Teachers Association Journal,* Vol. 54, p. 31, November, 1958.
9. HESS, CLAIRE, "Developmental Mathematics," *Grade Teacher,* Vol. 75, p. 63, February, 1958.
10. JENKINS, J., "Teaching the Formula for Circle Area," *The Mathematics Teacher,* Vol. 49, pp. 548–549, November, 1956.
11. KEISLAR, EVAN R., "Development of Understanding in Arithmetic by a Teaching Machine," *Journal of Educational Psychology,* Vol. 50, pp. 247–253, December, 1959.
12. MCKEEN, G., "Measures Make Arithmetic Meaningful," *Arithmetic Teacher,* Vol. 3, pp. 247–248, December, 1956.
13. LARSEN, HAROLD D., *Arithmetic for Colleges,* Chapter 10. New York: The Macmillan Company, 1958.
14. MUELLER, FRANCIS J., *Arithmetic, Its Structure and Concepts,* Chapter 6. Englewood Cliffs, N.J.: Prentice-Hall, Inc., 1956.
15. OSBORN, ROGER, AND OTHERS, *Extending Mathematics Understanding,* Chapter 11. Columbus: Charles E. Merrill Books, Inc., 1961.
16. PARKER, HELEN C., "Teaching Measurement in a Meaningful Way," *Arithmetic Teacher,* Vol. 7, pp. 194–198, April, 1960.
17. PAYNE, JOSEPH, AND ROBERT C. SEBER, "Measurement and Ap-

proximation," *The Growth of Mathematical Ideas,* 24th Yearbook. Washington, D.C.: The National Council of Teachers of Mathematics, 1959.

18. SCHAAF, WILLIAM L., *Basic Concepts of Elementary Mathematics,* Chapter 7. New York: John Wiley and Sons, Inc., 1960.
19. SCOTT, LLOYD, "Measurement and the Number Line," *Updating Mathematics,* Vol. 4, No. 6, 1962.
20. SPITZER, HERBERT F., *The Teaching of Arithmetic,* Chapter 9. Boston: Houghton Mifflin Company, 1961.
21. SUELTZ, B. A., "How Many? How Much?", *National Education Association Journal,* Vol. 48, pp. 30–31, February, 1959.
22. SWAIN, ROBERT L., *Understanding Arithmetic,* Chapter 11. New York: Rinehart and Company, 1957.
23. WILLIAMS, ALLAN S., "Ali's Four Weights," *Arithmetic Teacher,* Vol. 7, p. 209, April, 1960.

CHAPTER *13*

Developing Problem-Solving Ability

Some authorities in the field of elementary school arithmetic curriculum have stated that the major purpose of teaching children arithmetic is to provide them with a method of thinking.[1] Others have felt that the major purpose is to provide children with the skills they will need to meet the mathematical situations arising from their activities in life outside and inside the schoolroom.[2] In either case the importance of developing the problem-solving abilities of the pupils is implied, and its importance is always recognized by competent teachers. Traditionally, the arithmetic program in the elementary school has relied heavily upon verbal problems, which are referred to often as "word problems" or "story problems," to develop the pupils' problem-solving abilities.

The extent to which a person can increase his innate or natural ability to solve problems is still debatable, but the possibility of increasing the effectiveness with which a person uses the innate ability he possesses has been established. This effectiveness is

[1] H. G. Wheat, *The Psychology and Teaching of Arithmetic* (Boston: D. C. Heath and Co., 1937), p. 140.

[2] Foster E. Grossnickle and Leo J. Brueckner, *Discovering Meanings in Arithmetic* (Philadelphia: John C. Winston Co., 1959), p. 1.

noted as a person develops skill in using the "mental tools" available to solve each particular type of problem. Arithmetic provides us with many tools to attack problems. Teaching a child to use these tools to solve various problems increases his effectiveness at least in those areas of problem solving in which he receives practice. Good classroom experience indicates, moreover, that as pupils gain experience in solving arithmetic problems of a certain type, some of them seem to gain in the ability to solve arithmetic problems of types new to them.

Much research has been undertaken to determine how to improve the ability of pupils to solve verbal problems in arithmetic, but no quick way of attaining this objective has been ascertained. The research [3] in this area and the experience of teachers indicate that the development of a child's ability to solve verbal problems depends upon several factors, and that various procedures, each of which makes certain contributions, are required to increase this ability.

After identifying various factors contributing to the child's growth in ability to solve problems, a teacher may do much to increase the competence of the pupil in this respect. A continuing effort should be directed toward increasing the pupil's competence in problem solving throughout every stage of the arithmetic program. There is general agreement that much practice is needed.[4] As each new step in arithmetic is developed, its application to problem solving should be made clear to pupils by having them solve quantitative problems in social settings. One of the important skills gained from this practice is that of learning how to analyze a problem situation in order to determine the steps leading to its solution.

Either of two types of procedure may be followed successfully by pupils while analyzing verbal problems. One procedure is used when dealing with problem situations which are unfamiliar to the pupil. The other is followed when the pupil is able to identify a

[3] Robert H. Koenker, "Twenty Methods for Improving Problem Solving," *Arithmetic Teacher,* 5:74–78, March, 1958; Herbert F. Spitzer and Frances Flournoy, "Developing Facility in Solving Verbal Problems," *Arithmetic Teacher,* 3:177–182, November, 1956.

[4] Harry C. Johnson, "Problem Solving in Arithmetic: A Review of the Literature, I," *Elementary School Journal,* 44:396–403, March, 1944.

problem as belonging to a familiar pattern or combination of patterns, and so proceeds to use a familiar series of steps to meet the situation. Probably most of the problems in arithmetic which are met in the business world and in social situations in life outside the school are those which will fit into some familiar pattern. Problems relating to per cent are used to compute interest, profit and loss, increase and decrease, and in many other familiar business situations, and these fit often into well-defined patterns. Problems dealing with area, volume, and the various aspects of mensuration fit into other patterns. In such instances, the objective of the teacher might be to prepare pupils to recognize the types of common problems which are solved by using some well-defined pattern, and then to have pupils practice the skills involved in using such patterns until they can solve related problems efficiently.

A more difficult and challenging task is that of developing in pupils a mental attitude which will encourage them to work successfully on problems new to them and which do not fit into any pattern with which they are familiar. This necessitates the pupils' gradual development of attitudes of persistence, confidence in their own ability, and desire for the satisfaction of solving the new problems with a minimum of assistance. This will involve their analyzing an unfamiliar problem and trying various promising procedures until they are successful with one.

For pupils to develop this attitude it is likely that they will need considerable practice in solving problems successfully through their own efforts and discovery. The general method or procedure which the teacher uses in the daily arithmetic period becomes very important in fostering this attitude of discovery on the part of pupils.

The experienced teacher knows that certain patterns of solutions will be needed by pupils and that these patterns should be learned. Instead of "giving" these patterns to pupils and then having pupils practice them, it is preferable to require pupils to think through the problems and to discover the patterns for themselves. The practice they get while doing this, and the sense of satisfaction they derive from their success, will contribute to their being able later to discover solutions for problems for which no particular pattern has been taught or where the problem cannot be solved through using any pattern pupils have learned previously.[5]

The ability of the teacher to foster this attitude of discovery on the part of his pupils is one characteristic of an outstanding arithmetic teacher. It is noted in the daily work of the teacher who uses questions to lead pupils to think for themselves rather than "giving" them information which they could have deduced through their own observation or reasoning. Certain questions which are found to be too difficult for pupils may be broken down by asking further questions which are within their ability to answer. As emphasized by Wheat,[6] the skillful use of the teacher-question and pupil-answer technique contributes to building an attitude of self-reliance in pupils. This procedure takes more time in the initial stages, but the gain in the pupils' attitudes toward attacking problems independently will compensate the teacher for the extra time spent.

The "puzzle element" in arithmetic should be recognized as contributing considerably to the interest of children in this subject. The feeling of accomplishment which pupils experience when they are able to answer and "see through" a situation is a motivating factor which grows with success. The competent teacher does not overlook this positive intrinsic motivation.

Although the factors which enter into teaching children how to solve verbal problems are so closely interwoven that in practice they usually should not be separated, it is convenient for purposes of discussion to consider them under three headings, since they affect three important aspects of the teacher's work. These headings are:

1. Procedures to help pupils understand the setting of a verbal problem.
2. Procedures to help pupils identify the mathematical relationships involved in each problem situation, and identify the steps needed in dealing with each situation.

[5] Howard F. Fehr, "The Role of Insight in the Learning of Mathematics," *Mathematics Teacher,* 47:386–392, October, 1954.

[6] Harry Grove Wheat, *How to Teach Arithmetic* (Evanston: Row, Peterson and Co., 1951), p. 315.

3. Procedures to help pupils become more successful in carrying out the computations necessary to arrive at a satisfactory solution.

Suitable activities to achieve these three purposes should be carried on concurrently and the abilities concerned developed together. All three purposes must be achieved if pupils are to become competent in solving verbal problems in arithmetic.

Helping Pupils to Understand the Setting of a Verbal Problem

The use of textbook problems. As noted above, one of the important purposes in teaching children arithmetic is to enable them to use number effectively to solve quantitative problems which arise in everyday living. To accomplish this purpose, the teacher should take advantage of the numerous opportunities which arise in school life to help the children learn how arithmetic may be used to meet their daily needs. For example, a situation involving computation which might arise during a social studies lesson[7] or during a construction period provides an opportunity for the pupil to use his arithmetic in a way that is useful and meaningful to him.

Although solving arithmetic problems which arise in activities of school life is particularly helpful to pupils, the teacher cannot depend always on the availability of real situations at the exact time when pupils need practice in developing certain arithmetical concepts or skills. For this reason, it is necessary to have available numerous "described" problems of a textbook nature. There is some evidence to show that when pupils are able to visualize clearly a verbal problem, it becomes almost as easy for them as if the problem had occurred within their experience.[8]

Modern textbooks in arithmetic are written for the pupils' use and they provide many situations for practicing problem solving.

[7] John Jarolimek, "Teaching Quantitative Relationships in the Social Studies," *Arithmetic Teacher,* 4:70–74, March, 1957.

[8] L. L. Hydle and F. L. Clapp, *Elements of Difficulty in the Interpretation of Concrete Problems in Arithmetic.* Research Bulletin No. 9 (Madison: Bureau of Educational Research, University of Wisconsin, 1927), 84 pp.

Unfortunately, the difficulties in reading this arithmetic material often present new stumbling blocks for some children.[9] A pupil may have sufficient general reading ability to profit to some extent from the textbook material but still lack the special reading skills which are required to attain full competency in using the material. As it is important for a pupil to get a clear, vivid visualization of a problem situation from his reading, teaching the pupils how to read arithmetic material should be considered to be an important part of the arithmetic program. Good reading skills contribute directly toward the pupil's success in solving verbal problems.

Learning to read arithmetic material. Modern textbooks in arithmetic are written with considerable thought to the level of the reading ability of the pupils who will use them, but the teacher probably will find that there are children in each class who are not able to read at the level required to understand fully the settings of the problems. These children will need extra help in order to read the textbooks with sufficient understanding to profit from the use of these books. In most instances, the teacher should endeavor to build up the pupil's reading ability rather than to seek procedures which will enable a pupil to omit the reading material prepared for his grade level in the arithmetic textbooks. A modern arithmetic textbook contains material which the pupil should be able to use independently for reference purposes and for self-instruction. If a pupil is unable to read his textbook, he will be handicapped in the average arithmetic program.

The pupil should be taught that his procedures in reading arithmetic material should differ somewhat from his procedures in reading narrative material. Instead of reading rapidly to get the general thought of a sentence, as he does in reading narrative material, the pupil should learn how to read arithmetic material slowly enough to be able to note every word, because often a word which seems relatively unimportant might change the meaning of the arithmetic problem. He should learn that usually it will be necessary for him

[9] John P. Treacy, "The Relationship of Reading Skills to the Ability to Solve Arithmetic Problems," *Journal of Educational Research,* 38:86–96, October, 1944.

to read an arithmetic problem at least three times. During the first reading he should try to grasp the general situation and get the information needed to enable him to visualize the main aspects of the problem as they are described in the social setting. A second reading probably will be necessary in order to decide which operation (addition, subtraction, multiplication, or division) he will need to use for arriving at a solution or for completing each of several steps leading to a solution. A third reading enables him to direct his attention to the numerals which are in the problem, and to consider how to use them in computation.

If the pupil has developed the habit of reading through an arithmetic problem rather rapidly, and only once, in the manner in which he has become accustomed to read narrative material, probably he will have little success in reading arithmetic material.

To give pupils practice in reading the arithmetic textbook in such a way that they will learn how to use it for reference purposes, and also to enable pupils gradually to increase their vocabularies to keep pace with the new material, the teacher should arrange for the pupils, as a group, to spend a few minutes each day in reading the textbook and discussing the material. The pupils first should read silently, and then read aloud either phrases or sentences in answer to questions designed to test their understanding of the material. The significance of diagrams, graphs, or illustrations used in the textbook should be discussed. New vocabulary should be noted, and the meanings clarified.[10] A few minutes spent daily in this type of activity may be very profitable. This procedure enables the teacher to evaluate the abilities of the children to read arithmetic material, and thus he can emphasize those aspects of reading which are needed by certain pupils.

Developing the vocabulary of arithmetic. Even though a pupil can read and pronounce a word correctly it does not guarantee that he understands its meaning. In arithmetic material, it is particularly important for the pupil to understand the meaning of each word he is reading. Very frequently a whole arithmetic concept or series of concepts is implied in one word. Words such as

[10] Foster E. Grossnickle, "How to Use the Arithmetic Textbook," *NEA Journal,* 47:41–42, January, 1958.

"denominator," "perimeter," "volume," "discount," and many others imply concepts which may not be understood by the pupils.

The meaning of words new to the pupils should be developed carefully when these words are first encountered in the arithmetic material.[11] It is helpful to list new words on wall charts and review them as often as needed. Modern textbooks give vocabulary lists at intervals, and time should be taken to ensure that the pupils give sufficient attention to these lists. Pupils should be encouraged also to use the correct arithmetic terms when discussing their work. For example, with encouragement, pupils will soon learn to use the word "numerator" instead of calling this term of a fraction "the top number."

If the teacher maintains a steady emphasis upon the importance of the pupils' thorough understanding of the vocabulary of arithmetic, this fact should contribute considerably to the pupils' abilities to read and understand the material. When the teacher himself takes advantage of opportunities to use new words frequently in the proper context, this will contribute also to the pupils' vocabularies by giving them familiarity with new words.

Making use of the pupils' textbooks. Today's teacher is fortunate in having available modern textbooks which have been written carefully with expert attention to the psychological factors involved in the organization of subject matter and with insight into how children learn. Textbooks prepared for children of the third grade or higher levels present a sequence of learning steps which have been graded carefully so that each step leads easily into the succeeding step. For this reason, the teacher is following a psychologically sound progression of topics by using the sequence presented in a good modern textbook.

Due to the limits imposed upon the size of a textbook, often there are not enough problems and exercises included to meet the needs of all children in all situations. There are always enough problems, however, to indicate to the teacher the type and degree

[11] Harry C. Johnson, "The Effect of Instruction in Mathematical Vocabulary upon Problem Solving in Arithmetic," *Journal of Educational Research,* 38:97–110, October, 1944; Clarence Phillips, "The Relationship Between Arithmetic Achievement and Vocabulary Knowledge of Elementary Mathematics," *Arithmetic Teacher,* 7:240–242, May, 1960.

of difficulty of the problems suggested for each step. It should not be too difficult for a competent teacher to design similar problems at the same level whenever the children need extra practice.

The modern textbook differs from those written a number of years ago by giving much more space to the explanation of new steps. Diagrams, pictures, graphs, and other illustrations assist the pupils in understanding the concepts being presented. As has been noted above, the teacher should give pupils time to discuss this textbook material and ensure that their grasp of the explanations is sufficiently strong to enable them to use the textbook as a reference when they are reviewing material or when they need to relearn some step which is not remembered clearly.

Usually it is preferable for the teacher not to use the textbook when first introducing a new step. A new step is best introduced through class discussion of some pertinent aspect of the new situation which might arise within the social experience of pupils or adults. By using visual materials and familiar illustrations, the teacher may thus provide readiness activities for the new step and then introduce it through class discussion. A question-and-answer technique will enable him to ascertain how much pupils already know about the new topic and permit him to clarify those points needing particular emphasis. This type of instruction does not call upon the reading skills of the pupils until after the new concept has been introduced and clarified. Pupils who are weak in reading are able to profit by the introduction and the oral explanations.

When the pupils understand the new concept, the teacher should require them to take their textbooks and consider the explanations presented therein. As was mentioned above, it is at this point that the teacher should place considerable emphasis upon clarifying the reading of the arithmetic material for the weaker readers.

Understanding the social setting of a problem. Many verbal problems in arithmetic are expressed in some rather familiar social setting, and one of the first tasks of a pupil when he reads a problem is that of visualizing this social setting. After he understands the social setting he still must recognize the mathematical relationships involved. Often the social setting is taken from the adult business world, and is only vaguely understood by the pupil. Helping a pupil to understand the social setting of a verbal problem thus becomes an important part of the teacher's work.

The social implications of a problem situation may be clarified sometimes by a brief classroom dramatization of the social setting.[12] For instance, when learning about discounting notes, one pupil could take the part of the person borrowing money and giving a note. A second pupil could act the part of the person who is lending the money. A third pupil could act as the banker who is discounting the note. The teacher should be the narrator who leads the discussion regarding the steps which are being taken during the transaction. A few minutes spent thus in an impromptu dramatization of each of the common types of problems as they are encountered, will help familiarize the pupils with the business setting of a situation which would otherwise be strange to them.

In some types of problems the pupils may be helped by working from actual business forms in their computations. For instance, when learning to compute the cost of electrical consumption, the pupils could use electric light bills recently paid by their parents. Advertisements cut from newspapers may supply the material for practicing calculations involving buying and selling, price discount, or instalment buying. Such material makes the social setting seem more real and interesting to the pupils, and thus assists them in visualizing verbal problems in social settings.

Conclusions from many studies have indicated that at times there are advantages in having pupils make up their own problems.[13] The pupils should make up problems to show the applications of an arithmetic step they are learning to possible situations which might arise within their experience. Both the preparation of the problems and their solutions pose a challenge for the bright pupils. They find this type of practice interesting, as it provides them with an opportunity to do thinking of a creative nature,

[12] Robert H. Koenker, "Twenty Methods for Improving Problem Solving," *Arithmetic Teacher,* 5:74–78, March, 1958.

[13] William L. Connor and Gertrude C. Hawkins, "What Materials Are Most Useful to Children in Learning to Solve Problems?" *Educational Method,* 16:21–29, October, 1936.

and they often construct problems with a far more elaborate social setting than those usually found in textbooks.

Identifying Mathematical Relationships in Problem Situations

Studies to determine the types of errors children make in problem solving show that many errors are due to the children's not having adequate mathematical concepts. These findings imply that the emphasis a teacher gives to having pupils understand the "meaning" of arithmetic contributes to developing the pupils' problem-solving abilities. As the pupils gain an understanding of the nature of the arithmetical processes and the decimal numeration system, the application of this knowledge to problem solving is facilitated to some extent.

During the time that the pupils are learning the meaning of the computational processes for each of the operations of addition, subtraction, multiplication, and division, they should be required to solve many verbal problems in which each of the processes is used typically. This will enable them to understand what can be accomplished through using each particular operation and its related algorism. Pupils should understand, too, that usually there are various ways of solving each problem, although often it is more efficient to use one operation than it is to use another. Studies have shown that pupils may gain insight by considering various ways of solving a problem.[14] For instance, they might note that in a problem requiring them to find the combined total of two or more groups, the solution may be found by addition, counting, or in instances where the groups are all the same size, by multiplication. Selecting the operation to use in solving a particular problem thus becomes an early step toward its solution, and the operation selected by a pupil depends upon his ability to use a mature procedure when the choice is offered.

To give pupils practice in identifying the most efficient operation

[14] Herbert F. Spitzer and Frances Flournoy, "Developing Facility in Solving Verbal Problems," *Arithmetic Teacher,* 3:181, November, 1956.

to use in various situations, they sometimes may be asked to read a number of verbal problems and then suggest in each instance which procedure or procedures would be suitable to use in arriving at a solution. While this use of "problems without numbers" provides little or no practice in computation, several problems may be considered in a relatively short time, providing concentrated practice in recognizing the mathematical relationships in a verbal problem.[15] Another advantage of this type of activity is that the teacher is given many opportunities to note the types of difficulties the pupils are having in recognizing mathematical relationships. This evaluation permits the teacher to identify and emphasize those aspects of the work which need additional attention.

Using diagrams to indicate mathematical relationships. Many authorities refer to the value of encouraging pupils to make diagrams to indicate the mathematical relationships in certain types of problems.[16] Diagrams are particularly helpful where the problems involve aspects of measurement and deal with concepts of area or volume. In such instances the pupils should start with a diagram upon which they have recorded the relevant information, and by working from this, decide upon the steps which are needed to solve the problem.

Problems involving price discounts, profit and loss, increase and decrease, and various phases of per cent may sometimes be clarified by using diagrams to represent the numerical relationships which should be considered. Examples of how such diagrams might be drawn are shown in Figure 13.1.

Selecting verbal problems. As has been implied in the suggestions already given for selecting verbal problems for children, the quality of problems should be considered as carefully as the quantity. In order to select verbal problems similar to those arising in a life situation outside of the schoolroom, some thought should be

[15] *Ibid.*

[16] John L. Marks, C. Richard Purdy, and Lucien B. Kinney, *Teaching Arithmetic for Understanding* (New York: McGraw-Hill Book Co., 1958), pp. 323–325.

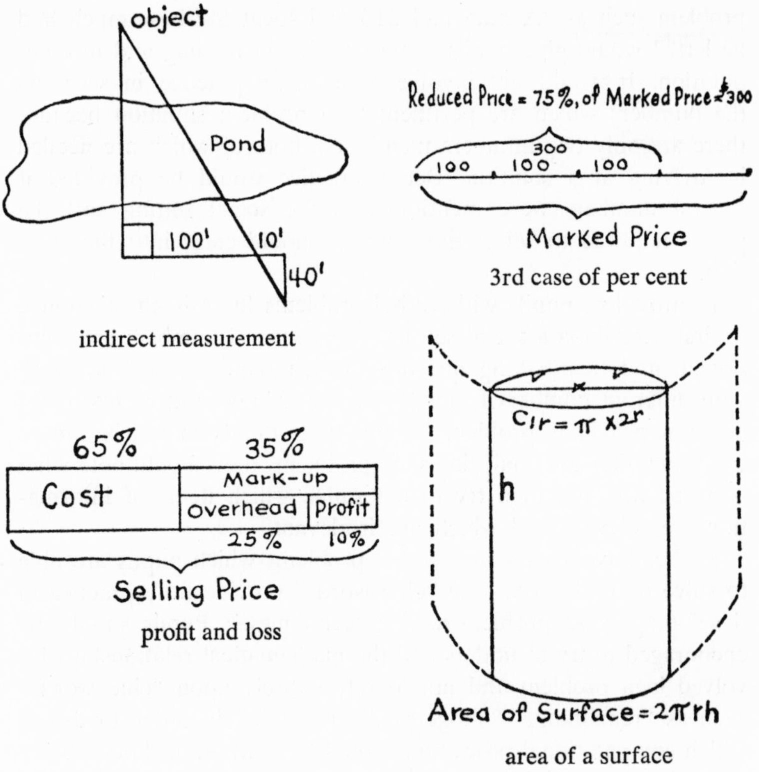

Figure 13.1 Examples of diagrams which might be used to facilitate an understanding of number relationships in certain problem situations.

given to problems which require pupils to make a choice between relevant and irrelevant details.

One difference between out-of-school problems and textbook problems is that in an out-of-school situation a person often is confronted with many factors from which the relevant information must be selected to solve his problems. Textbook problems are stated often quite briefly, with irrelevant details omitted. Because one factor in successfully solving problems is the ability to select the relevant information and ignore the irrelevant details, pupils should be given practice in this type of activity. For example, a problem such as "A man had $16 and spent $8; how much had he left?" would give pupils some practice in reading and in computation. It would not involve appreciable practice in selecting the numbers which are pertinent to a problem situation because there are only two numbers mentioned, both of which are needed in arriving at a solution. Better practice would be provided if several numbers were mentioned in the social setting and the pupils required to select those which should enter into the solution.

In providing pupils with verbal problems there is an advantage in first describing a social setting where several numbers are mentioned, and then asking questions which require pupils to work with different numbers from this setting. Many modern textbooks are now providing problems of this type. Pupils should be taught that when they are analyzing such problems, they should note what is asked for, and then try to determine which items of information are relevant and which are irrelevant.

Studies have shown that verbal problems which pupils are able to solve by noting only the "clue words" provide little practice in developing good problem-solving techniques.[17] Pupils should be encouraged to try to understand the mathematical relationships involved in a problem and not to rely entirely upon "clue words" such as "remaining," "altogether," or "each," in order to decide which computational procedure should be used, even though using such clues may make it easier for them to solve some textbook problems.

The verbal problems commonly called "two-step" problems may be particularly helpful in that they require pupils to do the type of thinking needed to improve problem-solving ability. These are problems in which two or more partial solutions are determined first and then used together to reach a complete solution. This type of problem requires the pupil to plan each of the steps needed to reach a partial solution, and then to grasp the relationships among the various steps.

Hartung and others have emphasized the importance of teach-

[17] Henry Van Engen, "The Child's Introduction to Arithmetic Reasoning," *School Science and Mathematics,* 55:358–363, May, 1955.

ing children to rewrite verbal problems as mathematical sentences.[18] For example, a verbal problem might be: "Mary has 5 pencils. After her mother gave her some more she had 12 pencils. How many did her mother give her?" The child would be taught first to express this in the mathematical sentence $5 + n = 12$ and then to find the value of "n" which would make the statement true. This procedure has much to recommend it, as it has the advantage of requiring the child to think about the relationships involved in the verbal problem and to express them in writing before beginning the needed computation. The practice pupils receive through solving such equations through informal procedures will enable them to appreciate the more formal procedures which they will be taught at higher grade levels.

Improving Computational Procedures in Problem Solving

Various studies have indicated that many errors made in solving verbal problems are errors in computation. As success in solving verbal problems requires accuracy in all computation as well as the adequate selection of procedures,[19] the teacher should persevere in encouraging the pupils to develop attitudes and habits of work which will contribute to accuracy.

The teacher should maintain a steady emphasis upon the importance of accuracy throughout all phases of the arithmetic program, until pupils fully understand the importance of accuracy in computations and have developed positive attitudes toward checking their work and using other safeguards against making errors. Sometimes the importance of accuracy may be impressed upon the pupils by the teacher's refusing to give marks on an arithmetic test for answers which are only partially correct. When the teacher adopts this policy, however, he should make sure that the pupils have sufficient time to check their work before handing it in. Any

[18] Maurice L. Hartung, Henry Van Engen, Lois Knowles, E. Glenadine Gibb, *Charting the Course For Arithmetic* (Chicago: Scott, Foresman and Co., 1960), p. 111.

[19] William A. Brownell, "Meaning and Skill—Maintaining a Balance," *Arithmetic Teacher,* 3:129–136, October, 1956.

time-pressure during a test would tend to decrease the care pupils might give to checking their computations.

Encouraging the habit of checking all computations tends to emphasize the importance of accuracy. At the same time it provides the pupils with more practice in completing algorisms, because the act of checking in itself involves more computation. To help impress upon the pupils the importance of checking their work, it is suggested that when the teacher has made computations on the chalkboard, he should go through the motions of checking the work even though he is sure that it is correct. These motions, which indicate that checking is taking place, may be done quite rapidly and with little loss of time. Their effect, however, is to impress upon the pupils the idea that checking is an activity which everyone, even the teacher, should complete as a usual procedure following each computation.

As new computational procedures are taught, the effective procedure for checking them should be developed at the same time. The pupils should try continually to reach the goal of having accurate solutions for all of the verbal problems which they have had time to complete. The amount of work covered may be slowed up somewhat at first, but as the pupils gain skill in computation, the gains in accuracy will compensate for the extra time taken.

Pupils should learn to check the computations needed at each step of a solution of a verbal problem as they proceed, rather than waiting to check all the steps after the answer to the whole problem has been determined. Once the final answer has been determined, the pupils should apply another check, that of deciding whether or not the answer is a reasonable one. This is usually done by substituting easily handled approximations through rounding the numbers given in the problem, and then comparing the estimate derived in this way to the calculated answer. This procedure of estimating the answer and using it as a check against the computed answer is helpful at all grade levels, but it is particularly helpful in solving problems involving common fractions, decimal fractions, or per cent.

Any practice which the pupils receive in "mental" arithmetic, that is, in carrying out computations without using pencil and paper, will increase their efficiency in estimating answers. Flournoy [20] has stated that practice in mental arithmetic improved pupils' ability to solve verbal problems. Increasing a pupil's ability to compute without pencil and paper should be expected to facilitate his effectiveness in checking answers by estimating.

It should be remembered that during the elementary school years pupils are meeting many new mathematical concepts in a relatively short space of time. It would be unrealistic to expect them to remember all that they had learned without their being provided with carefully selected reviews of their earlier learning. To provide sufficient review, a teacher frequently should include problems which mix the types of fundamental operations required for their solutions. For example, if all the practice problems given on a certain day required division procedures, there is a possibility that the pupils would use this operation rather mechanically and without troubling to study the mathematical relationships involved in the problem situation. The value of mixed drill in the fundamental processes has been established by early studies,[21] and the reasons for providing mixed drill in the fundamental processes apply equally well to providing mixed types of verbal problems.

It should be noted that the selection of problems should be made with careful thought to the grouping which must be planned in most classes in order to provide for the individual differences among the children.[22] The importance of selecting problems which will evoke the type of thinking needed for developing good problem-solving ability is recognized by authorities. It has been emphasized often in statements such as that of Hildebrandt, who wrote, "One should remember, however, that the nature or choice of the problem and the manner in which it is presented are of the greatest importance. These factors must be geared to the age

[20] Frances Flournoy, "The Effectiveness of Instruction in Mental Arithmetic," *Elementary School Journal,* 55:148–153, November, 1954; Olan Petty, "Non-Pencil-and-Paper Solutions of Problems," *Arithmetic Teacher,* 3:229–235, December, 1956.

[21] Austin C. Repp, "Mixed versus Isolated Drill Organization," in *Report of the Society's Committee in Arithmetic,* 29th Yearbook Part II, N.S.S.E. Bloomington, Ill.: Public School Publishing Co., 1930, pp. 535–549.

[22] Frances Flournoy, "Meeting Individual Differences in Arithmetic," *Arithmetic Teacher,* 7:80–86, February, 1960; Agnes G. Gunderson, "Arithmetic for Today's Six- and Seven-Year-Olds," *Arithmetic Teacher,* 2:95–101, November, 1955.

level and the experience of the group or individual." [23] These two factors, the choice of the problem and the manner in which it is presented, should be considered by the teacher to be of primary importance, irrespective of the techniques or procedures he is using to develop the pupil's problem-solving ability.

Suggested Learning Activities

1. At a grade level of your choice, examine ten pages of verbal problems from a current arithmetic textbook series. For each question asked, note what experience background would contribute best to an understanding of the social setting, e.g., living in rural, urban, seashore, mountain, plain or forest area; coming from low-, middle-, or upper-class home; having travelled widely. What conclusions might you draw from such an analysis?
2. Examine twenty verbal problems in a children's textbook and note how many have word or phrase clues through which pupils might identify processes to use in reaching solutions. In how many are similar clues misleading? In how many are no clear-cut clues recognizable? Report your findings for class discussion.
3. Compare the reading difficulty of a fifth grade arithmetic textbook with that of a reading textbook for the same level. In general, which do you estimate to be the more difficult? Do you think the disparity you found was planned? Why?
4. Make a plan for teaching children to read arithmetic problems from a textbook of your choice.
5. At a grade level of your choice write ten problems intended to give practice in a particular phase of problem solving, e.g., subtracting dimes and pennies at second grade level. Since slow learners generally need more practice than do others, adjust the reading difficulty accordingly. What out-of-school background are you assuming?
6. From a newspaper, cut an advertisement for a sale (groceries, drugs, dry goods, or the like) and make up a set of problems appropriate to children of a grade level of your choice.
7. Write ten two-step "problems without numbers" in each of which pupils need to determine the processes needed for solution.

[23] E. H. C. Hildebrandt, "Mathematical Modes of Thought," *The Growth of Mathematical Ideas,* p. 384. Twenty-fourth Yearbook of the National Council of Teachers of Mathematics, Washington, D.C.: The National Council of Teachers of Mathematics, 1959.

8. From a pupil's textbook in arithmetic, select five problems and illustrate each by the use of diagrams or other drawings.
9. Examine a modern arithmetic textbook at a grade level of your choice. Find two examples of verbal problems related to an introductory description of a social setting. Are all of the problems directly related to the setting described; that is, are all data needed for solution found in the description? Do some questions, though similar to those arising from the social setting, include different data?

Guided Supplementary Reading

1. What does Banks give as the main purpose of problem solving in grades 1 through 6?
2. What steps does Blecha recommend pupils be taught to follow in solving verbal problems?
3. What five steps in problem solving did Brewer find helpful for her pupils?
4. What five suggestions does Buswell make to improve problem-solving ability?
5. What do Clark and Eads say about children who try to solve problems for which they are too immature?
6. Does Curtin believe that social studies or other nonarithmetic teaching units should be selected for their arithmetic content?
7. At a grade level of your choice, select a social studies unit topic and analyze it for arithmetic activities much as Dumas does.
8. What did Flournoy find in her study of sixth grade children's reactions to quantitative statements in social studies materials?
9. What recommendations does Flournoy make with regard to arithmetic textbooks and mental arithmetic?
10. What means did Green use to motivate children to study two-step problems?
11. Grossnickle and Brueckner name a number of major skills and abilities needed by children in successfully reading arithmetic materials. What are they?
12. What does Herriott attempt to discover about pupils through the procedure he describes?
13. What reason does Jarolimek give for including incidental and planned arithmetic applications in the curriculum?
14. What values does Klas attribute to giving pupils problems without specific data?

15. Marks, Purdy, and Kinney list four common difficulties in problem solving. What are they?
16. What point of view do McSwain and Cooke take with regard to the matter of speed in problem solving?
17. What criticism does Olander make of teaching children "cues" to arithmetic processes?
18. What advantage does Osborn claim for the use of models in teaching and learning mathematics?
19. Why does Petty suggest that pupils be taught some mental solution of problems?
20. What is creative thinking in arithmetic, according to Reed?
21. Why does Serviss prefer to speak of problem solving as "problem-situation solving"?
22. Sinner makes some good suggestions for teaching problem solving. What are they?
23. What conclusion does Sister Josephina reach regarding the presentation of mental arithmetic problems?
24. What do Spitzer and Flournoy conclude with regard to the adequacy of problem-solving programs presented in textbooks?
25. How does Spitzer identify each of two roles of problems in arithmetic instruction?
26. What values does Thorpe ascribe to the learning of using equations in arithmetic?
27. According to Van Engen, the children in the lower elementary school must learn to avoid thinking about the objects described in a problem and center attention on what?
28. In nonoccupational uses of arithmetic, what did Wandt and Brown find was the proportion of mental to paper-and-pencil arithmetic?

Suggested Supplementary References

1. BANKS, J. HOUSTON, *Learning and Teaching Arithmetic,* Chapter 13. Boston: Allyn and Bacon, Inc., 1959.
2. BLECHA, MILO K., "Helping Children Understand Verbal Problems," *Arithmetic Teacher,* Vol. 6, pp. 106–107, March, 1959.
3. BREWER, S. S.,"Scientific Method of Problem Solving," *Arithmetic Teacher,* Vol. 3, pp. 117–118, April, 1956.
4. BUSWELL, GUY T., "Solving Problems in Arithmetic," *Education,* Vol. 79, pp. 287–290, January, 1959.
5. CLARK, JOHN R., AND LAURA K. EADS, *Guiding Arithmetic Learning,* Chapter 9. New York: World Book Company, 1954.

6. CURTIN, JAMES J., "Arithmetic in the Total School Program," *Arithmetic Teacher,* Vol. 4, pp. 235–239, December, 1957.
7. DUMAS, ENOCH, *Arithmetic Learning Activities.* San Francisco: Fearon Publishers, 1957.
8. FLOURNOY, FRANCES, "Interpreting Definite Quantitative Reference Materials," *Elementary School Journal,* Vol. 58, pp. 208–211, January, 1958.
9. FLOURNOY, FRANCES, "Providing Mental Arithmetic Experiences," *Arithmetic Teacher,* Vol. 6, pp. 133–139, April, 1959.
10. GREEN, ARTHUR S., "Give Reality to Arithmetic Problems," *Instructor,* Vol. 67, p. 18, February, 1958.
11. GROSSNICKLE, FOSTER E., AND LEO J. BRUECKNER, *Discovering Meanings in Arithmetic,* Chapter 13. Philadelphia: The John C. Winston Company, 1959.
12. HERRIOTT, ROBERT E., "Aid in the Analysis of Verbal Problems," *Arithmetic Teacher,* Vol. 5, pp. 143–145, April, 1958.
13. JAROLIMEK, JOHN J., "Teaching Quantitative Relationships in the Social Studies," *Arithmetic Teacher,* Vol. 4, pp. 70–74, March, 1957.
14. KLAS, WALTER L., "Problems Without Numbers," *Arithmetic Teacher,* Vol. 8, pp. 19–20, January, 1961.
15. MARKS, JOHN L., C. RICHARD PURDY, AND LUCIEN B. KINNEY, *Teaching Arithmetic for Understanding,* Chapter 12. New York: McGraw-Hill Book Company, 1958.
16. MCSWAIN, E. T., AND RALPH J. COOKE, *Understanding and Teaching Arithmetic in the Elementary School,* Chapter 11. New York: Henry Holt and Company, 1958.
17. OLANDER, HERBERT T., "Organizing a Program in the Reading of Mathematics," *Organizing Reading Programs in the Schools,* Pittsburgh: University of Pittsburgh, 1955.
18. OSBORN, ROGER, "The Use of Models in the Teaching of Mathematics," *Arithmetic Teacher,* Vol. 8, pp. 22–24, January, 1961.
19. PETTY, OLAN, "Non-Pencil-and-Paper Solutions of Problems," *Arithmetic Teacher,* Vol. 3, pp. 229–235, December, 1956.
20. REED, CALVIN H., "Developing Creative Thinking in Arithmetic," *Arithmetic Teacher,* Vol. 4, pp. 10–12, February, 1957.
21. SERVISS, TREVOR K., "Problem Solving," *Grade Teacher,* Vol. 73, p. 43, April, 1956.
22. SINNER, CLARICE, "The Problem of Problem Solving," *Arithmetic Teacher,* Vol. 6, pp. 158–159, April, 1959.
23. SISTER JOSEPHINA, "Mental Arithmetic in Today's Classroom," *Arithmetic Teacher,* Vol. 7, pp. 199–200, April, 1960.

24. SPITZER, HERBERT F., AND FRANCES FLOURNOY, "Developing Facility in Solving Verbal Problems," *Arithmetic Teacher,* Vol. 3, pp. 177–182, November, 1956.
25. SPITZER, HERBERT F., *The Teaching of Arithmetic,* Chapter 10. Boston: Houghton Mifflin Company, 1961.
26. THORPE, CLEATA B., "Equation: Neglected Ally of Arithmetic Processes," *Elementary School Journal,* Vol. 60, pp. 320–324, March, 1960.
27. VAN ENGEN, HENRY, "Child's Introduction to Arithmetic Reasoning," *School Science and Mathematics,* Vol. 55, pp. 358–363, May, 1955.
28. WANDT, EDWIN, AND GERALD W. BROWN, "Non-Occupational Uses of Mathematics; Mental and Written, Approximate and Exact," *Arithmetic Teacher,* Vol. 4, pp. 151–154, October, 1957.

CHAPTER *14*

Evaluation and Provision for Individual Differences

Objectives of Evaluation Procedures in Arithmetic

Importance of the teacher's understanding the capabilities of the pupils. Evaluation procedures in arithmetic are aimed at finding ways for improving the learning situation of the pupils. At times, the administrative purposes of evaluation, such as grouping pupils for assignment to certain classes or the need for reporting to parents, may receive particular emphasis. At other times, the emphasis in evaluation might be directed particularly toward increasing the motivation of pupils by making them more aware of their own progress.

In order to do the most effective teaching, it becomes essential for the teacher to know what progress pupils are making, because it is only then that the teacher can plan his work most efficiently. As has been emphasized many times throughout this book, one important characteristic of a good teacher is his ability to recognize the individual differences among the pupils in his class and to adjust his teaching to meet the needs of the children. Some of the teaching procedures which have been suggested in earlier chapters have been given priority because they are designed to facilitate the evaluation of the work being done, and thus make it easier for the teacher to determine the arithmetical needs of his pupils.

Every teacher soon learns through experience that pupils have different rates of learning. Some pupils, more than others, need to have certain steps in learning broken down into smaller steps. These pupils take longer to grasp the concepts new to them, and as they forget more quickly, they need more practice and more review work in order to retain what they have learned. As these slower learners have to expend more energy in order to make progress, it is often more difficult to motivate them, and they tend to become discouraged and lose interest unless the work is paced so that they feel that they are succeeding. On the other hand, the brighter pupils in the class become bored and tend to become careless if they are required to practice skills in which they are already proficient. It is necessary, therefore, to keep the brighter pupils challenged in order to keep them moving forward.

Maintaining the interest of children in arithmetic thus necessitates continual evaluation by the teacher, and a pacing of the work by providing a judicious mixture of new work and practice on the needed skills. Interest inventories may help the teacher to some extent, but his most valid index of the pupils' interest in arithmetic is the apparent attitude of the children during the daily arithmetic period. It should be noted that the attitude of the children may change quickly over a period of a few days if the work becomes too difficult for them. If the pupils appear to be losing interest, then other difficulties may be expected to follow.

Making use of cumulative records. The use of intelligence tests has now become so widespread in the schools that a teacher should have no difficulty in securing information regarding the intellectual capabilities of the pupils from their cumulative records. Such information is very helpful, particularly for identifying children who are working much below the standard which might be expected of them. Usually some of the pupils who are bright but who are doing average work tend to be overlooked by the teacher, although he well may be aware of the pupils who have low ability.

A fact which might not be fully recognized by beginning teachers is that any given pupil may have very uneven accomplishment in the various areas of arithmetic. For instance, many studies have shown that a pupil may be strong in computational skills but weak in his ability to reason mathematically or to think through problems involving the need for applying mathematical concepts to described situations. For this reason, the teacher needs to evaluate the pupil's knowledge in each aspect of arithmetic, and he should not draw conclusions regarding the pupil's general arithmetic ability from a test or other evaluation device which measures progress in only part of the arithmetic program. This implies that it is necessary for the teacher to use various evaluation devices which have been designed to measure the competence of a pupil in all the important aspects of the program.

The four most easily recognized aspects of the pupil's accomplishment in arithmetic which must be evaluated in order to avoid uneven progress are: computational ability, insight into mathematical relationships, ability to apply the knowledge of arithmetic to situations arising throughout daily activities, and interest in arithmetic. Any evaluation of the pupil's arithmetic ability should be made with at least these four phases in mind.

Making pupils aware of their own progress. To provide motivation, each pupil should be aware of any progress he is making. Self-evaluation is needed also to enable the pupil to recognize specific difficulties or lack of particular skills. He should be encouraged to analyze continually his work in arithmetic, and to look for those areas in which he feels the need for more help or more practice.

In the lower grades, this self-analysis may be stimulated best by evaluation procedures which enable a pupil to compare his present achievement with his past achievement, rather than only with the achievement of others. This tends to prevent the weaker pupils from becoming discouraged when their work is compared with that of the brighter pupils, and at the same time it tends also to keep brighter pupils from becoming too self-satisfied with their work when it is compared with the work of weaker pupils. As the pupils become older and move into the upper grades, it becomes more important for them to know how their arithmetic achievement compares with that of other pupils at their age level, as well as to know how their achievement compares with their own earlier achievement. Parents also wish to know how their children compare with other children, as well as what progress their children are making in relation to their own abilities.

Comparisons among pupils with regard to their arithmetic achievement often may be made best through the use of standardized tests.

The Selection and Use of Standardized Tests

Many standardized tests in the area of arithmetic are now available. For classroom purposes they may be classified into four types according to their main functions: survey tests, diagnostic tests, readiness tests, and progress tests. Up-to-date catalogues describing the specific tests may be obtained quite easily by writing to publishers, some of whom are listed at the end of this chapter.

Survey tests. A survey test in arithmetic is designed to enable a teacher to compare the general achievement of a pupil with that of children in a large group upon which the test has been standardized. It does this by providing test items which give a sample of arithmetic problems associated with the various levels in learning in an arithmetic program through which children usually pass during several grade levels. Tables of norms are provided, usually in the teacher's manual, which enable a teacher to compare the achievement of his pupils with regard to both grade level achievement and the achievement of age level groups.

Before selecting a survey test for use in his class, a teacher should examine it to see whether or not the test attempts to measure those things which he wishes to have measured. Most tests will have items designed to measure the pupil's computational skill and his ability to solve problems in described situations. Some tests attempt also to measure other aspects of the pupil's learning, such as knowledge of quantitative measures, knowledge of numerical facts, terms, and symbols, knowledge of the number system, and ability to make quantitative estimates.

Survey tests are normally most useful to a teacher at the beginning of the school year when he wishes to get information regarding the general arithmetic ability of the pupils in his class, before he has had time to evaluate their abilities more closely by other means.

Diagnostic tests. Unlike survey tests which attempt to give a general indication of what a pupil knows, a diagnostic test attempts to locate those aspects of arithmetic which a pupil does not know. For this reason, the scope of a good diagnostic test is much narrower than that of a survey test. It often is confined to one operation in one area of arithmetic—for example, in the area of addition of common fractions. Diagnostic tests of this nature have one or more items for each of the small learning steps within the scope of the test, and thus enable the teacher to pinpoint the type of difficulty which a pupil is encountering in that specific area. Certain tests combine some of the features of both a survey test and a diagnostic test by covering a wider area of arithmetic than a diagnostic test but, by grouping items which test similar competencies, they are able to indicate the more general points of difficulty the pupils may be having.

Usually diagnostic tests are administered after the pupil has completed a block of work. Thus they are able to indicate points of weakness in the pupil's achievement which provide important topics for review or for further practice.

Readiness tests. Readiness tests are designed to provide the teacher with information regarding the needs of pupils before they undertake a new topic in arithmetic. An understanding of a certain step in arithmetic may be dependent particularly upon an understanding of steps which have been learned earlier. A suitable readiness test would be made up of items which the pupils have been taught previously and which are needed in order to understand the new topic. For example, a readiness test in the addition of unlike fractions would contain items dealing with an understanding of like fractions, as well as with finding fractions equivalent to a given fraction but which have different denominators. In this way the readiness test would indicate where more preparation was needed before the class was introduced to the new topic.

Progress tests. The important characteristic of a good progress test is that it is geared to some particular series of arithmetic textbooks. Tests of this type are arranged in series consisting of nine or ten tests, and are designed to be administered a few weeks apart as the pupils proceed through the textbook.

Since the tests are designed to evaluate the material learned from a particular textbook, they do not suffer from a common criticism of many standardized tests. This is that often a standardized test does not "fit" the class, meaning that the test includes items which are beyond the scope of the work covered by the pupils.

Progress tests are designed to be administered often enough to permit each test of the series to include a relatively small portion of the total content being presented, but each test still includes a sample sufficiently large to give good coverage of the new work met during each period of a few weeks. Since each important learning step may be tested, a good progress test has many of the advantages possessed by a diagnostic test. Furthermore, as the tests of the series are administered at frequent intervals, the pupils are able to compare their progress monthly with their own earlier progress and thus are provided with a strong motivating factor.

Many publishers of arithmetic textbooks provide progress tests for the convenience of those using their textbooks. As this type of test becomes more popular, teachers will find that progress tests provide a very effective means for making a close evaluation of some of the important aspects of the arithmetic program.

The Use of Teacher-made Tests

One important advantage in using his own test is that the teacher can measure the learnings he feels are important at a given time. After examining the program in arithmetic which he has been developing for his class, the teacher can select the particular objectives which he considers important for the group of pupils at a particular time, and design a test to measure the pupils' progress toward these objectives.

Evaluating the pupil's insight into mathematical concepts. Modern arithmetic textbooks contain short tests which are comparable to three of the types mentioned above: the diagnostic test, the readiness test, and the progress test. By using these tests from the textbook, and as many teacher-made tests of a similar nature as are needed, the teacher may obtain a good measure of the pupil's insight into the mathematical concepts which are developed in the textbook, at least to the extent that these concepts may be measured by pencil-and-paper tests. As will be noted later, some of the pupil's mathematical concepts may be evaluated by means other than pencil-and-paper tests.

Evaluating the pupil's computational ability. The computational ability of the pupil may also be evaluated by using the tests from a modern textbook, along with similar teacher-made tests. Where the pupils are using workbooks along with a textbook, frequent examination of the pupils' workbooks will provide the teacher with information of the pupils' computational abilities.

Subjective Evaluation by the Teacher

As mentioned in Chapter 2, one of the most effective types of evaluation available to the teacher in the elementary school is the subjective evaluations he makes as a result of the direct observation of the pupil's work from day to day. Although subjective evaluation may be suspect on the grounds that the reliability of a single subjective judgment is usually low, the wide sample of the pupil's reactions which are observed daily and over a long period of time by a competent teacher should increase the reliability of the teacher's judgment considerably. As the teacher comes to know his pupils better, these daily observations form a very important part of the evaluation program in the elementary school, although generally teachers do not try to associate numerical values with these subjective ratings of a pupil's performance.

Observation and analysis of the pupil's written work. The pupil's success in his daily written work is a strong indication of his understanding, and it serves as an indication of how fast new concepts should be introduced as well as what work needs to be reviewed and which skills need to be practiced further.

Besides understanding arithmetical concepts, pupils must develop skill in computation and this requires practice, the amount of which varies according to the needs of different individuals. The progress made in developing skills in computation may be evaluated during the daily arithmetic period by noting the speed with which the pupil works and the maturity with which he uses various computational processes. For example, once a pupil has learned how to add or to multiply, he should not use counting procedures in situations where addition or multiplication would be more efficient. His use of immature procedures would indicate that the pupil does not feel familiar with the procedure and is not sure of himself when he is using it. Consequently, his performance suggests to the teacher that more practice is needed until the pupil reaches the point where he can employ more mature procedures with efficiency.

Observing the pupil's class participation. The manner in which a pupil answers questions orally during an arithmetic lesson also provides a further indication of how well he understands mathematical concepts and which aspects of the work must receive further clarification.

As mentioned previously, when pupils are using concrete materials, such as counters or tickets, to illustrate mathematical concepts in the lower grades, it often enables the teacher to see at a glance whether or not a pupil has grasped the concept being developed. In somewhat the same way, a teacher often may evaluate the mathematical insights obtained by a pupil in the intermediate or upper grades by noting how he uses concrete materials, such as a place-value chart, to illustrate certain ideas. Each time a pupil discusses a diagram or explains the nature of a chart which illustrates mathematical ideas, the teacher is provided with an opportunity for judging the pupil's grasp of the concept being presented, and is enabled, thereby, to note misconceptions or errors which indicate faulty learning.

During class discussions, while the pupils are considering the relative efficiency of the various ways for solving a given problem, the teacher has further opportunities to evaluate the mathematical insights of the children. At such times, the teacher may challenge the brighter pupils by asking them to think of other ways in which the problem could be solved, and by questioning them closely, making them prove the validity of their suggestions.

Individual interviews with pupils. One of the most effective ways for determining the specific difficulties of a pupil who is having trouble with arithmetic is to take a few minutes to interview him from time to time while he is engaged in solving arithmetic problems, and to note the manner in which he attacks each problem and carries out the necessary computations. Often further insight may be gained into how the pupil is thinking by asking him to express verbally the thinking he is doing as he works to find a solution. This is a very effective procedure for detecting misconceptions held by the pupil, and four or five minutes of the teacher's time spent in an individual interview may provide more help for the pupil than a much longer time used in group instruction. The teacher will find that he has no difficulty in noting gross misconceptions held by the pupil, and probably will have little difficulty in noting smaller points which would otherwise be overlooked during the regular arithmetic period.

Evaluating the pupil's ability to apply arithmetic in social settings. The extent to which pupils can apply their knowledge of arithmetic to solving problems which arise in daily living may be evaluated subjectively by observing how they handle incidental arithmetic situations which arise in connection with their other school activities. Some of these situations which are connected with the school activities in the primary grades already have been identified in Chapter 5. In the intermediate and upper grades, situations requiring the use of arithmetic arise daily in connection with other areas of the curriculum, such as social studies, science, physical education and health. Consequently, there should be abundant opportunities to observe how competently the children apply arithmetic in various activities.

The extent to which children use arithmetic during their school activities may be increased by directing the attention of the pupils to mathematical relationships which otherwise might be overlooked: for example, measuring layouts for posters in the primary grades (size of paper, placement of lettering, size of letters) or reporting in the intermediate grades on the relationships between imports and exports in selected countries (graphs, tables, per cent of increase and decrease).

When the pupils are applying their knowledge of arithmetic to situations which arise daily outside of the arithmetic period, they do so without being given clues as to the most efficient procedures to use. Consequently, the teacher is able to observe the degree of maturity and the method of working with which they approach each task. The teacher may derive further opportunities for evaluating subjectively the insights of pupils into mathematics by encouraging the class to discuss the way a pupil is using arithmetic to solve a problem in a given situation and to consider the relative efficiency of this and other approaches.

Evaluating the pupil's interest in arithmetic. As mentioned earlier, probably the most direct way to evaluate a pupil's interest in arithmetic is to observe the zest with which he enters into the work of the arithmetic period. The nature of his questions, the persistence with which he works to solve an arithmetic problem, and the interest he shows in the recreational aspect of arithmetic—all give a teacher clues for evaluating the pupil's interest.

Interest inventories, such as those described by Dutton,[1] may be prepared in order to secure additional information concerning pupils' attitudes toward arithmetic. These inventories take the form of a list of statements such as "I think arithmetic is fun" or "I don't enjoy studying arithmetic" which the pupils are asked to check to indicate their feelings toward arithmetic. The teacher may also prepare a list of the names of the various subject-matter areas which the children are studying, and then ask them to rate these areas in order of preference.

Since it is very important for the teacher to try to increase the pupil's interest in arithmetic, this important phase of evaluation should not be minimized in any way.

Making Provision for Individual Differences

Probably the most difficult problem facing a teacher in the elementary school is that of trying to develop a program which is suited to the needs of each child in a large group of from twenty-five to thirty-five children. By selecting and arranging learning activities, the teacher attempts to provide learning experiences

[1] Wilbur H. Dutton, "Measuring Attitudes Toward Arithmetic," *Elementary School Journal,* 55:24–31, September, 1954.

which are most valuable for the low achievers in the class during the same period of time in which learning experiences are provided for the high achievers. This problem is made more difficult by the fact that since children within any group have different rates of learning, the fast learners gradually will increase their lead over the slow learners, and consequently, when good instruction is provided, the spread in accomplishment between the fast learners and the slow learners will keep increasing.

The problem of providing for the individual differences of the children in a class has engaged the attention of educators for many years. Although no perfect solution to this problem has been found, research has provided many suggestions which are helpful in alleviating certain types of situations, thus making it possible for a good teacher to function effectively where the extreme differences are not too great.

Some of these suggestions are described in the remainder of this chapter. The teacher should remember, however, that there are weaknesses as well as strengths in each of the procedures suggested. The needs of the particular class in which the teacher is interested must be kept in mind in selecting procedures to provide for the individual differences of children. The teacher should weigh the advantages and disadvantages of each procedure in the light of its probable effectiveness in each particular situation. To be effective, a procedure may need to be modified within the course of a school year. In some instances one procedure may need to be replaced by another when the pupils are introduced to an arithmetic topic either more difficult or less difficult than topics which have been studied earlier. During the following school year, with a different group of children, the teacher may find that a different procedure is preferable.

The three general procedures for providing for individual differences which will be discussed are:

1. Organizations within a school to provide groups of pupils with somewhat similar achievement for each class in arithmetic.
2. Grouping pupils within a single class to enable those with similar needs to work together.
3. Pacing the instruction during an arithmetic lesson to provide for differences within the group of children being instructed.

In any type of grouping, there will be differences still remaining among the pupils. Consequently the third procedure, that of pacing the instruction during the arithmetic lesson, should be carried on irrespective of the organization of the class as a whole.

Organization within a School to Group Pupils According to Their Arithmetic Ability

When a school's population is large enough to have two or more classes at a certain grade level, it is possible to arrange for the arithmetic instruction in the classes concerned to be given at the same period of the day, and then have the high achievers separated from the average achievers and the low achievers by placing them in different classrooms during that period. As this will result in a smaller range of differences within each class with respect to general arithmetical ability, it reduces somewhat the teacher's problem of providing suitable activities, and also enables each teacher to introduce new material at a rate which is more nearly suited to the needs of each child in each of the classes. A disadvantage of this procedure is that it tends to divorce the arithmetic program from the other school activities of the pupil; and consequently, in the primary grades and intermediate grades, the advantages gained by this type of organization may be nullified by other factors.

In the upper grades, where the differences among the pupils usually are greater than those found in the lower grades, the advantages of this type of organization are more noticeable. At the present time, many schools are experimenting with this type of organization,[2] especially in situations where the arithmetic program is differentiated sharply in order to provide more advanced content for the high achievers.

[2] Grant C. Pinney, "Grouping by Arithmetic Ability—An Experiment in the Teaching of Arithmetic," *Arithmetic Teacher,* 8:120–123, March, 1961.

Grouping Pupils within a Single Class to Enable Those with Similar Needs to Work Together

The teacher may make some provision for individual differences within his own class by grouping pupils in various ways. The procedure used will vary according to how wide a spread in achievement is found among the members of the class, as will be noted below.

A grouping procedure where there is a very wide spread of individual differences. Where the differences in achievement among members of a class are very great, the teacher may have no recourse other than that of dividing the class into two or three groups, according to the arithmetic achievement of the pupils, and then proceeding as if he were teaching separate classes. Each group would then proceed at the pace which the teacher finds to be most suitable for that group. This procedure is similar to that which is often followed in organizing the reading program in the lower grades, and it presents somewhat the same problems for the teacher. When employing a class organization such as this, the teacher will have less time to spend on the direct instruction of each group in the class. Often it is better, however, for the children to be studying suitable content and to proceed at a rate which is suitable for them, even though they do not have as much of the teacher's time devoted to their direct instruction. To be most successful when using this organization, the teacher must prepare the individual practice assignments (sometimes called "seatwork") of the pupils very carefully. Unless this is done, the relatively large amount of time which the pupils spend in their individual work will not be used effectively.

A grouping procedure where there is a relatively narrow spread of individual differences. When the spread of individual differences in arithmetic ability among the pupils in a class is not very great, it sometimes happens that all the children in the class may be introduced at the same time to the new material for each step in the arithmetic program. The teacher then may make provision for individual differences within the class by varying the amount of practice exercises and review work for each of two or three groups of pupils who have similar needs. For example, a fifth grade class might be introduced to the topic involving the addition of unlike fractions, and for one or two lessons the children could work together as one group. By the third or fourth lesson, the teacher might feel that the pupils would profit more by not working as a single group, and he would divide the class into two or more groups and assign different types of practice exercises to each group. This will permit the slower achievers to get the type of practice they need, while the high achievers, who do not need as much practice, are provided with enrichment activities in arithmetic. These enrichment activities would be designed to broaden the scope of the arithmetic program for the children, while still holding their interest by challenging them with interesting applications of arithmetic and with interesting information.

When the teacher considers that the class as a whole is ready for the next new topic, the new work will be presented first to the class as a whole, and then a somewhat similar grouping procedure will be followed for providing the needed practice in subsequent lessons.

When using such a procedure, the teacher should endeavor to be aware continually of the achievement of each pupil so that the groups may be kept sufficiently flexible to permit pupils to be grouped suitably in various ways in accordance with the difficulty of each new topic as it is introduced.

It should be noted that any grouping procedure will require more skill and probably much more effort on the part of the teacher in order for him to do the most effective teaching, but the necessary skill is not beyond the capabilities of a competent teacher, and the effort should be repaid by the satisfaction the teacher derives from noting the improved progress of individual pupils.

Pacing Instruction during an Arithmetic Lesson

It is helpful to think of the learnings a child needs in arithmetic as comprising both understandings (or insights into mathematical relationships) and skills, which include the ability to respond immediately to some of these relationships without each time having to go through the steps in the thought process from which the child originally derived the understanding. For example, we wish children to understand how a given basic multiplication fact may be derived and why it is reasonable, for instance, to conclude that forty-five is the product of five times nine when they are using a decimal numeration system. During the early stages of learning the multiplication facts, we encourage the children to represent each basic multiplication fact by using concrete materials, and to construct tables which enable them to understand certain relationships among various basic facts. In such instances, we are helping the children to gain insight into each situation, thereby helping them to see meaning in what they are doing. Once the children understand the meaning of the basic facts, we then wish them to practice using them in various ways until they reach the point where they can respond immediately to a question such as "What is five times nine?"

Children vary greatly both in their ability to gain insight into the meaning of arithmetic and in regard to the time and practice they need in order to make a given response habitual. Brownell [3] has used the term "meaningful habituation" to describe the level in learning at which a pupil is able to answer almost automatically with the required response as a result of varied practice which has followed the thorough understanding of the mathematical rationale for the response.

When we speak of a teacher's "pacing" a lesson, we refer to the teacher's placing emphasis at just those points where the pupils in the class need help during a lesson. This help may be needed either to gain insight into the mathematical relationships involved or to enable the pupil at some point to arrive at a more mature level of meaningful habituation. The needed emphasis may be secured either by the number and difficulty of the questions asked by the teacher or by the degree to which he breaks down the more difficult learning steps into smaller or easier steps.

As pointed out earlier in this chapter, the individual differences

[3] William A. Brownell, "Meaning and Skill—Maintaining the Balance," *Arithmetic Teacher,* 3:129–136, October, 1956.

among the children of any class will cause various members of the class to reach certain levels of understanding of a concept at different times. By pacing the lesson carefully, the teacher is making the compromises necessary to allow those pupils who need a little more help to receive it, and at the same time he is endeavoring to hold the interest of the faster pupils without unduly retarding their progress. For example, by directing the more difficult questions to the brighter pupils and requiring them to clarify the points needing additional emphasis, the teacher helps to hold their attention and interest while giving the average achievers additional time and additional opportunities to grasp the implications in the explanations. This procedure still might provide insufficient help for the slower pupils. Consequently, when the teacher notes that the larger part of the group is ready to make some applications of the new concept in individual practice assignments, he gets this group started, and then proceeds to give further help, for a few minutes, to the slower pupils who need more assistance. When this latter group has started on the individual assignment, the teacher then moves around the classroom in order to note and give individual attention to those pupils who need additional help.

As noted above, when pacing a lesson a teacher is in reality making a compromise between the needs of the faster pupils and those of the slower pupils; but because the procedure is flexible, it provides a very effective means for making some provision for the individual differences of children. The amount of time which the teacher devotes to the individual children in the group is thus varied from day to day, according to the difficulty of the topic being presented and the needs of the children. At the same time, the rate at which the class proceeds as a whole is regulated by the amount of time needed to emphasize the difficult points during each lesson.

As noted above, pacing a lesson is a useful procedure in whatever type of class organization the teacher is using to provide for individual differences. Its effectiveness will be closely related to how well the teacher has evaluated the arithmetic abilities of the individual pupils in his class.

Enriching the Arithmetic Program

The presence of children who are rapid learners in arithmetic presents school administrators and teachers with the challenge of providing an arithmetic program which is commensurate with the abilities of these pupils. How this challenge will be met depends upon the many factors which are found in any school situation, but one of two procedures is usually considered. One of these procedures consists in placing the main emphasis upon accelerating the fast learners by grouping them in separate classrooms. The separation of the high achievers from the low and average achievers may be carried out either by organizing special classes for them, in which case all of their curriculum is adjusted and they remain in these special classes for all of their work, or by following the practice mentioned earlier in this chapter in which the pupils are placed in less heterogeneous groups only during certain periods of the day. Either of these two latter procedures will facilitate the use of an accelerated program in which the pupils proceed at a rate which is faster than that of the average achievers.

A second general procedure for meeting the needs of the high achievers in arithmetic consists of broadening the scope of their arithmetic program by emphasizing enrichment activities. The term "enrichment" is sometimes used to refer to any arithmetic activities which are used over and above those suggested in the pupils' textbooks. It is hoped that all pupils will enjoy some enrichment activities in this sense of the term.

In this book, we are using the term "enrichment" to refer to arithmetic activities in excess of those provided for the large group of average achievers in the regular arithmetic program. The types of activities in an enriched program are not different necessarily from those found in the regular program, but the extent of these activities will be greatly increased for the high achievers, since their fast rate of learning provides them with more time for engaging in such activities.

As mentioned above, there are many factors which should be considered before deciding upon the procedure most suitable in a given situation. In general, the relevant factors in the lower and intermediate grades tend to give more weight to the use of enrichment procedures which will broaden the scope of the program, while the relevant factors in the upper grades give more emphasis to the advantages found in some type of acceleration.

In any classroom situation, a teacher will find a need for considering enrichment activities in arithmetic, but in a situation where the emphasis on providing a program for high achievers consists mainly or entirely in broadening the scope of the program with enrichment activities, a knowledge of the principal considerations in using this procedure becomes very important for the teacher. By giving thought to the manner in which these considerations will apply to the particular situation in which he is interested, the teacher is guided in the selection and organization of the enrichment activities he will use with the group of high achievers he is teachıng. A number of enrichment activities are suggested at the end of this chapter.

Maintaining the interest of the pupils. One of the foremost considerations to be kept in mind while selecting suitable enrichment activities is that these activities should tend to maintain or increase the pupil's interest in arithmetic. If the pupil's interest in the subject is lost through misguided overemphasis on the part of the teacher, the eventual result of the program may be negative. This does not mean that the work should be "watered down" or made too easy. Challenging work often will increase the interest of bright pupils. It does mean that the teacher should be sensitive continually to the interest of the pupils in those activities which are provided. It may be assumed correctly that all of the pupils will not be interested equally in the same material, and consequently the teacher should vary the activities and provide a wide range of mathematical topics for the pupils' consideration. At times, when the teacher considers it suitable to permit the pupils to choose the topics for investigation, he should encourage them to do so and thus help ensure that the pupils' interests are being given consideration. This would apply particularly to instances in which pupils are preparing reports on various mathematical topics.

Providing a basis for a further study of mathematics. Another important consideration which a teacher should keep in mind while selecting and organizing enrichment activities for high achievers, particularly those in the upper grades, is that many of these pupils later may pursue science programs and other programs at the secondary school and college levels which will include courses in mathematics. Consequently, although the recreational aspects of arithmetic should be utilized to increase the interest of the pupils in the subject and to broaden the scope of their program, it is important that a suitable portion of the pupils' time should be utilized in providing a basis for further studies in mathematics. The elementary aspects of algebra, geometry, set language, logic, number theory, and probability well might provide a large portion of the enrichment activities for high achievers in the upper grades.

Suggestions for emphasizing this phase of the program will be discussed in Chapter 15 in connection with the procedures for introducing pupils to contemporary mathematics.

Maintaining computational skills. At all grade levels a teacher should select a sufficient number of activities to encourage the high achievers to maintain or to increase their computational skills. As pointed out by Brownell,[4] skills in computation do not come automatically as a result of increased insight into mathematical relationships, but need to be developed through suitable practice. Many suggestions for enrichment activities, such as some of those listed at the end of this chapter, have a high interest value but are not of the nature which provides practice in computational skills. The teacher should ensure that such activities do not constitute the whole enrichment program for high achievers. On the contrary, he should make certain that a sufficient number of enrichment activities which require important computational skills is included in order to provide the pupils with a well-balanced program.

Types of Activities for Enriching the Arithmetic Program

A great deal of material is available at the present time which lists and describes various enrichment activities in detail.[5] The fol-

[4] Brownell, *op. cit.*
[5] William L. Schaaf, *Recreational Mathematics, A Guide to the Literature.* Washington, D.C.: National Council of Teachers of Mathematics, 1958.

lowing list indicates types of material. The numbers in parentheses after each type of activity indicate references listed in the last section of this chapter which describe many enrichment activities of the type indicated.

RECREATIONAL ACTIVITIES

- Puzzles and "brain-twisters" (2, 19, 20, 25)
- Number tricks (4, 5, 10)
- Magic numbers (10)
- Magic squares (10, 17)
- Number games (6, 14)
- Number problems (16, 17)
- Problems in geometric construction (9)
- Codes and ciphers (8)

INTERESTING SOCIAL APPLICATIONS OF MATHEMATICS

- A classroom "stock market" (18)
- A classroom "insurance company"
- Scientific applications of mathematics (13, 26)
- Topics related to concepts of time (3, 23)
- The work of computers and calculators
- Cost of using an automobile (12)
- Map arithmetic (31)

INTERESTING COMPUTATIONAL PROCESSES

- Short cuts in computation (17)
- Different ways of computing (17)
- Different ways of checking computation (10, 17)
- Mental arithmetic
- Slide rule
- Abacus (15)
- Logarithmic tables
- Tests of divisibility (17, 22)

TOPICS LEADING TO FURTHER INSIGHT INTO MATHEMATICS

- Number bases and numeration systems (22)
- Prime and composite numbers (22)
- "Clock" arithmetic (22)
- Negative numbers (22)
- Number line (22)
- Number progressions (22)
- Units on elementary topics from geometry, algebra, or set theory

READING ACTIVITIES

Historical material of interest (3, 17, 28)
Origin of terms in mathematics and measurement (17)
Books giving a simplified introduction to important mathematical concepts (9, 11, 27)

MATHEMATICS CLUBS

SPECIAL PROJECTS

Mathematics exhibits
Mathematics contests
Mathematics bulletin boards

References for Enrichment

1. BAER, HOWARD. *Now This, Now That*. New York: Holiday House, 1957. Primary level.
2. BAKST, A. *Mathematical Puzzles and Pastimes*. Princeton, N.J.: Van Nostrand, 1954. Upper level.
3. BEHN, HARVEY. *All Kinds of Time*. New York: Harcourt, Brace, 1950. Primary level.
4. BRANDES, L. G. *Math Can Be Fun*. Portland, Maine: J. Weston Walch, 1956. Intermediate and upper levels.
5. DEGRAZIA, J. *Math Is Fun*. New York: Gresham Press, 1948. Upper level.
6. DUMAS, ENOCH. *Arithmetic Games*. San Francisco: Fearon Publishers, 1960. Through the sixth grade.
7. DUMAS, ENOCH. *Arithmetic Learning Activities*. San Francisco: Fearon Publishers, 1957. Through the sixth grade.
8. EPSTEIN, SAM, AND BERYL EPSTEIN. *The First Book of Codes and Ciphers*. New York: Watts, 1957. Intermediate and upper levels.
9. FREEMAN, M., AND I. FREEMAN. *Fun with Figures*. New York: Random House, 1946. Intermediate level.
10. GILLES, W. F. *The Magic and Oddities of Numbers*. New York: Vantage Press, 1953. Upper level.
11. HOGBEN, L. *The Wonderful World of Mathematics*. New York: Garden City Books, 1955. Intermediate and upper levels.
12. HUNTINGTON, HARRIET E. *At the Service Station*. Los Angeles: Melmont Publishers, 1957. Primary level.
13. HYDE, MARGARET O. *Exploring Earth and Space: The Story of I.G.Y.* New York: Whittlesey House, 1957. Intermediate and upper levels.

14. KOHL, MARGUERITE, AND F. YOUNG. *Games for Grownups.* New York: A. A. Wyn, 1951. Intermediate and upper levels.
15. KOJIMA, TAKASHI. *The Japanese Abacus.* Rutland, Vt.: Tuttle, 1954. Upper level.
16. KRAITCHIK, MAURICE. *Mathematical Recreations.* Second Rev. Ed. New York: Dover, 1953. Intermediate and upper levels.
17. LARSEN, H. D. *Enrichment Program for Arithmetic.* Evanston: Row, Peterson, 1956. Grades three through eight.
18. LEEMING, JOSEPH. *From Barter to Banking.* New York: Appleton, Century, 1940. Intermediate and upper levels.
19. LEEMING, JOSEPH. *Fun with Puzzles.* Philadelphia: Lippincott, 1946. Intermediate and upper levels.
20. LEEMING, JOSEPH. *More Fun with Puzzles.* Philadelphia: Lippincott, 1947. Intermediate and upper levels.
21. MADACHY, JOSEPH S., *Recreational Mathematics Magazine.* Box 1876, Idaho Falls, Idaho. Upper level.
22. MARKS, JOHN L., AND OTHERS. *The Ginn Arithmetic Enrichment Program.* Boston: Ginn, 1961. Intermediate and upper levels.
23. MARSHAK, ILIN. *What Time Is It?* Philadelphia: Lippincott, 1932. Intermediate and upper levels.
24. MEYER, JEROME S. *Fun with Mathematics.* Cleveland: World Publishing, 1952. Intermediate and upper levels.
25. NORTHROP, EUGENE P. *Riddles in Mathematics: A Book of Paradoxes.* New York: Van Nostrand, 1944. Intermediate and upper levels.
26. SAWYER, W. W. *Designing and Making: A Book for Boys, Girls and Inventors.* London: Blackwell, 1950. Upper level.
27. SHACKLES, G. L. S. *Mathematics at the Fireside.* Chicago: University of Chicago Press, 1952. Upper level.
28. SMITH, DAVID E. *Number Stories of Long Ago.* Washington, D.C.: National Council of Teachers of Mathematics, 1919. Intermediate and upper levels.
29. SMITH, DAVID E., AND J. GINSBERG. *Numbers and Numerals.* Washington, D.C.: National Council of Teachers of Mathematics, 1937. Intermediate and upper levels.
30. SPITZER, HERBERT F. *Practical Classroom Procedures for Enriching Arithmetic.* St. Louis: Webster Publishing, 1956.
31. TANNENBAUM, BEULAH, AND MYRA STILLMAN. *Understanding Maps: Charting the Land, Sea, and Sky.* New York: Whittlesey House, 1957. Intermediate and upper levels.
32. WIRTZ, ROBERT W., AND MORTON BOTEL. *Math Workshop for*

Children. Wilmette, Illinois: Encyclopaedia Britannica Films, 1961.

Some Publishers of Standardized Tests [6]

Acorn Publishing Company, 9 Front Street, Rockville Centre, New York

Bureau of Publications, Teachers College, Columbia University, New York 27, New York

California Test Bureau, 5916 Hollywood Boulevard, Los Angeles 28, California

C. A. Gregory Company, 345 Calhoun Street, Cincinnati 19, Ohio

Educational Test Bureau, Educational Publishers, Inc., 720 Washington Avenue, S.E., Minneapolis 14, Minnesota

Educational Testing Service, Cooperative Test Division, Princeton, New Jersey

Harcourt, Brace and World, Inc., 750 Third Avenue, New York 17, New York

Houghton Mifflin Company 2 Park Street, Boston, Massachusetts.

Public School Publishing Company, 345 Calhoun Street, Cincinnati 19, Ohio

Science Research Associates, 57 West Grand Avenue, Chicago 10, Illinois

Suggested Learning Activities

1. At a grade level of your choice, examine the test records of pupils to note how each varies with respect to those aspects of arithmetic achievement tested. Report the greatest and the least variation found. Note also the highest and lowest achievement levels.
2. Interview two teachers to find by what means pupils are helped to become aware of their progress in learning arithmetic.
3. Examine a readiness test in a modern children's textbook to note types of items included. If you were to make a readiness test to check pupils' readiness to undertake learning to multiply by two-place multipliers, what would you include?
4. Name some outcomes of the arithmetic program which are difficult to judge through the use of common formal tests. Tell how you might evaluate them in day-to-day classroom situations.

[6] Sheldon S. Myers, *Mathematics Tests Available in the United States.* Washington 6, D.C.: National Council of Teachers of Mathematics, 1959.

5. Make an interest inventory designed to discover pupils' attitudes toward various aspects of problem solving.
6. Interview two teachers to learn how individual needs are met in teaching arithmetic. Look for class organization, individual help, out-of-arithmetic-class activities, home study, independent activities.
7. Observe an arithmetic lesson and then make a plan for how you would teach the next day's activity with full regard for the individual differences you noted.
8. Interview an elementary school principal to ask how he organized the pupils and assigned the teachers to make meeting individual differences most manageable. In what other way does he assist in the process?
9. Make a list of arithmetic enrichment activities suitable for fast learners at a grade level of your choice and for a topic of your selection. Note all sources of materials needed; be specific (for example, if you have selected the topic of adding unlike fractions at fifth grade level and you suggest a game might be played, tell what game and where directions can be found).
10. Examine and report on three standardized tests in arithmetic. In what ways are they alike? In what ways are they different?

Guided Supplementary Reading

1. What four widely used methods of appraising the behavior of learners does Brueckner develop?
2. What four methods or procedures for meeting the needs of superior students are suggested by Brueckner, Grossnickle, and Reckzeh?
3. Clark and Eads point out that the better the teaching, the greater will be the differences in learning. What reasons are given for this?
4. What are some of the ways Coburn suggests a teacher may attempt to meet individual differences?
5. Collier lists eight blocks to learning arithmetic. What are they?
6. Why does Dubins think it important to teach arithmetic with science applications?
7. What does Dumas mean when he says a teacher must "be judicious about the time" for children to play arithmetic games?
8. For children who are well above average in arithmetic ability, Dumas and others suggest a "twofold plan." What is its general nature?

9. Dutton and Adams give a scale for studying children's attitudes toward arithmetic. Why do the authors think the results obtained might be valuable?
10. From his study, what does Erickson conclude is the relationship of socio-economic status to arithmetic achievement?
11. How does Flagg propose that pupils can be assisted in developing confidence and self-reliance in arithmetic?
12. What major ways of varying instruction does Flournoy describe?
13. What purposes does Grossnickle list for enrichment for fast learners?
14. Grossnickle and Brueckner identify three "levels of diagnosis." What are they?
15. According to Hamilton, who are the remedial cases in arithmetic?
16. Hartung does not think that most schools need more drill to improve their arithmetic programs. What does he think they need?
17. What does Hildebrandt point out as a common characteristic of mathematically gifted children?
18. From Howard's limited survey, would one get the impression that British teachers who used the Cuisenaire-Gattegno materials reacted favorably or unfavorably toward their use?
19. What unique procedure for meeting individual differences is described by Ivie and others?
20. What functions does Johnson ascribe to classroom games?
21. What does Junge point out as learning characteristics of gifted children?
22. Lankford lists fourteen statements on which learning theorists are said to agree. What source is given credit for the points made?
23. What does McMeen mean by "vertical differentiation" as a way of meeting individual differences?
24. What do Michaelis and Dumas conclude with regard to the use of standardized tests in arithmetic?
25. Miller found a wide variation in the amount of time devoted to arithmetic instruction. What range did he find at fifth grade level? What was the average?
26. Phillips gives three techniques for meeting individual differences. What are they?
27. What did Sister Josephina's study of arithmetic achievement in June, as compared to that in September, reveal?
28. What do Spencer and Brydegaard mean when they say, "There are many *good* errors"?
29. Spitzer has suggested a considerable variety of enrichment activities. What does he give as the main purpose in so doing?

30. What are some of the suggestions made by Spitzer regarding kinds of instructional materials sixth grade pupils might prepare?
31. What were some of the "alternate methods" used by pupils in Stephens's class contests?
32. Stokes describes a "basic plan" for evaluation of learning in arithmetic. What are the main features of such a program?
33. What four characteristics of slow learners does Sueltz point out?

Suggested Supplementary References

1. BRUECKNER, LEO J., "Evaluation in Arithmetic," *Education,* Vol. 79, pp. 291–294, January, 1959.
2. BRUECKNER, LEO J., FOSTER E. GROSSNICKLE, AND JOHN RECKZEH, *Developing Mathematical Understanding in the Upper Grades,* Chapter 14. Philadelphia: The John C. Winston Company, 1957.
3. CLARK, JOHN R., AND LAURA K. EADS, *Guiding Arithmetic Learning,* Chapter 9. Yonkers: World Book Company, 1954.
4. COBURN, MAUDE, "Flexibility in the Arithmetic Program," *Arithmetic Teacher,* Vol. 2, pp. 48–54, April, 1955.
5. COLLIER CALHOUN C., "Blocks to Arithmetical Understanding," *Arithmetic Teacher,* Vol. 6, pp. 262–268, November, 1959.
6. DUBINS, M. IRA, "Integration of Arithmetic with Science through the Study of Weather in the Elementary School," *School Science and Mathematics,* Vol. 57, pp. 121–130, February, 1957.
7. DUMAS, ENOCH, *Arithmetic Games.* San Francisco: Fearon Publishers, 1960.
8. DUMAS, ENOCH, JACK KITTELL, AND BARBARA GRANT, *How to Meet Individual Differences in Teaching Arithmetic.* San Francisco: Fearon Publishers, 1957.
9. DUTTON, WILBUR H., AND L. J. ADAMS, *Arithmetic for Teachers,* Chapter 15. Englewood Cliffs, N.J.: Prentice-Hall, Inc., 1961.
10. ERICKSON, LELAND H., "Certain Ability Factors and Their Effect on Arithmetic Achievement," *Arithmetic Teacher,* Vol. 5, pp. 287–293, December, 1958.
11. FLAGG, ELINOR B., "Developing Confident, Self-reliant Learners in Arithmetic," *School Science and Mathematics,* Vol. 55, pp. 381–388, May, 1955.
12. FLOURNOY, FRANCES, "Meeting Individual Differences in Arithmetic," *Arithmetic Teacher,* Vol. 7, pp. 80–86, February, 1960.
13. GROSSNICKLE, FOSTER E., "Arithmetic for Those Who Excel," *Arithmetic Teacher,* Vol. 3, pp. 41–48, March, 1956.

14. Grossnickle, Foster E., and Leo J. Brueckner, *Discovering Meanings in Arithmetic,* Chapter 16. Philadelphia: The John C. Winston Company, 1959.
15. Hamilton, Jean F., "Remedial Arithmetic in the Regular Classroom," *School Science and Mathematics,* Vol. 56, pp. 197–209, March, 1956.
16. Hartung, Maurice L., "Distinguishing between Basic and Superficial Ideas in Arithmetic Instruction," *Arithmetic Teacher,* Vol. 6, pp. 65–70, March, 1959.
17. Hildebrandt, E. H. C., "Mathematical Modes of Thought," *The Growth of Mathematical Ideas,* 24th Yearbook. Washington, D.C.: National Council of Teachers of Mathematics, 1959.
18. Howard, Charles F., "British Teachers' Reactions to the Cuisenaire-Gattegno Materials; the Color-Rod Approach to Arithmetic," *Arithmetic Teacher,* Vol. 4, pp. 191–195, November, 1957.
19. Ivie, Claude, and others, "Grouping in Arithmetic in the Normal Classroom," *Arithmetic Teacher,* Vol. 4, pp. 219–221, November, 1957.
20. Johnson, Donovan, "Commercial Games for the Arithmetic Class," *Arithmetic Teacher,* Vol. 5, pp. 69–73, March, 1958.
21. Junge, Charlotte, "Gifted Ones: How Shall We Know Them?" *Arithmetic Teacher,* Vol. 4, pp. 141–146, October, 1957.
22. Lankford, Francis G., Jr., "Implications of the Psychology of Learning for the Teaching of Arithmetic," *The Growth of Mathematical Ideas,* 24th Yearbook. Washington, D.C.: National Council of Teachers of Mathematics, 1959.
23. McMeen, George, "Differentiating Arithmetic Instruction for Various Levels of Achievement," *Arithmetic Teacher,* Vol. 6, pp. 113–120, April, 1959.
24. Michaelis, John U., and Enoch Dumas, *The Student Teacher in the Elementary School,* Chapter 11. Englewood Cliffs, N.J.: Prentice-Hall, Inc., 1960.
25. Miller, G. H., "How Much Time for Arithmetic?" *Arithmetic Teacher,* Vol. 5, pp. 256–259, November, 1958.
26. Phillips, Jo McKeeby, "One Classroom, with Arithmetic and Justice for All," *Arithmetic Teacher,* Vol. 5, pp. 165–167, October, 1958.
27. Sister Josephina, "Differences in Arithmetic Performance," *Arithmetic Teacher,* Vol. 6, pp. 152–153, April, 1959.
28. Spencer, Peter L., and Marguerite Brydegaard, *Building*

Mathematical Concepts in the Elementary School, Chapter 10. New York: Henry Holt and Company, 1952.

29. SPITZER, HERBERT F., *Practical Classroom Procedures for Enriching Arithmetic.* St. Louis: Webster Publishing Company, 1956.
30. SPITZER, HERBERT F., *The Teaching of Arithmetic,* Chapter 13. Boston: Houghton Mifflin Company, 1961.
31. STEPHENS, HAROLD W., "They Love Arithmetic!" *Arithmetic Teacher,* Vol. 2, pp. 60–61, April, 1955.
32. STOKES, C. NEWTON, *Teaching the Meanings of Arithmetic,* Chapter 10. New York: Appleton-Century-Crofts, Inc., 1951.
33. SUELTZ, BEN A., "Slow Learner," *Grade Teacher,* Vol. 73, p. 41, April, 1956.

CHAPTER 15

Contemporary Mathematics in an Elementary School Program

In 1944 the Post-War Commission on Mathematics of the National Council of Teachers of Mathematics [1] recommended changes in the mathematical programs of public schools in this country. In 1952, the University of Illinois Committee on School Mathematics undertook an extensive project in an effort to develop material for the secondary schools which would introduce the viewpoint of contemporary mathematics.[2]

Following the launching of "Sputnik" in 1957, grants provided by the National Science Foundation and other organizations gave increased emphasis to a critical examination of mathematics programs in the elementary and secondary schools. Of the large studies dealing with mathematics programs, those conducted by the School Mathematics Study Group (SMSG) and the University of Illinois

[1] "The First Report of the Commission on Post-War Plans," *Mathematics Teacher,* 37:226–232, May, 1944; "The Second Report of the Commission on Post-War Plans," *Mathematics Teacher,* 38:195–221, May, 1945; "Guidance Report of the Commission on Post-War Plans," *Mathematics Teacher,* 40:315–339, November, 1947.

[2] UICSM Project Staff, "The University of Illinois Mathematics Program," *School Review,* 65:457–465, Winter, 1957.

Committee on School Mathematics (UICSM) have attracted nationwide attention and have exerted considerable influence on school curriculums. The following statement by Dr. E. G. Begle, Director of the School Mathematics Study Group, indicates the general aim of these studies:

We have set a goal to aim at, a decision as to what we would like to have our students know when they finish high school. For example, our goal for the college-capable student is a program in high school which will enable him to take in his first college year a substantial course in calculus. For the less capable student, our goal is a mastery and an understanding of as many mathematical skills as the student is capable of, and at the same time an understanding of the nature of mathematics and of the role of mathematics in our society.[3]

The School Mathematics Study Group took as its starting point a consideration of the mathematical competencies which would be desirable for students entering college mathematics courses, because the purpose of the group was to recommend content and teaching procedures in the secondary schools which would facilitate the acquiring of such competencies. Next, those mathematical competencies considered desirable for secondary school students were examined in order to determine what changes were needed in the elementary school program in order to prepare pupils to enter the secondary school mathematics programs.

The changes in the arithmetic programs which have been recommended by various study groups are related to the content of the program, to the gradation of the various topics introduced into the program, and to the methods of instruction.

Changes in Content

Although the gradation of the content differs considerably in the reports of the various study groups, the nature of the content suggested by these groups is very much alike and is exemplified in the recommendations of the Maryland Mathematics Project, which suggests the following topical units for a seventh grade course: [4]

[3] E. G. Begle, Report of a Conference on Elementary School Mathematics (New Haven: Yale University Press, 1959), p. 1.

[4] *Studies in Mathematics Education.* A Brief Survey of Improvement Programs for School Mathematics Prepared by the Scott, Foresman and Company. Chicago: Scott, Foresman and Company, 1959.

1. Systems of Numeration
2. Symbols
3. Natural Numbers
4. Factoring and Primes
5. The Number One
6. The Number Zero
7. Mathematical Systems
8. Powers and Scientific Notation I
9. The Number System of Ordinary Arithmetic
10. Points, Lines, Curves, Planes
11. Logic and Number Sentences
12. Systems of Integers under Addition
13. Powers and Scientific Notation II
14. Plane Figures I
15. Plane Figures II
16. Systems of Measures
17. Systems of Rational Numbers
18. Estimating
19. Graphs on a Plane
20. Averages

Experimental programs conducted by the School Mathematics Study Group introduced some of the above-mentioned topics to children in the fourth, fifth, and sixth grades of the elementary school through the following units: [5]

GRADE 4

Concept of Sets
Numeration
Properties and Techniques of Addition and Subtraction, I
Properties of Multiplication and Division
Sets of Points
Properties and Techniques of Addition and Subtraction, II
Techniques of Multiplication and Division
Recognition of Common Geometric Figures
Linear Measurement
Concept of Fractional Number

GRADE 5

Extending Systems of Numeration
Factors and Primes

[5] Begle, *op. cit.*, p. 438.

Extending Multiplication and Division
Congruence of Geometric Figures
Addition and Subtraction of Fractional Numbers
Measurement of Angles
Area
Ratio

GRADE 6

Exponents
Multiplication of Fractional Numbers
Side-Angle Relationships of Triangles
The Integers
Coordinates
Division of Fractional Numbers
Volume
Organizing and Describing Data
Sets and Circles

The general nature of the content recommended for secondary school students is exemplified in the following list included in the first and second courses of a four-course series recommended by the University of Illinois Committee on School Mathematics for students in the ninth through the twelfth grades.[6]

FIRST COURSE

Distinction Between Numbers and Numerals
Real Numbers
Principles of Real Numbers
Inverse Operations
Relations of Inequality
Numerical Variables
Generalizations about Real Numbers
Notation and Some Concepts of the Algebra of Sets
Solutions of Equations, Linear and Quadratic
Solution of "Worded" Problems
Ordered Pairs of Numbers
Graphing Equations and Inequations

SECOND COURSE

Sets and Relations
Linear and Quadratic Functions

[6] *Studies in Mathematics Education, op. cit.,* p. 31.

Systems of Linear Equations
Measures of Intervals, Arcs, Angles, and Plane Regions
Elementary Properties of Angles, Polygons, and Circles
Further Study of Manipulations of Algebraic Expressions

There is general agreement among various study groups that new content should be included which gives more emphasis to a study of the structure of number through the use of a unifying language of sets, and that the content should be such as will form a basis for a further study of mathematics.

Gradation of Content

The suggestions of the various study groups for the gradation of new material for the elementary school program indicate that although some of the new material will be introduced in the intermediate grades, the main emphasis on introducing the new concepts will be placed at the seventh and eighth grade levels. In instances where differentiated programs are provided for the more able pupils, the new material may be introduced very early in the elementary school program. Before making recommendations in this area, we should await the outcomes of experimental programs now in progress, which include intuitive geometry, the introduction of mathematical logic, and other aspects of contemporary mathematics in the intermediate, and in some instances in the primary, grades. The purpose of these programs is to prepare pupils for a much more extensive study of contemporary mathematics at the secondary school level.

Many of the topics which have been introduced in traditional programs at the seventh and eighth grade levels will be introduced in the intermediate grades. This would be noted particularly in the introduction of topics involving per cent, equations, and some geometrical concepts.

In order that the vocabulary which is used to describe number and number relationships might be more precise, some elementary set concepts would be introduced as the need for them arises in the intermediate grades.

Changes in Method

The importance of bringing meaning into arithmetic—that is, emphasizing an understanding of the rationale of the computational procedures and the structure of number—has been stressed by all of the groups which have been studying the mathematics programs. Consequently this aspect of method probably will receive more emphasis. The use of a "controlled discovery" technique whereby the children are led through questioning to grasp a new concept is recommended.

A change which will affect teaching procedure is that which suggests that children in the intermediate grades be taught how to state the mathematical relationships in a given problem situation in the form of mathematical sentences, before they begin the computation needed to solve the problem.

It is recommended that more attention be given to using precise language when discussing number and number operations, so that the mathematical concepts and vocabulary developed by the children will be compatible with that which they learn at the secondary school level.

As the "meaning approach" to teaching arithmetic has been given increasing emphasis in the elementary school for over a decade, the changes in method will not be as noticeable to the elementary school teacher as will the changes in the content of the arithmetic program.

Important Concepts Introduced from Contemporary Mathematics

Some of the concepts from contemporary mathematics well might be woven in with those from the traditional program throughout all the grades of the elementary school, so that there is a smooth progression of mathematical ideas, and an opportunity for the pupil to understand how mathematical topics are related. In the upper grades of the elementary school, the new material might be studied in more depth by arranging the material in topics which would lead on to similar topics studied in the secondary school program. As new textbooks are developed for the pupils, the new concepts and the traditional material will be developed within one sequence, so that the whole program will be psychologically sound from the learner's viewpoint. When this is done, a teacher would be well advised to follow the sequence provided in a well-planned textbook when introducing and developing new topics.

Although in the pupils' arithmetic program the new material should be interwoven with the traditional material, for the purposes of the following discussion the important aspects of contemporary mathematics programs for the seventh and eighth grades will be discussed apart from the traditional school programs.

ALGEBRA IN THE ELEMENTARY SCHOOL PROGRAM

Elementary Set Concepts

An important characteristic of contemporary mathematics programs is the use of set concepts and symbolism to describe and express various ideas in arithmetic, algebra, geometry, and in fact in all mathematics. Although an extensive study of set-theoretics would have little value for elementary school children, some of the simpler concepts and some symbolism are very useful and should be introduced as soon as the need arises in discussing the nature of number. The following concepts, employing set language and symbolism, have been selected as useful to elementary school children, and particularly useful to those in the upper grades. At the intermediate grade level, the purpose for introducing set concepts is to enable the pupils to express more precisely some of the ideas found in arithmetic. Consequently, the concepts relating to sets may be developed as they are needed through the study of number, but at the seventh and eighth grade levels a more systematic study of set concepts is needed as an introduction to further work in mathematics at the secondary school level.

The nature of a set. A set may be thought of as some well-defined group or collection of elements of either a concrete or an abstract nature. Thus we may speak of a set of pupils in a classroom, the set of boys in a class, the set of natural numbers between seven and eleven, the set of points on a line, or the set of the sides of a given triangle. A given set may be indicated by naming each of the elements, or members, which make up the set (called the *roster* notation) or it may be indicated by a sentence which describes the members which belong to the set. For example, we may speak of the set of natural numbers between 7 and 11, or we may refer to the same set by speaking of the set whose members are 8, 9, and 10. This set is described more explicitly by the symbolism $\{8, 9, 10\}$, read as, "The set whose members are the numbers eight, nine, and ten." Another way symbols could be used to designate this set is to use braces to include the description of the set and write $\{x \mid x \varepsilon N \wedge 7 < x < 11\}$, which could be read as, "A set of all x such that x is a natural number and x is greater than seven and less than eleven" (See Figure 15.1). In this instance,

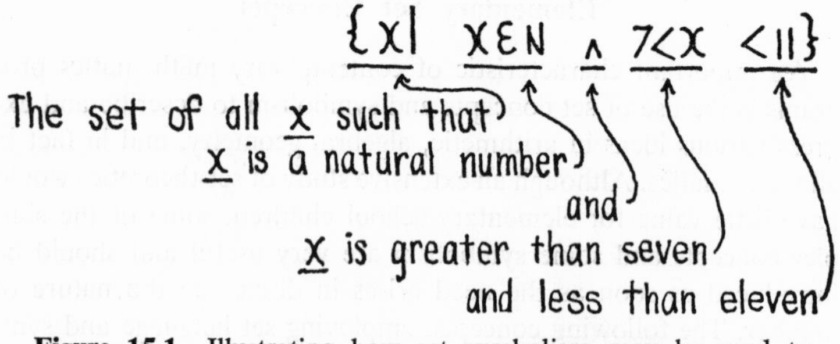

Figure 15.1 Illustrating how set symbolism may be used to express a mathematical sentence.

"N" is being used to indicate the set of natural numbers and "ε" is used to denote "is a member of." This notation technically is called the *set-builder* notation, and will be explained further below.

It will be noted in the example given above that the set is defined by including a condition which has to be satisfied in order for an element to qualify as a member of the set, namely, the condition that x must be replaced by a natural number which is more than seven and less than eleven. It will be noted that the symbolism provides a concise, as well as a precise, way of expressing certain ideas regarding numbers.

The following list includes symbols relating to sets and to certain relations of equality and inequality which are used very frequently in contemporary mathematics. These symbols should be introduced to children in the elementary grades as they are needed to express new concepts.

Symbol	*Meaning of Symbol*
$=$	"is equal to"
$\neq$	"is not equal to"
$<$	"is less than"
$\nless$	"is not less than"
$>$	"is greater than"
$\ngtr$	"is not greater than"
$\cong$	"is congruent to"
$A \subset B$	"Set *A* is a proper subset of set *B*" or "Set *A* is contained in set *B*"
$A \subseteq B$	"Set *A* is a subset of set *B*" (This allows the inclusion of the case where $A = B$.)
U	"The universe" (The set of all elements under discussion from which replacements for the variable may be selected.)
$A \cap B$	"Intersection of set *A* and set *B*"
$A \cup B$	"Union of set *A* and set *B*"
A'	"Complement of set *A*"
$\emptyset$ or $\{\ \}$	"The null set" or "The empty set"
$\{1, 2, 3\}$	"The set whose members are 1, 2, and 3" (Braces are used to enclose the description of a set.)
$\{x \mid x > 7\}$	"The set of all *x* such that *x* is greater than 7"
ε	"is a member of"
$\wedge$	"and"
$\vee$	"or"
(x,y)	"The ordered pair *x*, *y*"

Subsets. Set *A* is said to be a *subset* of set *B* when every member of set *A* is also a member of set *B*. For example, the boys in a given school class would form a subset of the members of a whole class which is made up of both boys and girls. If the class were made up of boys alone, the set of boys still would be a subset of the whole class, because every member of the set of boys would be a member of the whole class. If *A* is a subset of *B*, but does not include every member of *B*, then *A* is said to be a *proper subset* of *B*. The symbols $A \subset B$ may be read as "*A* is a proper subset of *B*," while the symbols $A \supseteq B$ are read as, "*A* is a subset of *B*." Diagrams called Euler circles, or Venn diagrams, according to the ideas which they illustrate, are used often to illustrate relationships among sets and subsets. In current usage, however, the term *Venn diagram* is being used to name all diagrams which indicate the relationships among sets.

The *universe,* or *universal set,* is the set from which the sets under discussion are drawn. For example, if we were discussing natural numbers as members of a set, then the universal set would consist of all the natural numbers. When drawing Venn diagrams, the universal set is generally represented as a rectangle. In Figure 15.2 the universe consists of a designated group of children, such

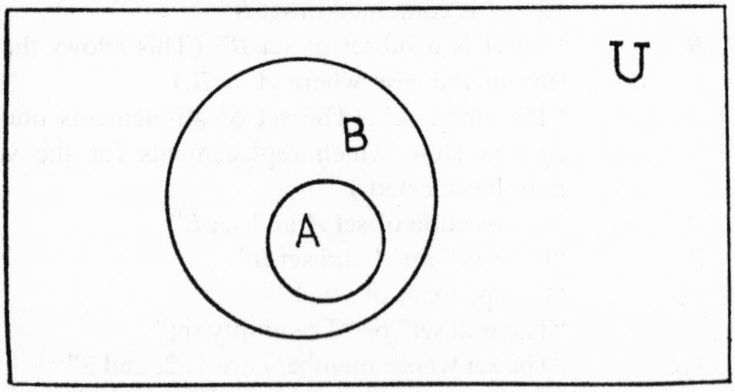

$U =$ The universal set consisting of all pupils in a certain school.
$B =$ The set of pupils in a given class.
$A =$ The set of boys in the given class.
$A \subset B$

Figure 15.2 Euler circles (sometimes called Venn diagrams) illustrating how a set of boys may be thought of as being a subset of a given class.

as all the children in a given school. The circle labeled "*B*" represents a fourth grade class in this universe, while circle "*A*" represents the set of boys as being a subset of set *B*.

The concept of an *empty set,* or *null set,* is also useful. An empty set refers to a set which has no members. For example, in a situation where a school class is composed entirely of girls, the set of boys in that class would be the empty set. Symbols representing the empty set are "ϕ" or "{ }."

A set which has infinitely many members, such as the set of natural numbers, is called an *infinite set.* The set of natural numbers could be indicated by the symbols {1, 2, 3, 4, · · · }, which could be read as, "The set whose members are the numbers 1, 2, 3, 4, and so on." As the three dots within the brackets are not followed by a numeral, it is assumed that this series of numbers would continue endlessly, and that the pattern for continuing is established by the sequence of the numbers given.

A set which is not an infinite set is a *finite set.* For example, the symbols {1, 2, 3, 4, · · · 1,000,000} would refer to the finite set of numbers from one to one million inclusive.

Operations on sets. We may think of operations on sets as well as operations on numbers. Two common operations on sets are called *union* and *intersection.*

The operation of union is that in which all the distinct members of two or more sets are considered as a single set. For example, the operation of union on the two sets A and B, where $A = \{1, 2, 3, 4\}$ and $B = \{3, 4, 5\}$, would result in the set {1, 2, 3, 4, 5}. The symbol to indicate union is "$\cup$," and the operation on the two sets mentioned above could be expressed symbolically as

$$\{1, 2, 3, 4\} \cup \{3, 4, 5\}, \text{ or as } A \cup B,$$

and the set resulting from this union would be shown as

$$\{1, 2, 3, 4, 5\}$$

We read $A \cup B$ as "A union B."

Union could be indicated by the following Venn diagram. The shading indicates the union of sets A and B.

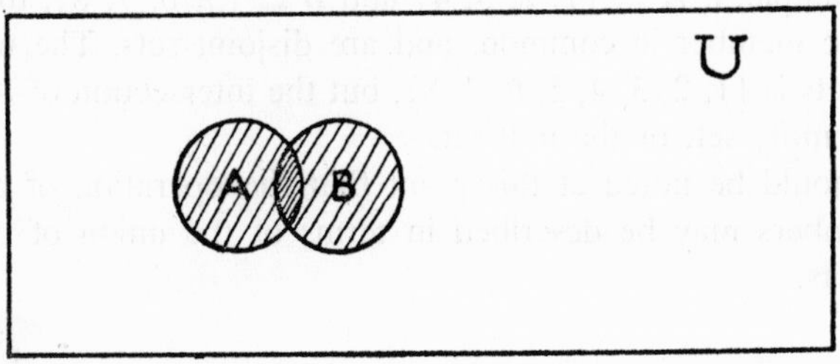

The operation of intersection on two sets is that which results in a set which is composed only of those members which are common to both sets. For example, if $A = \{1, 2, 3, 4\}$ and $B = \{3, 4, 5\}$, the operation of intersection on these two sets would result in $\{3, 4\}$. As the symbol to indicate intersection is "$\cap$," intersection on these two sets is indicated by $A \cap B$, which is read "*A* intersection *B*," and is illustrated by the following diagram where the shaded portion represents the set formed by this operation, in this instance $\{3, 4\}$.

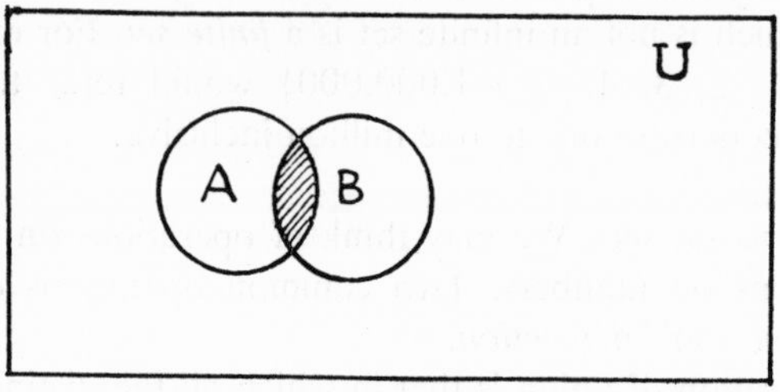

When two sets have no members in common they are called *disjoint sets*. Disjoint sets may be illustrated by the following diagram.

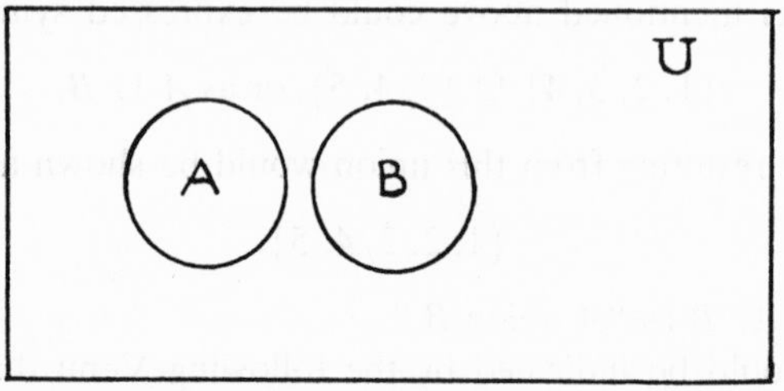

For example, if $A = \{1, 2, 3, 4\}$ and $B = \{5, 6, 7, 8\}$, these sets have no member in common, and are disjoint sets. The union of these sets is $\{1, 2, 3, 4, 5, 6, 7, 8\}$, but the intersection of A and B is the empty set, or the null set.

It should be noted at this point that the operation of addition on numbers may be described in terms of the union of two disjoint sets.

Another useful concept is that of the *complement* of a set. The complement of a set is made up of those members in the universe of which the set is a part but which are not members of the given set. For example, if the universe under discussion were the set of natural numbers, and if $A = \{1, 2, 3, 4\}$, then the complement of A would be $\{5, 6, 7, 8, \cdots\}$. The symbol for the complement of A is A', read as "A prime," and the shading in the following diagram indicates that the complement of the set A is made up of the members of the universe which are not included in A.

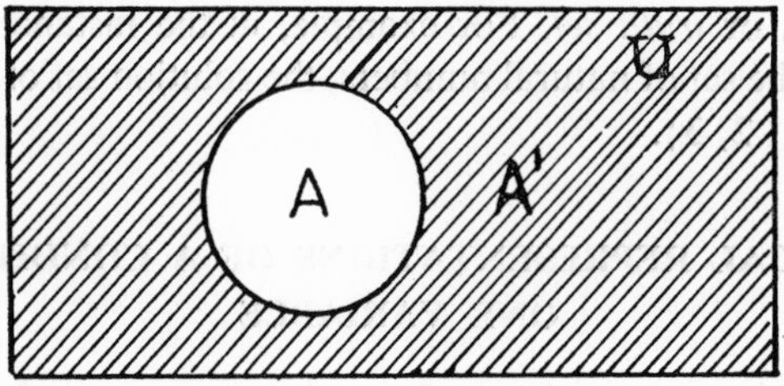

The set concepts and symbols mentioned above are useful in describing other mathematical concepts, and will be used often in the pages which follow.

EXPRESSING CONCEPTS BY MATHEMATICAL SENTENCES

As mentioned earlier, it is important that a distinction be maintained between a number, which is an abstraction, and a numeral, which is the symbol used to refer to a number. A written expression such as $3 + 4 = 7$ is a sentence, made up of numerals and other symbols. The idea, or abstraction, to which this sentence refers is called a *statement*. The sentence is thus a written expression of a statement. A sentence such as $x + 3 = 7$ is called an *open sentence* as it contains a symbol, "x" in this instance, which acts as a placeholder for a numeral. There is no way of knowing whether the statement expressed by an open sentence is true or false. When the placeholders are replaced by numerals in a sentence, then the statement to which the sentence refers has *truth value;* that is, the statement is either true or false. It cannot be both. Such a sentence sometimes is called a *closed* sentence.

In the sentence "$x + 3 = 7$" we shall speak of the symbol "x" as a placeholder for a numeral, but in the statement to which "$x + 3 = 7$" refers, which is the idea or abstraction, the referent for "x" will be called a *variable*. We shall think of a numeral replacing "x" in a sentence and of a number replacing a variable in a statement. The set of numbers which may be used to replace the variable in a statement will form the universe for that variable. Another common phrase for "universe of the variable" is "domain of the variable." The set of numbers which on replacing the variable will make the statement a true statement, will be called the *solution set,* or *truth set.* For example, in the instance where the universe is the set of natural numbers, the solution set of $x + 3 < 7$ would be $\{1, 2, 3\}$.

GRAPHICAL REPRESENTATIONS OF A CONDITION IN ONE VARIABLE

Graphical representations of number concepts often may be very helpful to pupils and should be used frequently by the teacher to promote insight into number relationships.

In Figure 15.3 a number line is used to represent a statement

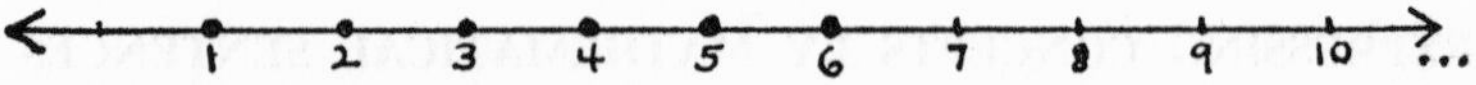

$U =$ Set of natural numbers $= \{1, 2, 3, 4, 5, \cdots\}$
$\{x \mid x < 7\} = \{1, 2, 3, 4, 5, 6\}$

Figure 15.3 A drawing illustrating the graph of the solution set of a condition in one variable.

expressed by the symbolism $\{x \mid x < 7\}$. On the drawing representing a line, marks are spaced at equal intervals. The arrowheads on the drawing of the line indicate that the line should be thought of as extending infinitely far in both directions. Numerals are placed by each mark to associate a natural number with the point represented by the mark. The three dots to the right of the numeral "10" indicate that the members of the set of natural numbers could continue to be associated with infinitely many points.

In this instance, the members of the set of natural numbers will be considered as replacements for the variable x. The dots indicate that $\{1, 2, 3, 4, 5, 6\}$ is the solution set, because any member of this set, and of this set only, will satisfy the condition that $x < 7$ when the universe is the set of natural numbers.

In Figure 15.4 the graph of the solution set for satisfying the

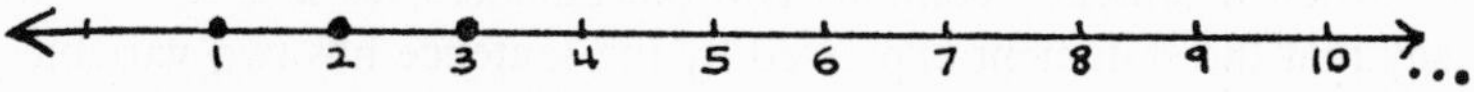

$U =$ Set of natural numbers $= \{1, 2, 3, 4, 5, \cdots\}$
$\{x \mid x + 3 < 7\} = \{1, 2, 3\}$

Figure 15.4 A drawing illustrating the graph of the solution set of a condition in one variable.

condition $x + 3 < 7$ is indicated by the dots on the drawing which represent the points associated with the natural numbers 1, 2, and 3.

In Figure 15.5 the graph of the solution set for satisfying the

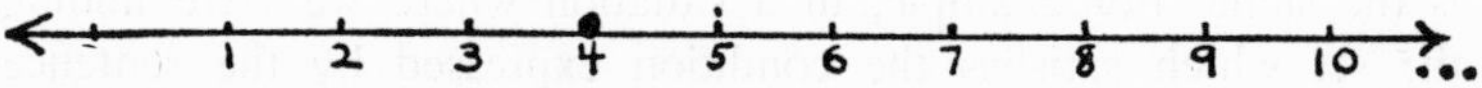

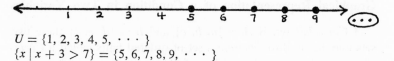

$U =$ Set of natural numbers $= \{1, 2, 3, 4, 5, \cdots\}$
$\{x \mid x + 3 = 7\} = \{4\}$

Figure 15.5 A drawing illustrating the graph of the solution set of a condition in one variable.

condition $x + 3 = 7$ is indicated by the dot which represents the point associated with the number 4.

In Figure 15.6 the graph of the solution set for satisfying the

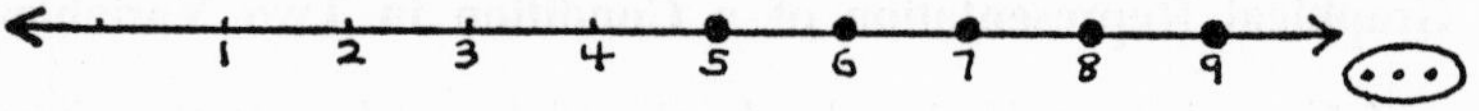

$U = \{1, 2, 3, 4, 5, \cdots\}$
$\{x \mid x + 3 > 7\} = \{5, 6, 7, 8, 9, \cdots\}$

Figure 15.6 A drawing illustrating the graph of the solution set of a condition in one variable.

condition that $x + 3 > 7$ is indicated by the dots representing points associated with the numbers 5 through 9 inclusively as well as the three dots to the right of "9" which indicate that all points to the right which are associated with natural numbers would be associated with numbers in the solution set. In this instance the solution set could be shown as $\{5, 6, 7, 8, \cdots\}$.

Ordered Pairs

When a sentence contains two placeholders, as $x + 4 = y$, we say that the statement expressed by the sentence has two variables. When two variables are used in a condition, the order of the variables is important, because the condition will determine the relationship between the variables. The expression (x,y) is read, "The ordered pair, x y," and the first element in the ordered pair is called *the first component* while the second element is called *the second component.*

In some situations the universe, or replacement set, for the first component may be different from the universe of the second component. In most situations, the universe for each of the components is the same. For example, in a situation where we were finding the set which satisfies the condition expressed by the sentence $\{(x,y) \mid x + 4 = y\}$ and where the universe for set A, which furnishes the replacements for x, is given as $A = \{1, 2, 3\}$ and the universe for set B, which furnishes the replacement for y, is given as $B = \{4, 5, 6\}$, the solution set would be $\{(1,5), (2,6)\}$. Although the nine ordered pairs, (1,4), (1,5), (1,6), (2,4), (2,5), (2,6), (3,4), (3,5), (3,6) could be used as replacements in the condition, only the ordered pairs (1,5) and (2,6) could be said to satisfy the condition.

Graphical Representation of a Condition in Two Variables

A Cartesian set. If $A = \{a, b, c\}$ and $B = \{d, e, f\}$ these two sets may be used to *generate* a set of ordered pairs called a *Cartesian set* by using each member of A as a first component of an ordered pair along with each member of B as the second component of these ordered pairs. For example, the Cartesian set $A \times B$, which is read as "A cross B," [7] and which is generated from $A = \{a, b, c\}$ and $B = \{d, e, f\}$ would be $\{(a,d), (a,e), (a,f),$

[7] The Cartesian set $A \times B$ is called also "The Cartesian product of A by B."

(b,d), (b,e), (b,f), (c,d), (c,e), $(c,f)\}$. Figure 15.7 shows how this concept may be illustrated graphically.

$A = \{a, b, c\}$

$B = \{d, e, f\}$

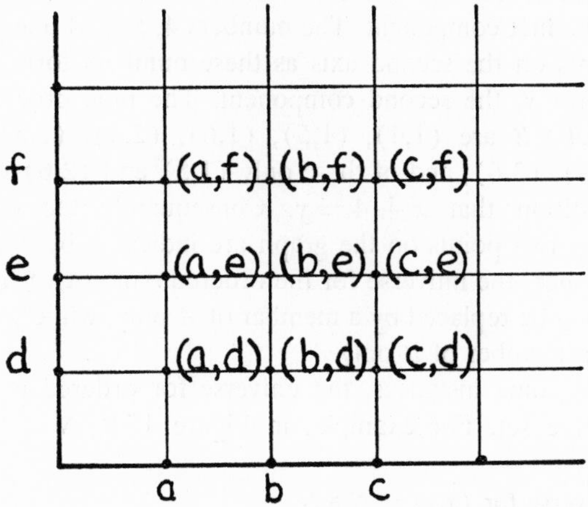

$A \times B = \{(a,d), (a,e), (a,f), (b,d), (b,e), (b,f), (c,d), (c,e), (c,f)\}$

Figure 15.7 A graph of a Cartesian set of ordered pairs which has been generated from two sets.

Figure 15.8 illustrates the graph of the solution set $\{(x,y) \mid x + 4 = y\}$, where x may be replaced by any member of $A =$

If $A = \{1, 2, 3\}$ and $B = \{4, 5, 6\}$, then $\{(x,y) \mid x + 4 = y\} = \{(1,5), (2,6)\}$.

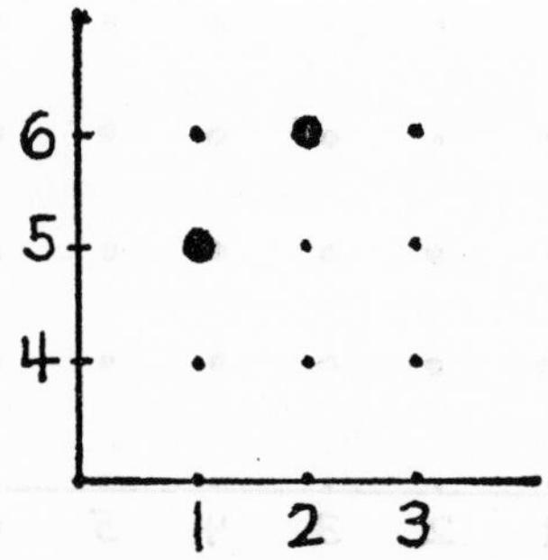

Figure 15.8 The graph of the solution set is represented by the large dots.

$\{1, 2, 3\}$ and y may be replaced by any member of $B = \{4, 5, 6\}$. In this instance, the numbers 1, 2, and 3 are associated with points on the first axis as these are the numbers in the replacement set for x, the first component. The numbers 4, 5, and 6 are associated with points on the second axis as these numbers form the replacement set for y, the second component. The nine ordered pairs formed by $A \times B$ are (1,4), (1,5), (1,6), (2,4), (2,5), (2,6), (3,4), (3,5), (3,6), and of these only (1,5) and (2,6) would satisfy the condition that $x + 4 = y$. Consequently the dots representing these two points on the graph are indicated by larger dots. In this instance, the universe for the ordered pair, (x,y), is $A \times B$ because x may be replaced by a member of A only, while y may be replaced by a member of B only.

In some instances, the universe for ordered pairs might be an infinite set. For example, in Figure 15.9, $N = \{1, 2, 3, \cdots\}$

Universe for $(x,y) = N \times N$
$\{(x,y) \mid x + 1 > y\}$

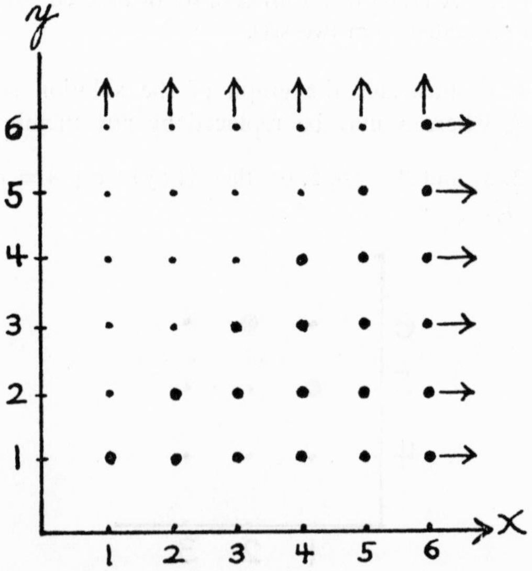

Figure 15.9 The graph of the solution set is represented by the large dots. The graph is incomplete.

and the universe for $(x,y) = N \times N$. The graph of the solution set $\{(x,y) \mid x + 1 > y\}$ is illustrated by the larger dots. As the graph is the graph of an infinite set, the diagram must of necessity be incomplete, but the part which is represented illustrates the relationship of the solution set to the universe, and is a useful device for gaining insight into this relationship.

The concept of ordered pairs which a pupil utilizes when he finds the solution set which satisfies a condition in two variables is very important, as it is basic to many other mathematical ideas. It is one of the many ways in which we may define an association from one set of numbers to another, and thus leads on to the concept of a relation and a function. A clear understanding of the nature of functions will be needed later by a student if he is to understand certain aspects of mathematics which he will study at secondary school and college levels. A discussion of the nature of functions is beyond the scope of this book.

GEOMETRY IN THE ELEMENTARY SCHOOL PROGRAM

As noted earlier in Chapter 5, pupils are introduced to familiar geometrical shapes such as the circle, rectangle, square, and triangle in the first and second grades.

During the time that children are in the intermediate grades, they learn the procedure for finding the area and volume of two- or three-dimensional figures while they are developing concepts relating to measurement.

While children are in the intermediate grades they learn to use a straightedge, compass, and protractor in drawing triangles, rectangles, and circles, and in measuring angles in degrees. They also are introduced to simple constructions such as those involved in bisecting line segments and angles, and in drawing a perpendicular to a line.

Recent experimental studies involving the introduction of simple geometrical constructions along with appropriate vocabulary to younger children suggest that an introduction to this aspect of geometry might be begun successfully in the primary grades.

The traditional elementary school mathematics programs have always included simple constructions in geometry, and these have not proven difficult for average achievers in the intermediate grades. Informal geometry has been introduced at various places from the fourth through the eighth grades.

The new material being suggested in contemporary mathematics programs is related to the viewpoint which emphasizes the importance of children's learning to think of geometrical figures as abstractions, and learning to use set concepts and set language in describing these figures.

Nonmetric Geometry in the Elementary School Program

As used here, the term "nonmetric geometry" will refer to concepts of geometry being considered in terms of set concepts where measurement is not involved. An important purpose in introducing nonmetric geometry into the elementary school program in the upper grades is to familiarize pupils with an approach to geometry in which the concepts are interpreted in terms of sets of points.

The need for an inductive-deductive approach. The experiences of generations of teachers indicate that it is desirable to employ an inductive-deductive approach when helping children to develop concepts at the elementary school level. This is particularly so with regard to concepts in mathematics. In such an approach, the teacher will use concrete or physical representations to help pupils develop concepts regarding the abstract relationships among mathematical objects. In the literature of mathematics, such concepts are described as "intuitive concepts" inasmuch as they have not been developed and proven by mathematical logic.

These intuitive concepts developed by the children lead to their forming broad generalizations regarding mathematical objects, and once a mathematical generalization has been understood, it may be used in solving problems through deductive reasoning. In other words, a mathematical generalization is developed inductively, through a pupil's observing many of its instances, but when the generalization is understood, it is used as a basis from which, by deductive reasoning, the pupil is able to solve many other problems to which the generalization is applicable. This is what is meant by the phrase "an inductive-deductive approach."

Although a certain background of intuitive mathematical concepts is expected of the more mature secondary school students, a more rigorous approach to mathematics is desirable at that level. At the secondary school level, a mathematical system is developed deductively through the use of certain axioms, undefined terms, and the theorems derived from these. One of the values expected of such an approach is that the students will become conversant with a deductive type of reasoning.

Although the mathematical concepts developed by the pupils in the primary and intermediate grades of elementary school are "intuitive" and the approach should be largely inductive in nature, by the time the pupils reach the upper grades of the elementary school a start may be made in showing them how mathematical systems are developed deductively. Here the approach need not be entirely deductive, but the material should be organized psychologically so that new concepts and new vocabulary are made to seem consistent with, and follow from, the concepts which the pupils have developed through their former experiences. It is desirable at this level for the content to be arranged and developed in a pattern which will prepare the child to understand the nature and purpose of the more rigorous presentation of mathematics that he will experience at the secondary school level.

As mentioned above, one of the values derived from a study of geometry is that it provides the pupils with an illustration of the nature of deductive reasoning and proof. The pupils should understand that they will be using an "if—then" type of reasoning while studying mathematics, in which it is agreed that if certain given assumptions are accepted then, through a sequence of related statements, the validity of a conclusion may be established.

In the upper grades of the elementary school, an introduction to nonmetric geometry will provide a bridge, as it were, between the geometrical concepts which the pupils have learned intuitively and the more rigorous deductive procedures which they will meet later. In nonmetric geometry the pupil learns how his intuitive concepts may be stated more precisely through using set concepts and set symbolism. He should learn also how his earlier concepts may be related and extended into an integrated system of ideas by starting with certain undefined terms, such as "point," "line," or "plane," and then using a deductive procedure.

In the discussion which follows, emphasis will be given only to the concepts which are identified with nonmetric geometry in contemporary mathematics programs, rather than to the geometry presented in traditional programs. The steps the pupils take in leading up to each concept will not be described here, but they should be those pursued in some well-planned textbook for the pupils.

The best general teaching procedure to use is one of "controlled discovery" in which the teacher directs the pupil's attention to the aspects of a given problem through a questioning technique which enables the pupil to make each discovery for himself, rather than through a demonstration technique. The technical terms and definitions should be applied to each new concept only after the concept itself has been understood by the pupil. Informal definitions and descriptions suggested by the pupils should be considered prior to formal definitions.

"Point," "Line," "Space," and "Plane" as Undefined Terms, and Some of Their Relationships

In algebra, the axioms and theorems deal largely with mathematical objects called "numbers." In geometry, as the axioms deal largely with spatial relationships, undefined terms such as "point," "line," "space," and "plane" are needed. Although these terms are undefined, they will become characterized by their properties during discussion.

The term "space" is undefined, but may be thought of as the set of all points. The term "point" is undefined also, but a point has the property of having a location in space. In geometry, the term "line" is used to refer to a straight line only, and is thought of as extending infinitely far in each of its directions. It is a set of points, any two of which will *determine* the line; that is, any two points in a line will fix its location and direction. The symbol "$\overleftrightarrow{AB}$" may be used to designate a line which has been determined by the points *A* and *B*. Three or more points which are in the same line are said to be *collinear* points, while points which are not in the same line are *noncollinear*.

A point is said to separate a line into two *half-lines* as shown in Figure 15.10. The point itself is the *boundary* between the half-

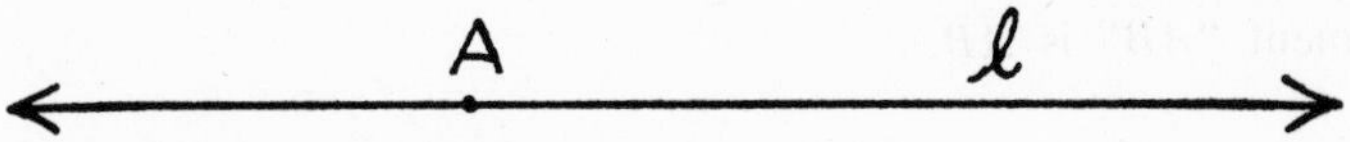

Figure 15.10 The point A separates the line l into two half-lines.

lines, and is not thought of as being part of either of the half-lines to which it forms the boundary. In Figure 15.11, the line l is

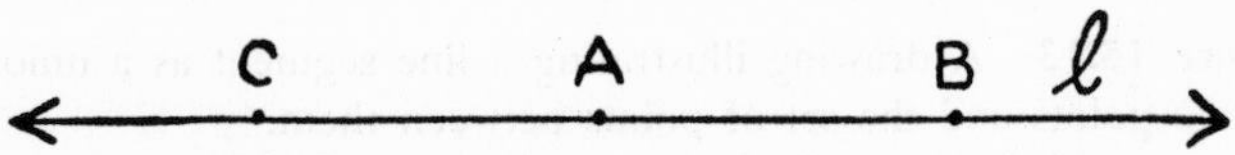

If R = set of points in the half-line from the point A on point B, and S = set of points in the half-line from the point A on the point C, and T = set of points of which the point A is the only member, then line $l = R \cup S \cup T$

Figure 15.11 A drawing illustrating how a point A separates the line l into two half-lines, and is the union of two half-lines and their boundary.

the set of points which is the union of the sets of points in both of the half-lines $\overrightarrow{AB}$, $\overrightarrow{AC}$ and the set whose only member is the point A.

A *ray* is the union of the set of points in a half-line and the point which forms the boundary of the half-line. The ray AB is symbolized by $\overset{\bullet\!\!\rightarrow}{AB}$, where A is the endpoint and B is another point on which the ray lies, as illustrated in Figure 15.12.

If R = set of points in the half-line, $\overrightarrow{AB}$ and S = set of which the point A is the only member = A, then $\overset{\bullet\!\!\rightarrow}{AB} = R \cup S$

Figure 15.12 A drawing illustrating a ray as a union of a half-line and its boundary.

A *line segment* is the union of a set of two points and the set of points on the line between them. A segment includes its two endpoints, as illustrated in Figure 15.13. The symbol for the segment "*AB*" is $\overline{AB}$.

If R = set of points in line l between the points A and B, and S = set of which point A is the only member, and T = set of which point B is the only member, then $\overline{AB} = R \cup S \cup T$

Figure 15.13 A drawing illustrating a line segment as a union of two points and the set of points between them.

The term "congruence" is an undefined term which when applied to segments means that the segments are the same size. The symbol for congruence is $\cong$, and when used in the sentence $\overline{AB} \cong \overline{CD}$ is read, "The segment *AB* is congruent to the segment *CD*."

The idea of congruence along with the idea of "betweenness" may be used to define what is meant by "greater than" and "less than" as applied to segments.

In Figure 15.14a, let $\overline{AB}$ and $\overline{CD}$ be two segments of the lines

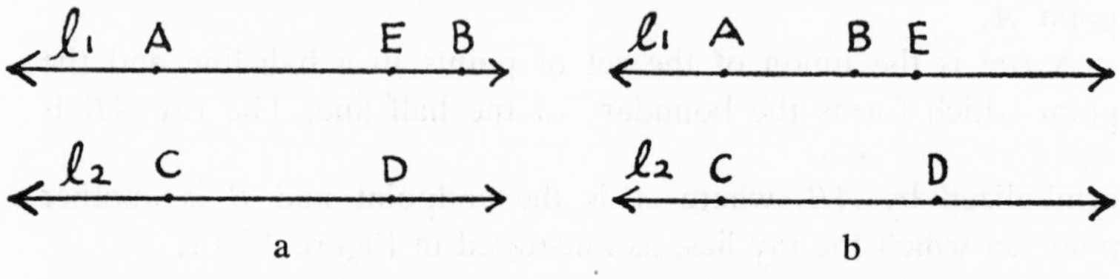

Figure 15.14 A drawing illustrating how the concepts of congruence and "betweenness" may be used to define the meaning of "greater than" and "less than" as these terms are applied to segments.

l_1 and l_2 respectively. As the point A separates the line l_1 into two half-lines, let E be a point in the half-line $\overrightarrow{AB}$ which makes $\overline{AE} \cong \overline{CD}$. If E is between the points A and B (Fig. 15.14a), then $\overline{AB} > \overline{CD}$; but if B is between A and E (Fig. 15.14b), then $\overline{AB} < \overline{CD}$.

The term "plane" is undefined, but a plane may be thought of as a set of points in space which may be represented by a flat surface, such as a floor or wall. As a plane is an infinite set of points and has no boundaries, it may be considered to be separated into two *half-planes* by any line which lies in it. A line separating a plane into two half-planes forms a boundary for each half-plane, but the line itself does not belong to either half-plane. In Figure 15.15, the points A and B would be in different half-planes, but the point C is in neither half-plane.

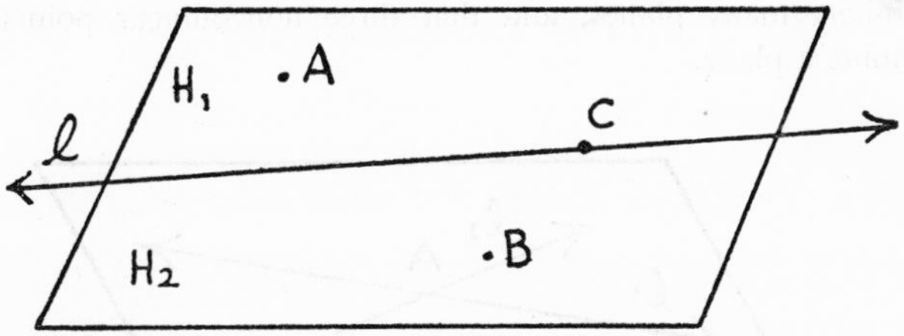

If A ε half-plane H_1, and B ε half-plane H_2, and C = point in line l, then $C \notin H_1 \cup H_2$.

Figure 15.15 A drawing illustrating a plane separated into half-planes.

A plane forms a boundary which separates space into two *half-spaces,* but the plane itself does not belong to either of these half-spaces.

As suggested in Figure 15.16, a line is included in infinitely many planes. The same figure suggests that a line $\overleftrightarrow{AB}$ and a point not in the line, such as C, will determine a plane. Furthermore, as a line itself is determined by two of its points, any three non-collinear points thus will determine a plane.

When lines have a point in common they are said to *"intersect"* (Figure 15.17). Two lines in the same plane but which have no point in common are *parallel lines* (Figure 15.18). Lines that are in different planes and are not parallel are called *skew lines,* as illustrated in Figure 15.19.

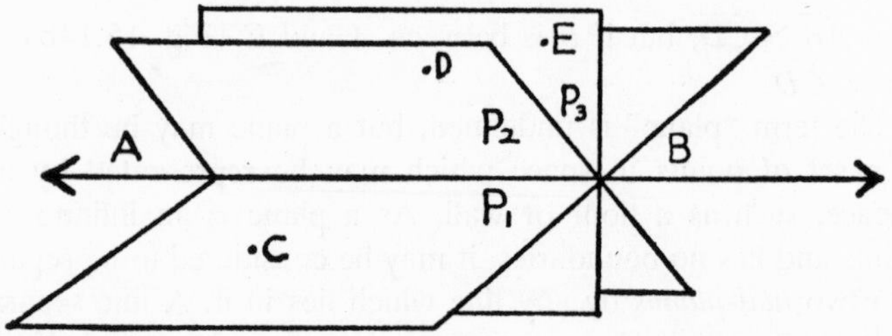

If $P_1 =$ set of points in plane$_1$, and $P_2 =$ set of points in plane$_2$, and $P_3 =$ set of points in plane$_3$, then $\overleftrightarrow{AB} = P_1 \cap P_2 \cap P_3$.

Figure 15.16 A drawing suggesting that a line is included in infinitely many planes, and that three noncollinear points determine a plane.

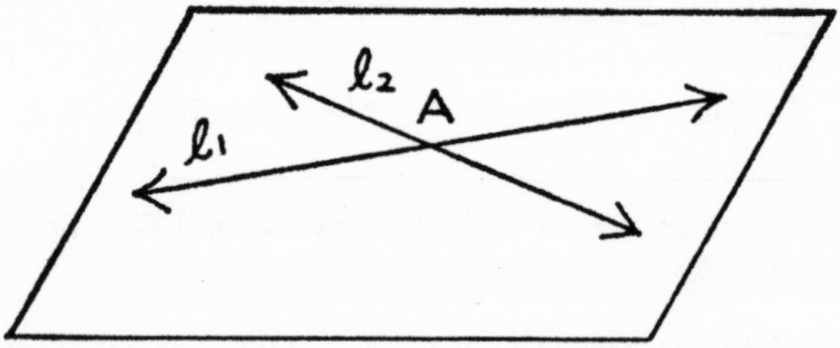

If $R =$ set of points in line l_1, and $S =$ set of points in line l_2, then $R \cap S =$ point A.

Figure 15.17 A drawing illustrating intersecting lines.

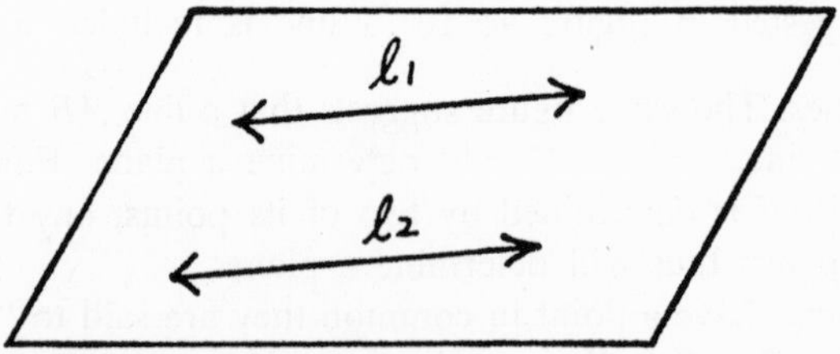

If $R =$ set of points in line l_1, and $S =$ set of points in line l_2, and $R \cap S = \emptyset$, then l_1 and l_2 are parallel.

Figure 15.18 A drawing illustrating parallel lines.

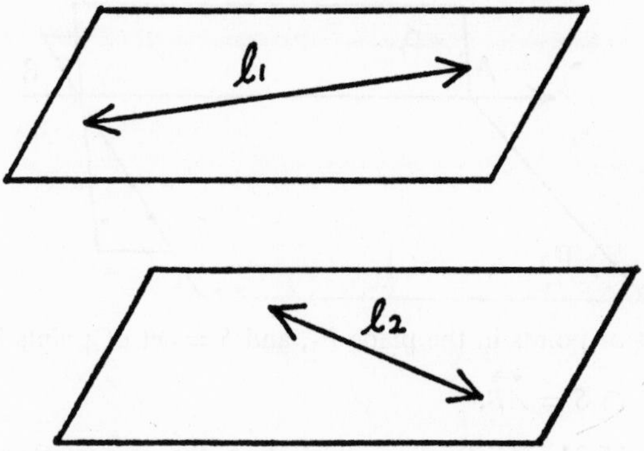

If $R =$ set of points in line l_1, and $S =$ set of points in line l_2 (line l_1 is not parallel to line l_2), and $R \cap S = \emptyset$, then l_1 and l_2 are skew lines.

Figure 15.19 A drawing illustrating skew lines. Note that line l_1 is not parallel to line l_2, and that these lines lie in different planes.

As indicated in Figure 15.20, when a plane is intersected by a line, the intersection is a point, but when two planes intersect, the intersection set is a line, as illustrated in Figure 15.21.

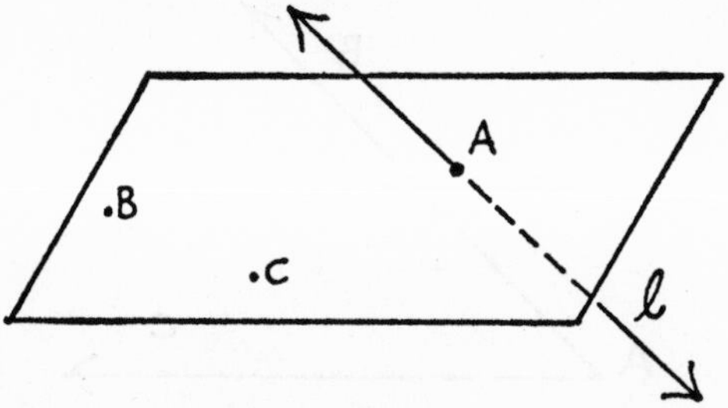

If $R =$ set of points in the plane determined by the points A, B, and C, and $S =$ set of points in line l, then $R \cap S =$ point A.

Figure 15.20 A drawing illustrating the intersection of a line and a plane.

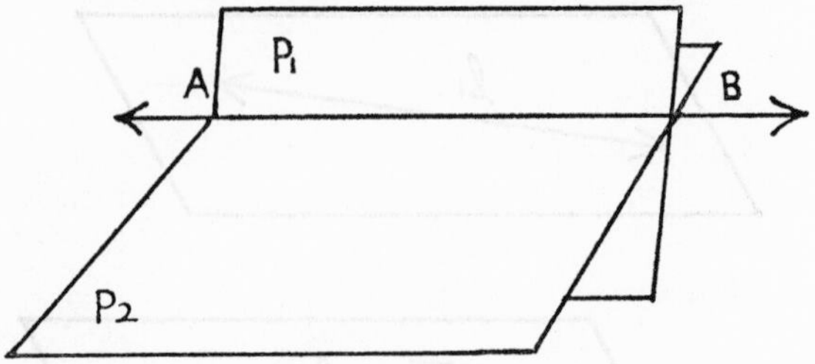

If R = set of points in the plane P_1, and S = set of points in the plane P_2, then $R \cap S = \overleftrightarrow{AB}$.

Figure 15.21 A drawing illustrating the intersection of two planes.

Angles and Some of Their Properties

Two rays which have a common endpoint, or *vertex,* but which do not form a line, make up an *angle.* The angle is the union of the sets of points in the two rays, and the intersection of these two sets would be the single point which is the vertex, as illustrated in Figure 15.22.

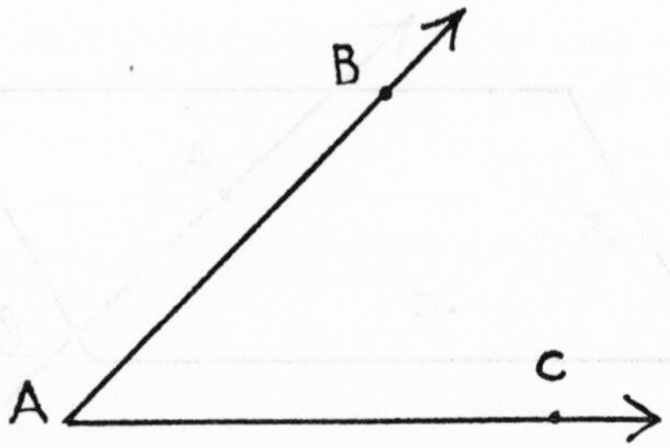

If R = set of points in $\overrightarrow{AB}$, and S = set of points in $\overrightarrow{AC}$, then $R \cup S = \angle BAC$, and $R \cap S$ = point A.

Figure 15.22 A drawing illustrating an angle.

An angle is named by including the name of the point which is its vertex between the names of two points, one on each of its sides, as may be noted in Figure 15.22. The symbol for the angle *BAC* is $\angle BAC$.

The *interior region* of an angle is the intersection set of points of the two half-planes of which the two lines which include the sides of the angle are the boundaries. The interior region of the $\angle BAC$ in Figure 15.23 is represented by the cross-shaded area.

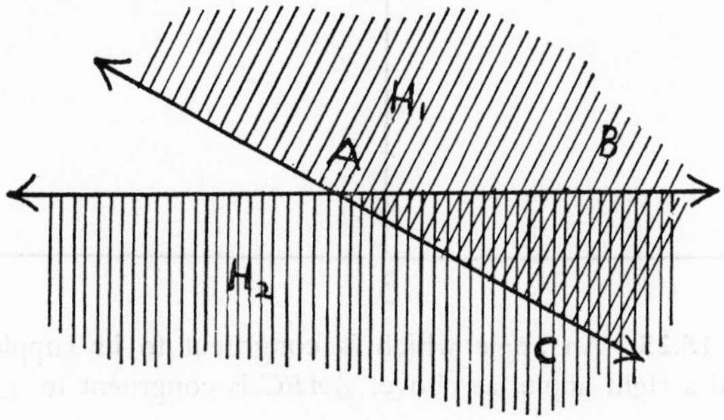

If R = set of points in half-plane H_1, and S = set of points in half-plane H_2, then $R \cap S$ = interior of $\angle BAC$.

Figure 15.23 A drawing illustrating the interior of an angle as the intersection of two half-planes.

An angle thus may be thought of as separating a plane into an interior region of the angle and an exterior region.

As illustrated in Figure 15.24, when two angles have a common vertex, a common side, and when the two sides which are not common form a line, then they are called a *linear pair of angles*.

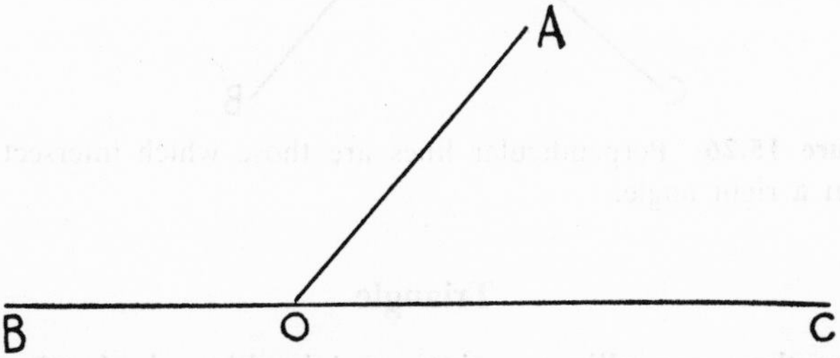

Figure 15.24 A drawing illustrating a linear pair of angles. $\angle AOB$ and $\angle COA$ are each the supplement of the other.

Each angle of a linear pair of angles is said to be the *supplement* of the other.

An angle which is congruent to its supplement, such as $\angle ABC$ in Figure 15.25, is called a *right angle.*

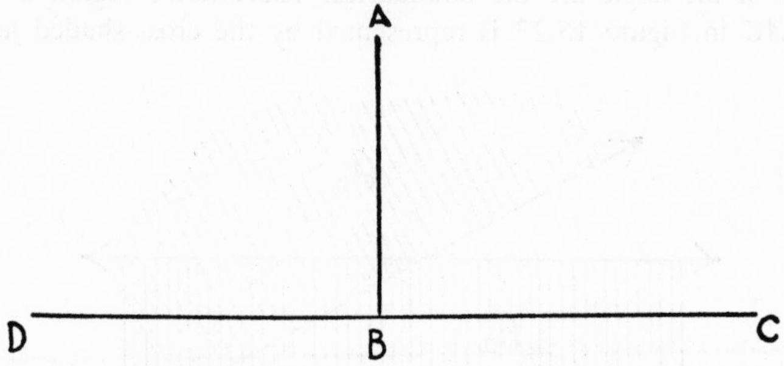

Figure 15.25 An angle which is congruent to its supplement is called a right angle, as above, $\angle ABC$ is congruent to $\angle ABD$.

Perpendicular lines are those which intersect to form a right angle, as illustrated in Figure 15.26.

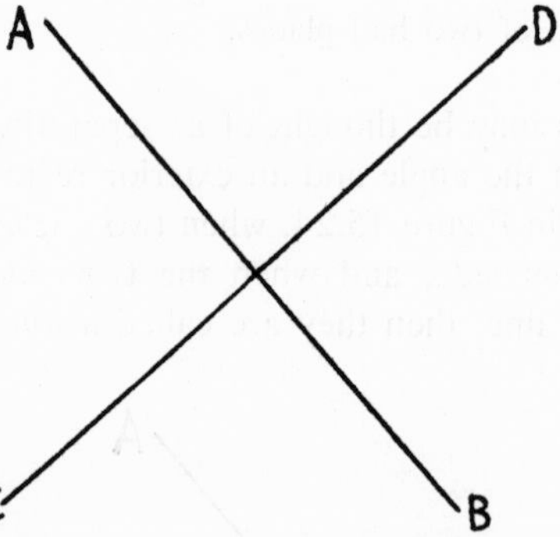

Figure 15.26 Perpendicular lines are those which intersect to form a right angle.

Triangle

When three noncollinear points are joined in pairs by three line segments, as indicated in Figure 15.27, the union of the three sets

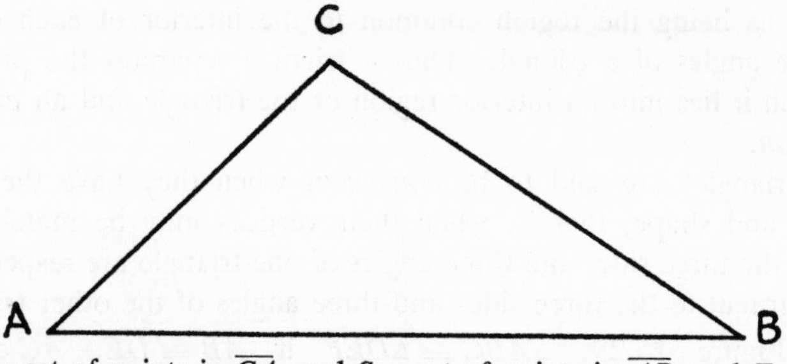

If R = set of points in $\overline{CA}$, and S = set of points in $\overline{AB}$, and T = set of points in $\overline{CB}$, then $\triangle ABC = R \cup S \cup T$.

Figure 15.27 A triangle is the union of the sets of points in the segments joining three noncollinear points.

of points in the three segments is a *triangle*. The points of intersection of the segments are called the *vertices* of the triangle, and the line segments are called the *sides* of the triangle.

The shaded portion of the diagram in Figure 15.28 indicates

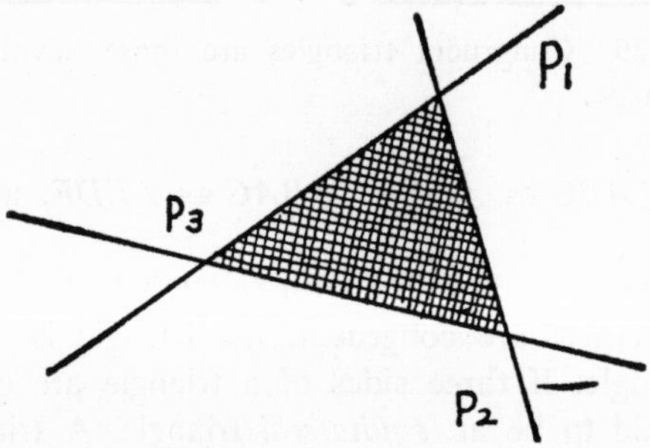

If R = set of points in half-plane P_1 and S = set of points in half-plane P_2 and T = set of points in half-plane P_3, then the interior region of the triangle = $R \cap S \cap T$.

Figure 15.28 A drawing illustrating that the interior region of a triangle is the intersection of half-planes.

the intersection of half-planes of which each of the lines containing the sides of the triangle forms a boundary. This intersection is called the *interior region* of the triangle, which may be defined also as being the region common to the interior of each of the three angles of a triangle. Thus a triangle separates the plane in which it lies into an interior region of the triangle and an *exterior region.*

Triangles are said to be *congruent* when they have the same size and shape; that is, when their vertices may be matched so that the three sides and three angles of one triangle are respectively congruent to the three sides and three angles of the other triangle. In Figure 15.29, $\Delta ABC \cong \Delta DEF$ if $\overline{AB} \cong \overline{DE}$, $\overline{AC} \cong \overline{DF}$,

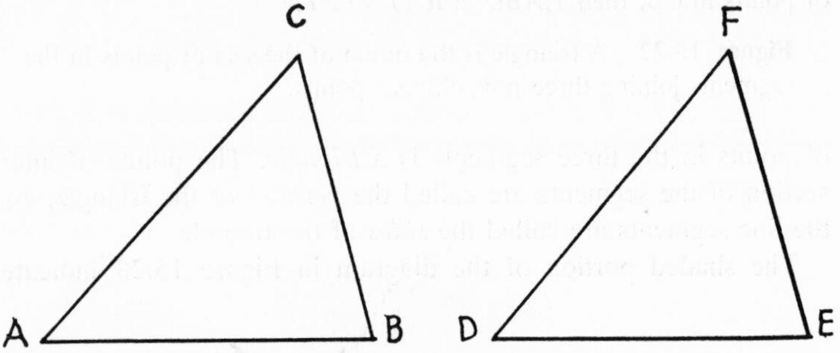

Figure 15.29 Congruent triangles are those having the same size and shape.

$\overline{BC} \cong \overline{EF}$, $\angle ABC \cong \angle DEF$, $\angle BAC \cong \angle EDF$, and $\angle BCA \cong \angle EFD$.

Triangles may be classified with relation to their sides. If two sides of a triangle are congruent, the triangle is said to be an *isosceles* triangle. If three sides of a triangle are congruent, the triangle is said to be an *equilateral* triangle. A triangle with no two sides congruent is said to be a *scalene* triangle.

Curves

A *curve* is a set of points. It may be represented by moving the point of a pencil over a sheet of paper in various ways, as in Figure 15.30. In geometry, a line is considered to be a type of curve. A curve may be made up of segments, as represented in Figure 15.30a, and then it is called a *broken curve.* A curve

Figure 15.30 Drawings representing curves.

such as each of those represented in Figure 15.30b,d may be illustrated by a pencil mark which does not cross over itself, and which intersects itself only at the point where it was begun. Such curves are *simple closed curves.* A triangle or a circle is an example of a simple closed curve.

A simple closed curve separates the plane in which it lies into an interior region, represented by shading in Figure 15.31, and an exterior region.

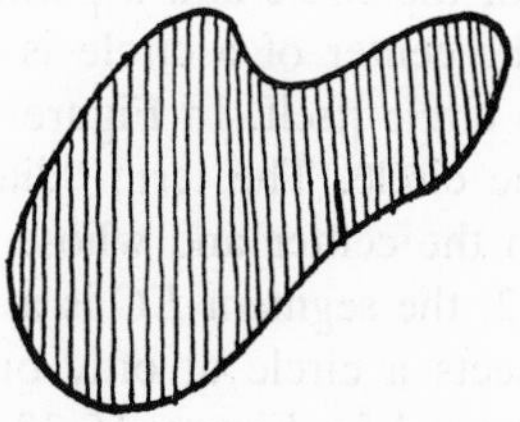

Figure 15.31 The shaded section represents the interior region of a simple closed curve.

Circles

A circle may be described in terms of the solution set of points which satisfies a geometric condition. For example, in Figure 15.32, if we say that the circle is the set of points "X" such that $\overline{AX} \cong \overline{AD}$, we will be describing the set of points forming a circle with a radius equivalent to $\overline{AD}$. If $\overline{AX}$ is less than $\overline{AD}$, then the set of points in the solution set would comprise the interior of the circle. If $\overline{AX}$ is greater than $\overline{AD}$, the solution set would be the points making up the exterior of the circle.

The term "radius" is used to refer to a segment whose end-

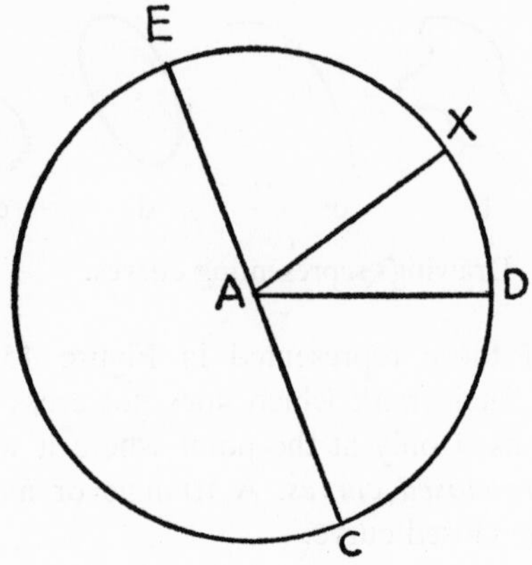

Figure 15.32 The circle *EDC* is a set of points, *x*, such that $\overline{AX} \cong \overline{AD}$.

points are the center of the circle and a point on the circle. It will be noted that while the center of a circle is in the interior of the circle, it is not on the circle itself. In Figure 15.32, points such as *E, D,* or *C* are on the circle. The term "diameter" refers to any segment which lies on the center and whose endpoints are on the circle. In Figure 15.32, the segment *EC* is a diameter.

When a line intersects a circle at only one point it is *tangent* to the circle, as illustrated in Figure 15.33. The point of intersection is the *point of tangency.*

Figure 15.34 illustrates how two points, *A* and *B,* might separate a circle into two parts. Each of these two parts is an *arc* of the circle. The endpoints of each arc are included in the arc. The symbol for the arc *AMB* is $\widehat{AMB}$, where *M* is a point contained in the arc whose endpoints are *A* and *B.*

A *semicircle* is an arc determined by the endpoints of the diameter of a circle. In Figure 15.34, $\widehat{ADC}$ is a semicircle.

An angle whose vertex is at the center of a circle and whose sides contain the endpoints of an arc is a *central angle,* as illustrated in Figure 15.34 by the $\angle$ *BOC.* An arc may be measured in terms of the measure of the central angle which contains the endpoints of the arc.

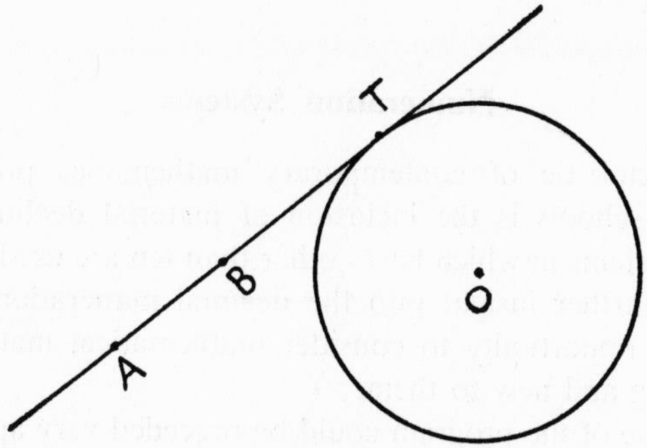

If $R =$ set of points on the circle, and $S =$ set of points in the line $\overleftrightarrow{AB}$, and $T =$ the point of tangency, then $R \cap S = T$.

Figure 15.33 The line *AB* is tangent to the circle if it intersects the circle at only one point.

The term "circumference" is used to refer to the length of the simple closed curve which is the circle. It should be noted that the word "radius" may be used to refer to the length of a radius as well as to the segment which has as its endpoints the center of a circle and a point on the circle. Similarly, the word "diameter" is used to refer to either the length of the diameter or to a segment which is named a diameter.

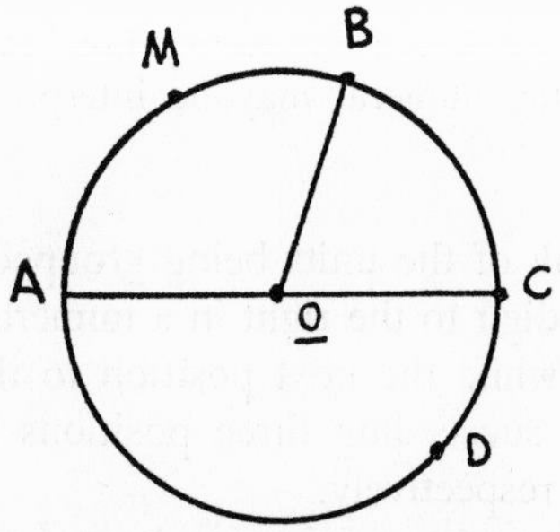

Figure 15.34 A drawing representing an arc *AMB,* a semicircle *ADC,* and a central angle $\angle AOB$.

Numeration Systems

A characteristic of contemporary mathematics programs for elementary schools is the inclusion of material dealing with numeration systems in which bases other than ten are used. This gives the pupils further insight into the decimal numeration system as well as the opportunity to consider mathematical material which is interesting and new to them.

This phase of the program could be preceded very appropriately by discussing historical aspects of numeration systems, such as those described in Chapter 6, and considering the symbols and grouping procedures used in writing numerals by various peoples at different times in history.

As noted earlier, an examination of the decimal numeration system discloses that the position of the digits in a numeral determines the value of the numeral. This property of place value may be utilized to construct numeration systems with bases other than ten.

Figure 15.35 illustrates that in the decimal numeration system,

10^4	10^3	10^2	10^1	10^0
ten thousands	thousands	hundreds	tens	ones

Figure 15.35 A diagram indicating how the place value of digits in a base-ten numeral may be interpreted as powers of ten.

where we may think of the units being grouped by powers of ten, the position of the digit to the right in a numeral for a whole number indicates 10^0, while the next position to the left of this indicates 10^1, and the succeeding three positions to the left indicate 10^2, 10^3, and 10^4, respectively.

With the exception of zero, any number taken to the zero power is the number 1. Thus, 10^0 is one, and the "5" in the numeral "345" indicates 5 ones. The second place from the right in the numeral "345" indicates groups of 10^1, or ten. Consequently the

"4" in the numeral "345" indicates 4 tens, or 40. The third place from the right indicates groups of 10^2, or hundreds, so the "3" in the numeral "345" indicates 300. The value of the numeral "345" is thus three hundred forty-five.

In the decimal numeration system, because the value of each digit in a numeral is some power of ten, we say that the *base* of this system is ten. The base-ten expanded form for the base-ten numeral 2345 is $2(10^3) + 3(10^2) + 4(10^1) + 5(10^0)$.

If a base other than ten were used, such as five, the value of each digit in a numeral would be changed accordingly. For example, as indicated in Figure 15.36, the digit to the right would indicate the

5^4	5^3	5^2	5^1	5^0
six hundred twenty-fives	one hundred twenty-fives	twenty-fives	fives	ones

Figure 15.36 A diagram indicating how the place value of digits in a base-five numeral may be interpreted as powers of five.

number of ones (5^0), the second place from the right would indicate the number of fives (5^1), the third place from the right would show the number of twenty-fives (5^2), and succeeding places in the numeral, to the left, would indicate values which were other powers of five. The base-ten expanded form for the base-five numeral 1234 is $1(5^3) + 2(5^2) + 3(5^1) + 4(5^0)$. For example, in a base-five system of numeration, the symbols "23" would indicate 2 fives and 3 ones, and this would correspond in value to 1 ten and 3 ones, or 13, in the decimal numeration system. This may be expressed as $23_{\text{five}} = 13_{\text{ten}}$, where the "five" as a subscript indicates the use of a base-five system and the subscript "ten" indicates the use of the base-ten numeration system. We are assuming here that the subscript which indicates the base is itself an expression of the base-ten numeration system.

Figure 15.37 represents, as an example, how a group of 23 objects could be regrouped so that numerals in bases other than ten could be represented by groups of objects.

BASE	NUMERAL	GROUPING OF OBJECTS
ten	23_{ten}	□□□□□□□□□□ □□□ □□□□□□□□□□
eight	27_{eight}	□□□□□□□□ □□□□□□□ □□□□□□□□
five	43_{five}	□□□□□ □□□ □□□□□ □□□□□ □□□□□
three	212_{three}	□□□ □□□ □□□ □□ □□□ □□□ □□□ □□□

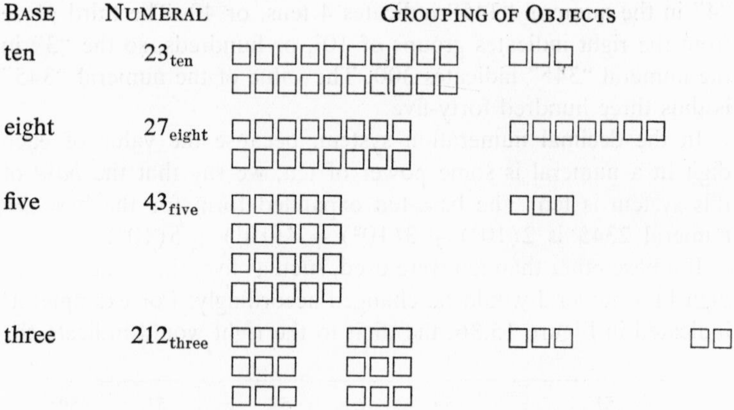

Figure 15.37 An illustration of how a group of 23 objects may be regrouped to represent numerals in various bases.

It will be noted in Figure 15.37 that in expressing 23 in the base-three numeration system, the first "2" in the numeral "212_{three}" indicates the number of groups of 3^2 (or nines in the base-ten system). Thus the numeral 212_{three} could be thought of as expressing 2 nines, plus 1 three, plus 2 ones in the base-ten system, and hence $23_{ten} = 212_{three}$.

A Base-Five Numeration System

Figure 15.38 compares some numerals in a base-five system of numeration with numerals in the base-ten system, or decimal numeration system.

An addition table for a base-five numeration system is shown in Figure 15.39.

A multiplication table for a base-five numeration system is shown in Figure 15.40.

Algorisms using base-five and base-ten numeration systems are illustrated in Figure 15.41 and Figure 15.42.

It will be noted in Figure 15.41 that the numeral 312_{five} indicates $3(5^2) + 1(5^1) + 2(5^0)$ when expressed in the decimal numeration system, and its value would correspond to the value of the numeral 82 in the decimal system.

DECIMAL NUMERATION	BASE-FIVE NUMERATION
1	1
2	2
3	3
4	4
5	10
6	11
7	12
8	13
9	14
10	20
11	21
12	22
25	100
26	101
50	200
51	201

Figure 15.38 A comparison of some numerals in a base-five numeration system with numerals of equal value in a base-ten numeration system.

+	0	1	2	3	4
0	0	1	2	3	4
1	1	2	3	4	10
2	2	3	4	10	11
3	3	4	10	11	12
4	4	10	11	12	13

Figure 15.39 An addition table for a base-five numeration system.

×	0	1	2	3	4
0	0	0	0	0	0
1	0	1	2	3	4
2	0	2	4	11	13
3	0	3	11	14	22
4	0	4	13	22	31

Figure 15.40 Multiplication table for a base-five numeration system.

BASE-TEN	BASE-FIVE
36	121
+46	+141
82	312

Figure 15.41 Addition algorisms using base-ten and base-five numeration systems.

BASE-TEN	BASE-FIVE
34	114
×7	×12
238	233
	114
	1423

Figure 15.42 Multiplication algorisms using base-ten and base-five numeration systems.

As 1423 in base-five numeration indicates $1(5^3) + 4(5^2) + 2(5^1) + 3(5^0)$ in the decimal numeration system, the numeral "1423_{five}" would have the same value as 238 in the decimal numeration system.

Changing from a base-five numeration system to a base-ten numeration system. A procedure for changing from a base-five numeration system to a base-ten numeration system is illustrated below.

BASE-FIVE BASE-TEN

$$1423_{five} = 1(5^3) + 4(5^2) + 2(5^1) + 3(5^0)$$

$$\begin{aligned} 1 \times 5^3 &= 125 \\ 4 \times 5^2 &= 100 \\ 2 \times 5^1 &= 10 \\ 3 \times 5^0 &= 3 \\ & \overline{238} \end{aligned}$$

$$1423_{five} = 238_{ten}$$

Changing from a base-ten numeration system to a base-five numeration system. To change 238_{ten} to a numeral in a base-five system, the following algorism is useful.

$$\begin{array}{ll}
\;\;47 & \\
5\overline{)238} & \text{remainder } 3 \\
\;\;\;9 & \\
5\overline{)47} & \text{remainder } 2 \\
\;1 & \\
5\overline{)9} & \text{remainder } 4 \\
\;0 & \\
5\overline{)1} & \text{remainder } 1
\end{array}$$

It will be noted that if the remainders are taken in order, starting from the last, the numeral 1423_{five} will be the numeral in base-five numeration which is equal in value to the numeral 238_{ten} in decimal numeration. Instead of using the long division form above, it is more convenient to use a short division form as shown below.

$$\begin{array}{rl}
5\underline{)238} & \\
5\underline{)\;\;47} & \text{remainder } 3 \\
5\underline{)\;\;\;\;9} & \text{remainder } 2 \\
5\underline{)\;\;\;\;1} & \text{remainder } 4 \\
0 & \text{remainder } 1
\end{array}$$

$$238_{ten} = 1423_{five}$$

A rationale for the above example is as follows: When 238 is divided by 5, the quotient (47) indicates the number of groups of 5, while 3 ones remain; thus the numeral "3" is shown in the ones place of the base-five numeral. When the 47 fives are divided by 5, the quotient (9) indicates 9 groups of 25 (5×5) and a remainder of 2 groups of 5, thus the second digit from the right in the base five numeral is 2. In the next division, when 9 twenty-fives are divided by 5, the quotient 1 shows 1 group of 125 ($5 \times 5 \times 5$) and the remainder of 4, which indicates 4 groups of 25, is placed in the third position from the right in the numeral. In the fourth division, the 1 group which represents 125 is divided by 5 and results in the quotient 0, indicating no group of 625 ($5 \times 5 \times 5 \times 5$); the remainder of 1 provides the fourth digit from the right in the numeral of the base-five numeral. Thus, $238_{ten} = 1423_{five}$.

A Binary Numeration System

A binary numeration system, which has a base of 2, is useful in the construction of electric computers. In the binary system only two numerals are needed, as noted in Figure 15.43, and conse-

BASE-TWO	BASE-TEN
110101	$1(2^5) + 1(2^4) + 0(2^3) + 1(2^2) + 0(2^1) + 1(2^0)$

$$\begin{aligned} 1 \times 2^5 &= 32 \\ 1 \times 2^4 &= 16 \\ 0 \times 2^3 &= 0 \\ 1 \times 2^2 &= 4 \\ 0 \times 2^1 &= 0 \\ 1 \times 2^0 &= 1 \\ & \overline{53} \end{aligned}$$

$110101_{two} = 53_{ten}$

Figure 15.43 A procedure for changing a numeral in base-two to a numeral of equal value in base-ten.

quently they may be represented by the condition of an electric circuit which is either open or closed. The procedure for changing from base-two to base-ten resembles that used in changing from base-five to base-ten.

Figure 15.44 indicates numerals in the binary system of numeration which have a value equivalent to some of the numerals in the decimal system.

Addition and multiplication tables for use with numerals in a binary system are shown below:

+	0	1
0	0	1
1	1	10

×	0	1
0	0	0
1	0	1

Numerals in Decimal System	Numerals in Binary System
0	0
1	1
2	10
3	11
4	100
5	101
6	110
7	111
8	1000
9	1001
10	1010
11	1011
12	1100
13	1101
14	1110
15	1111
16	10000
17	10001
32	100000
64	1000000
128	10000000

Figure 15.44 Some numerals in the decimal system and their equivalent values when written in the binary system.

A teacher in the intermediate grades of the elementary school will find that the more able children are capable of understanding the use of numeration systems with bases other than ten if the work is presented carefully to them. Introducing children to numeration systems with various bases will help them to make a distinction between a number and the symbol used to represent it, as well as provide them with insight into the decimal system of numeration.

Looking Ahead

While it is recognized that the topics presented in this chapter are only a few of those which make up contemporary mathematics, they provide an overview of the more important aspects of the new material which might be introduced during the elementary grades. A teacher should have a deeper understanding of these topics, of course, before presenting them to children, and attention is directed toward the many excellent books now available which deal with contemporary mathematics. Some of these books are listed at the end of this chapter.

During the next decade, answers will need to be found by those planning elementary school mathematics programs to certain questions such as the following which concern a philosophy of education:

1. What purposes should a program in elementary school mathematics serve?
   (a) What balance is needed between the selection of content to facilitate the use of arithmetic in everyday social situations and the content needed to lay a groundwork for mathematical study at the secondary and college levels?
   (b) To what extent are these purposes different for different children?
2. What balance should be maintained between the time allotted to studying mathematics and that allotted to other areas of the curriculum at the various grade levels?
3. How should the mathematics program serve the pupils
   (a) in other curriculum areas?
   (b) in out-of-school situations?

Answers also need to be found in the area of psychology for questions dealing with the gradation of content and with teaching procedures.

1. How and when should specific items be presented so that they may be learned with maximum efficiency?
   (a) Are provisions made to accommodate differences among children in interests, abilities, and needs?
   (b) Are adequate materials of instruction available to teachers at the levels needed?
2. What provisions may be made for transfer pupils while curriculum changes are in progress?
3. Can all teachers be expected to master both the mathematics needed and the teaching procedures to be used in the time available to them

in their preservice training? The recommendations of the Mathematical Association of America for teachers in kindergarten through the sixth grade suggest a year of college preparatory geometry and a year of college preparatory algebra followed by the equivalent of twelve semester units of college mathematics.[8] These recommendations seem unrealistic in view of the scope of material which teachers must master in other areas of the elementary school curriculum, but it is evident that teachers will need more background in mathematics than was needed when following the traditional program.

With some exceptions, the changes which may be expected in elementary school mathematics programs will be more in the nature of an evolution than a revolution. Suggestions for new content will be tried out in classrooms during the next decade, and those which seem most effective will find a permanent place at the grade levels where they may be learned most effectively by average achievers and be most useful for them. Enrichment materials and activities will be provided regularly for high achievers, while a modified curriculum will be available for low achievers. The principle that different curriculums should be provided for children who differ greatly in their learning abilities will be recognized.

In the primary grades, while more emphasis may be expected to be placed on arithmetic than was found in the traditional program, the amount of new content will depend, in most instances, upon the time which is made available from the remainder of the primary child's curriculum. The bulk of the new content will be carried through enrichment activities, rather than be part of the regular program for all children.

In the intermediate grades, some of the new material will be woven into the traditional program to provide more understanding for all pupils of the abstract nature of mathematics, while other new material will be included in the curriculum of high achievers. Numeration systems with bases other than ten, informal geometry, and the use of equations and inequalities in connection with problem solving, will find a permanent place in the program of most

[8] "Recommendations of the Mathematical Association of America for the Training of Teachers of Mathematics," *American Mathematical Monthly*, Vol. 67, pp. 982–991, December, 1960.

children. The principles of associativity, commutativity, and distributivity will be given attention at appropriate places. There will be more emphasis on using precise language when discussing abstract mathematical relationships, and the vocabulary and concepts which are included at the intermediate grade levels will be made more compatible with the work done in the upper grades and in the secondary school.

Some historical aspects of mathematics will be introduced to increase the pupils' interest in the subject. Abundant enrichment activities will be provided for high achievers to broaden the scope of their program and to increase their interest in mathematics.

At the upper grade levels of the elementary school, a more pronounced change from the traditional program will be evident. As much of the content of the traditional program concerning applications of per cent will be dealt with in the intermediate grades or reserved for general mathematics courses for terminal students in high school or junior college, time will be available to introduce average achievers to the more abstract aspects of mathematics. Extensive use will be made of set language and symbolism to develop concepts in elementary algebra and nonmetric geometry and to study the properties of numbers and the operations on numbers. Topics introducing pupils to elementary concepts of mathematical logic and probability will be included for the more capable pupils. The enrichment provided at upper grade levels for such pupils will be directed toward providing them with deeper insight into mathematics in the topics they are studying rather than with a superficial broadening of their program by including a wider range of topics.

The procedures for all grade levels will stress the use of such geometrical interpretations of mathematical relationships as may be shown with number lines, graphs, and diagrams. There will be an increasing emphasis also on using a "controlled discovery" technique in order to encourage desirable problem-solving attitudes in pupils and to increase their interest in mathematics.

Suggested Learning Activities

1. Visit a class being taught "new mathematics." Describe the reactions you note among pupils. Are they interested? Do they seem to be

learning the concepts being taught? What differences do you sense among the boys and girls with regard to their reactions to what and how they are being taught?

2. Interview a teacher who has taught some "new mathematics" for at least one year. How would he answer some of the questions asked on pages 432–433?
3. Using each of the two methods for designating sets given in your text (roster and set builder methods), designate the following sets:
   (a) The set of all natural numbers greater than five and less than ten.
   (b) The set of all digits.
   (c) The set of all natural numbers divisible by three.
4. Give a verbal description of each of the following:
   (a) $\{11, 13, 15, 17, 19\}$
   (b) $\{x \mid y \varepsilon N \wedge x = 2y\}$
   (c) $\{x \mid x \varepsilon E \wedge 0 < x < 12\}$, $E =$ even integers
5. Draw Venn diagrams to show:
   (a) Girls in this class who are wearing earrings, and all of the girls in this class; let the universe in this instance be all the students in the class.
   (b) Boys in this room, and persons who brought their lunches; in this instance let the universe be the pupils in the school.
   (c) Boys in a school who are student body officers, and who are transported on buses; in this instance let the universe be the pupils in the school.
6. Convert the following to base ten: (a) 327_{eight}, (b) 3213_{four}, (c) 101110_{two}.
7. Convert the following base-ten numerals to bases indicated: (a) 97 to base five, (b) 135 to base seven, (c) 22 to base two.

Guided Supplementary Reading

1. How does Adler use a pair of half-lines to illustrate the concept of multiplication?
2. What conclusions does Anderson reach from his study of the use of visual-tactual devices?
3. How does Banks differentiate arithmetic and algebra?
4. According to Breuer, what characteristic remains for a set when one disregards the physical nature of the elements of a set?
5. Brueckner and others cite some objectives of the teaching of algebra which have both mathematical and social implications. What are they?

6. Brumfiel and others credit the ancient Egyptians with knowing what aspect of the Pythagorean theorem?
7. What programs does Buswell advocate for the "upper third"? Why?
8. Which did Deery's subject find more difficult—converting from decimal to hexal or the reverse?
9. What advantage does Driscoll claim for teaching children to check by casting out 9's and other numbers?
10. What change in the treatment of algebra is taking place as reported by Dutton and Adams?
11. How does Freund differentiate between *abstract* and *applied* geometry?
12. According to Fujii, what does the term *universal set* denote?
13. With what teaching aid did Goodman surprise his eighth graders?
14. What reasons does Gramlich give for using the slide rule in the elementary school?
15. What mathematical items does Kingston point out can be used to advantage to clarify arithmetic at 7th and 8th grade levels?
16. In whose honor was the term "Cartesian product" named?
17. How does Larsen define a slide rule?
18. What is Mueller's point of view regarding the place of algebra in grades 7 and 8?
19. How do Osborn and others define addition of natural numbers using set terms?
20. What recommendations do Ruddell and others make regarding the value of the traditional algebra and geometry courses as suitable background for elementary school teachers of arithmetic?
21. What values does Sachs attach to teaching children about admirable numbers and compatible pairs?
22. Schaaf points out that geometry existed before the height of ancient Greek civilization. What peculiar contribution did the Greeks make to this area of mathematics?
23. From his examination of programs developing "modern" mathematics at grades 7 and 8, what categories does Schult find to be represented in all of the experiments?
24. Swain suggests that proof should not be associated in the child's mind with geometry alone. What does he mean?
25. Following Swain's notation, convert 7871 to the duodecimal scale.
26. What reason is given by Begle, as quoted by Weaver, for the development of an SMSG program in elementary schools?
27. What justification does Willerding give for teaching a unit in modular arithmetic to 8th graders?

28. How does the *roster* method of describing a set differ from the *rule* method?

Suggested Supplementary References

1. ADLER, IRVING, *The New Mathematics,* Chapter 1. New York: The John Day Company, 1958.
2. ANDERSON, GEORGE R., "Visual-Tactual Devices and Their Efficacy; An Experiment in Grade Eight," *Arithmetic Teacher,* Vol. 4, pp. 196–203, November, 1957.
3. BANKS, J. HOUSTON, *Elements of Mathematics,* Chapter 5. Boston: Allyn and Bacon, Inc., 1961.
4. BREUER, JOSEPH (translated by Howard F. Fehr), *Introduction to the Theory of Sets*. Englewood Cliffs, N.J.: Prentice-Hall, Inc., 1958.
5. BRUECKNER, LEO J., FOSTER E. GROSSNICKLE, AND JOHN RECKZEH, *Developing Mathematical Understanding in the Upper Grades,* Chapter 12. Philadelphia: The John C. Winston Company, 1957.
6. BRUMFIEL, CHARLES F., ROBERT E. EICHOLZ, AND MERRILL SHANKS, *Introduction to Mathematics*. Reading, Mass.: Addison-Wesley Publishing Company, 1961.
7. BUSWELL, GUY T., "Content and Organization of Arithmetic," *Arithmetic Teacher,* Vol. 6, pp. 77–83, March, 1959.
8. DEERY, R. T., "Linda Learns the Hexal System," *Arithmetic Teacher,* Vol. 5, pp. 251–254, November, 1958.
9. DRISCOLL, LUCY E., "Casting Out Nines and Other Numbers," *Arithmetic Teacher,* Vol. 5, pp. 82–83, March, 1958.
10. DUTTON, WILBUR H., AND L. J. ADAMS, *Arithmetic for Teachers,* Chapter 13. Englewood Cliffs, N.J.: Prentice-Hall, Inc., 1961.
11. FREUND, JOHN E., *A Modern Introduction to Mathematics,* Chapter 16. Englewood Cliffs, N.J.: Prentice-Hall, Inc., 1956.
12. FUJII, JOHN N., *An Introduction to the Elements of Mathematics*. New York: John Wiley and Sons, 1961.
13. GOODMAN, FREDERICK L., "Prime Numbers and Factoring," *Arithmetic Teacher,* Vol. 6, pp. 274–275, November, 1959.
14. GRAMLICH, JAY J., "Slide Rules for Upper Elementary Grades," *Arithmetic Teacher,* Vol. 5, pp. 29–33, February, 1958.
15. KINGSTON, J. MAURICE, "Some Arithmetical Fundamentals of Value to Junior High School Teachers," *Mathematics Teacher,* Vol. 48, pp. 232–236, April, 1955.
16. KRICKENBERGER, W. R., AND HELEN R. PEARSON, *An Introduc-*

tion to Sets and the Structure of Algebra. Boston: Ginn and Company, 1958.

17. LARSEN, HAROLD D., *Arithmetic for Colleges,* Chapter 13. New York: The Macmillan Company, 1958.
18. MUELLER, FRANCIS J., "Building Algebra Readiness in Grades Seven and Eight," *Arithmetic Teacher,* Vol. 6, pp. 269–273, November, 1959.
19. OSBORN, ROGER, M. VERE DEVAULT, CLAUDE C. BOYS, AND W. ROBERT HOUSTON, *Extending Mathematics Understanding,* Chapter 7. Columbus: Charles E. Merrill Books, Inc., 1961.
20. RUDDELL, ARDEN K., WILBUR DUTTON, AND JOHN RECKZEH, "Background Mathematics for Elementary Teachers," *Instruction in Arithmetic,* 25th Yearbook, Chapter 13. Washington, D.C.: The National Council of Teachers of Mathematics, 1960.
21. SACHS, F. M.,"Admirable Numbers and Compatible Pairs," *Arithmetic Teacher,* Vol. 7, pp. 293–295, October, 1960.
22. SCHAAF, WILLIAM L., *Basic Concepts of Elementary Mathematics,* Chapter 3. New York: John Wiley and Sons, Inc., 1960.
23. SCHULT, VERYL, "Whither Arithmetic in Grades 7 and 8?" *Education,* Vol. 79, pp. 280–286, January, 1959.
24. SWAIN, ROBERT L., "Modern Mathematics and School Arithmetic," *Instruction in Arithmetic,* Chapter 12. Washington, D.C.: The National Council of Teachers of Mathematics, 1960.
25. SWAIN, ROBERT L., *Understanding Arithmetic,* Chapter 6. New York: Rinehart and Company, Inc., 1957.
26. WEAVER, J. FRED, "The SMSG Project on Elementary-School Mathematics," *Arithmetic Teacher,* Vol. 8, pp. 32–35, January, 1961.
27. WILLERDING, MARGARET F., "Teaching Unit in Modular Arithmetic for Grade 8," *School Science and Mathematics,* Vol. 60, pp. 511–518, October, 1960.
28. WOODWARD, EDITH J., AND RODERICK C. MCLENNAN, *Elementary Concepts of Sets.* New York: Henry Holt and Company, 1959.

INDEX